MW01011658

FASA CORPORATION
1990

**CONCEPT, OVERALL STORY,
and GENERAL BLAME**
Tom Dowd
Sam Lewis

WRITING
Physical
Ken St. Andre
Hates
John Faughnan
Past
W.G. Armintrout
Loves
Jerry Epperson
Counterstroke
Paul R. Hume
Spiritual
Lester W. Smith
Future
James D. Long
**Present and
Additional Material**
Tom Dowd

DEVELOPMENT
Tom Dowd

EDITORIAL STAFF
Senior Editor
Donna Ippolito
Assistant Editor
Sharon Turner Mulvihill

PRODUCTION STAFF
Art Director
Dana Knutson
Cover Art
Todd Hamilton
Cover Design
Mike Nielsen
Illustration
Joel Biske
Jeff Laubenstein
Jim Nelson
Tim Bradstreet
Terry Pavlet
Larry MacDougall
Earl Geier
Layout
Tara Gallagher

Published by FASA Corporation
P.O. Box 6930 Chicago, IL 60680

T·A·B·L·E · O·F · C·O·N·T·E·N·T·S

DUEL AT DAWN: A Prologue

Emile:

I write to you this evening, driven by the need to tell you of the amazing event I witnessed today. As you know, my employment for the last season has been in the household of one Monsieur E., a nobleman of much culture, learning, and influence with this fair city's most illustrious citizens.

These past months have been the most joyous of my life. Never have I had the opportunity to remain so close to a mind as brilliant as Monsieur E.'s and never have I dwelled in a house where I am treated with such respect. As I told you, I believed for a time that all was glorious with the world.

A few weeks ago, just before the festival and just after my last letter, there began a sequence of events leading to the amazing occurrence that I just mentioned.

The first sign of the chaos to come was the disappearance of an illuminated manuscript that my master had lent to an acquaintance of his, a Monsieur R., of the university. From what I have been able to learn, the manuscript disappeared from Monsieur R.'s library under the oddest circumstances. Even more mysterious than the theft is the dagger of the strangest design and construction that Monsieur R. found in the exact place where the manuscript had been. He gave it to my master, thinking that Monsieur E. might recognize some connection between the dagger and the theft. Though I know not whether he has, I have witnessed him standing in the garden late at night, examining the dagger.

What followed was a bizarre series of thefts, disappearances, reappearances, misunderstandings, and allegations that culminated in a minor scandal in the palace that has damaged my master's reputation. In addition, these events contributed directly to the dissolution of a relationship between my master and a Mlle. M., the young lady with whom he was deeply enamored.

As it happened last evening, only I, a few scullery maids, and my master were present in the house, the rest having been sent on various trips and errands. After an uncommonly light day, I was up later than usual, reading a manuscript from the library. Monsieur E. must have noticed my light and come knocking at my door. When I opened it, I found him standing there in the hall, his face showing an expression I had never seen before. He appeared as I imagine might a veteran who has readied himself for the most important battle of his life.

Before I could say anything, Monsieur E. grabbed me roughly by the shoulders. "André," he said, "at dawn I finish this and I need you by my side. The time for reckoning with that fool is here." As you can imagine, I was aghast. By his words and tone, I could only infer that he intended a duel and was instructing me to be his second.

Though I am far from being an old man, the spring of youth is long since gone from my body. To expect me to fulfill the role required was sheer folly. In my surprise, I told him so directly. My master reacted only by smiling wider and reaching out to

twitch my left ear in a manner that seemed completely natural but completely out of character for him. "You need not worry," he said. "I require only your presence."

He grasped me again by the shoulders as though we were the oldest of friends, then released me and made off down the corridor toward his rooms. Stunned, I stood there watching him until he disappeared behind his doors, knowing he was happier than I had seen him in weeks.

I will spare you and my pride a description of the fear that tore at me during those few hours before sunrise. By the time the first glimmer of morning appeared, however, I had sufficiently steeled myself for what was to come. Monsieur E. wished me present and I would not disappoint him.

I found him in his study, carefully tending his sword in that odd manner of his. (You will perhaps remember a previous letter in which I described the mysterious silver stone he used to maintain the razor-sharpness of his arms. I must say this blade is one of the most lethal weapons I have ever seen.) As I entered, he finished his work, sheathed the weapon, and tossed it to me. He was wearing a simple white tunic, black breeches, and boots. Over that, he wore a full cloak cut from cloth the seamstress told me he'd brought back from Persia. His eyes were alight with a fire that, truth be told, frightened me.

"André," he said, "let us be on our way."

I followed him out, but instead of heading for the carriage as I had expected, we made our way on foot. We traveled south for a short distance, but I could not imagine where we were heading. As it turned out, our destination was the river, or rather, one of the new stone bridges crossing it.

Halfway across, Monsieur E. stopped and declared that we had arrived. With those words, the fear I had fought aside earlier returned with a cold vengeance. Not only did my master intend to duel that morning, but in a place as public as the town square! Now, admittedly, anyone's chance of discovering us would only become likely when the city awoke at dawn, but even in the dark, some travelers were about. Not to mention the likelihood of our being interrupted by a patrol.

No matter. I swallowed hard and dug my fingernails into my palms. My master needed me and I would be there.

We had stopped only a few moments when I spied two figures approaching the bridge from the opposite side. Closest to us was a tall man, who moved with the long strides and deliberation of someone with military training. My fear arose again, but the sight of the second man drove it from me.

As they approached the bridge, this other man quickened his stride and all but pranced ahead to the edge of the bridge. There he paused, bowed grandly, and turned to his companion. I glanced at my master and saw that a hard look had come into his eyes, but I could make out the barest trace of mirth about his mouth. I turned to look back across the bridge, and my master surprised me by placing his hand upon my shoulder. "Whatever happens, André, you will let it occur. The time for pawns is over. Now it is he and I again."

His words perplexed me, but before I could utter a question, the newcomers began to make their way toward us. The tall man hung back while the light-footed man led, his hands thrust into the side pockets of his long coat. As he neared, I could begin to make him out more clearly.

Of average height, that is, slightly taller than myself, he cut a careless figure, his hair uncoiffed and his clothes unkempt. I almost took him for a ruffian until I realized that what I had taken for shadows on his face were something else.

His visage was powdered properly enough, Emile, but it was also marked in a most outlandish fashion. I was immediately struck by the resemblance between him and a character in a farce-play that passed through early last spring. A more odd-looking fellow I have never seen.

When the painted man finally drew close to us, my master began to remove his gloves and addressed him. "My old friend," he said, "again we find ourselves at odds? Why do you vex me so? What have I done to deserve this treatment from one—"

As my master spoke, I could see the newcomer's face begin to cloud. He yanked his right hand free and began to wave it violently in front of him. Then he threw both hands into the air and called out to my master loudly in a language I did not understand. Emile, I do not claim a scholar's knowledge of language, but I do pride myself in being able recognize those tongues that I do not speak. You must believe me. Though this man spoke to my master in a mysterious, incomprehensible tongue, Monsieur E. understood him.

Not only that, but he replied in the same tongue! When the newcomer interrupted him, I saw my master's face grow hard for a moment. He then spoke in the tone that I have only heard him use to reprimand someone who has failed him. The newcomer responded by laughing uproariously! Never before have I seen a person lapse into such a sudden, unexpected peal of laughter. He then lashed into my master, still in that odd tongue, like some school teacher scolding an ill-prepared child. My master's eyes narrowed and I could see the tension build in his jaw. It was obvious that it galled him profoundly to be addressed in such a manner.

Finally, my master had enough and verbally lashed back, waving his right hand in hard, sharp, cutting motions. The other man smiled, nodded, and turned quickly, allowing his coat to spin. As the man walked the few steps to his second, my master turned toward me. "Why do I let that fool rile me so?" he said. (I should point out Emile that he did not say "fool." The word he used I could not understand, but I believe it had a similar meaning.)

I started to reply, but he held up his hand. "A rhetorical question, André. There is no answer. My sword, if you please." He stepped away from me, to my side, and held out his right hand. Holding the sheathed weapon flat before me, I placed the grip in his palm. Slowly, he drew it out, allowing the peeking sun to gleam off its fine edge. Across from us, the other man drew his blade in a quick, well-practiced manner. He slashed it once before him and then advanced a step.

My master's sword came clear and he held it vertical before him. Without turning, he spoke to me softly so that his opponent would not hear. "André, if I fall here, I ask that you burn the small black chest beneath my bed. Do so without opening it."

I assured him that I would, and he stepped forward to meet his foe.

What I witnessed next, Emile, mere words cannot describe. Indeed, I still wonder if it was part of some delusion I suffered. There, as the sun crested the hills to the east, before man and God, my master and his opponent did duel.

What a fight it was, Emile! Would that you could have seen it. I cannot claim to have witnessed many duels. Nor can I claim to have previously seen many displays of the art, but what occurred before me this morn was spectacular.

There is no doubt in my mind that my master and his foe are the two best swordsmen who ever lived. Better than those of the King's guard, and even better than those who duel to entertain in the traveling shows. Better, I dare say, based on your own descriptions, than that gentleman from Verona of whom you are so fond.

For what seemed like hours, my master and his foe fought, the art as we know it giving way to styles and techniques I have no words to describe. Lesser men would say they fought like ruffians, but the art was always with them.

And Emile, there is no doubt that each knew the other well, that they had fought in this manner before. As they dueled, they bantered, at least so I believe, in languages I know not. Once, maybe twice, I thought I recognized a word, but that is all. The longer they fought, the more joy appeared on their faces. I was so enraptured by their display that it took my poor mind a few moments to realize that it had ended.

My master's foe advanced with a lightning flurry of slashes and thrusts, which my master strongly deflected, losing only a few steps. Then, quickly, my master aimed his own low slashes at his foe, striking down and leaning left. The other parried deftly, then realized his mistake as my master shifted his weight, crossed him, dipped his point under his guard and thrust up and away.

At first it seemed that nothing happened, but the spray of blood from my master's foe said otherwise. My master had severed the man's ear, cleanly and sharply along the skull, taking much hair with it.

My master immediately withdrew, holding his sword vertically before him. His foe, stunned, dropped his sword, and brought his hand up to where his left ear had been. I glanced at my master and saw an odd look cross his face, as though he somehow regretted what he had done. His foe held his hand in place, looked at my master, and spoke to him calmly in that odd tongue. He said only a few words and then turned and walked from the bridge. His second soon followed.

I was overjoyed, Emile. My master had shown himself better than his opponent, and I sensed the trials of the last weeks were at an end. I turned to congratulate him, but the words froze on my lips. There was a sadness in his face, Emile, which I had not expected. He watched his opponent until the man was out of sight, then stood there, immobile. Finally, with a long sigh, he relaxed and lowered his blade. I immediately offered his sheath. He slid the sword into place without cleaning it.

Almost fearing to speak, I asked him if it was over. He did not turn, but answered me while still staring off down the road.

"Over?" he said. "No, in my haste, I have maimed him. Now it will never be over."

INTRODUCTION

Harlequin is a multi-part roleplaying adventure set in the world of **Shadowrun**. The year is 2050. Advances in technology are astonishing, with Humans able to blend with computers and travel through that netherworld of data known as the Matrix. Even more astonishing is the return of Magic. Elves, Dwarfs, Dragons, Orks, and Trolls have reassumed their true forms, while megacorporations (rather than superpowers) rule much of the world. Moving among it all like whispers in the night are the shadowrunners. No one admits their existence, but no one else can do their secret work.

GAMEMASTER'S NOTES

Harlequin is an adventure supplement that gamemasters can use to introduce a continuing subplot into any existing **Shadowrun** campaign. It is not intended that these eight adventures be run as one continuous whole, moving immediately from one story to the next. The idea is for the gamemaster to run them separately, interspersing other events and adventures between them. The gamemaster might, for example, run one of the **Harlequin** mini-adventures, then one of the other published **Shadowrun** adventures, then another mini-adventure, then an adventure of his own design, and so on. Play of the mini-adventures should be interspersed between, or run parallel to, other adventures that have no connection.

After having participated in one or two of the mini-adventures, players of **Harlequin** should begin to notice a connection (it is, after all, rather obvious). It is not until the final mini-adventure that some real truths, half-truths, and outright lies will be revealed, however. The gamemaster will find information, notes, and recommendations about using this book in the **Running Harlequin** chapter.

These adventures use a decision-tree format, meaning that the players' team could arrive at the same encounter via various different routes. Due to **Harlequin's** size, an abbreviated format has been used to pack plot and adventure into the book. For that reason, the various mini-adventures may contain plotlines that are more linear than the usual **Shadowrun** adventure. The gamemaster is encouraged to make any changes necessary to expand the plot by bringing more choices to it. Hints for gamemastering the various situations are included with the individual sections of each adventure.

To run the **Harlequin** adventures, the gamemaster needs a thorough familiarity with the contents of this book, as well as a working familiarity with the basic **Shadowrun** rules. It is also strongly recommended that the gamemaster familiarize himself with the **Shadowrun** magic sourcebook, **The Grimoire**, as it describes new magical powers and abilities used in these adventures. Gamemasters who do not own **The Grimoire** will need to do some tinkering with any plots that use these special powers and abilities.

The contents of this book are for the gamemaster's eyes only. Everything needed to roleplay **Harlequin** is included here.

Harlequin is designed for a team of four to seven player characters. The group should contain a variety of talent, including one or more Magicians. Though a Decker may not be an active participant (in terms of using his abilities) in all the adventures, it is encouraged that a single team, including a Decker, be used. It is possible, however, to use a team with flexible membership.

MAKING SUCCESS TESTS

During the course of the adventures, the players will make a number of Unresisted Success Tests using a skill and a given Target Number. These Unresisted Success Tests will be indicated by the name of the appropriate skill and the Target Number. For example, an Athletics (3) Test refers to an Athletics Success Test with a Target Number 3. Sometimes it is necessary to make the die rolls against a Success Table that includes different levels of information corresponding to different numbers of successes. In all instances, rolling a higher number of successes reveals all the information from the lower numbers as well. For example, a character achieving 3 successes would not only learn the information for 3 successes, but for 2 and 1 success as well.

HOW TO USE THIS BOOK

Aside from the basic **Shadowrun** rules and the advanced magic rules found in **The Grimoire**, this book includes everything needed to play these adventures. The gamemaster should read through the entire book before beginning the game. Some important plot developments will not become apparent until well into the adventure, but the gamemaster will have to lay the groundwork much earlier on. He can only do that by being familiar with the storyline.

The gamemaster should also examine the maps, plans, and diagrams included. Where appropriate, the maps are coded with letters and numbers to link an area to its description in the text.

Though this book tries to cover all the likely—and even unlikely—things that can happen during the adventure, it is impossible to foresee everything. The gamemaster may find that sometimes it is a good idea to just let the unexpected lead where it will.

Harlequin is made up of eight different mini-adventures, each written by a different author. Each contains a number of short sections describing each of the encounters and events the player characters will face or are likely to face in the course of roleplaying **Harlequin.**

Each section begins with either a relevant quote or a short fictional piece intended to contribute to the tone and feel of the mini-adventure to follow. Then comes a short **Introduction** tailored to that particular adventure, which may include additional general hints about the story to follow.

Most of the encounters begin with a section entitled **Tell It To Them Straight**. This is intended to be read to the players and describes where the player characters are and what is happening to them as though they were actually there. The gamemaster may find that he occasionally needs to adapt the text to special circumstances or the actions of the shadowrunners. **Any special instructions to the gamemaster are printed in boldface type.**

Next comes the information section entitled **Behind The Scenes**. This is the real story, for only the gamemaster knows what is really going on at any given moment in an adventure. If there is a map needed to play this encounter, it is included in this section. Non-player character stats needed to roleplay the section are usually included here as well, though in some cases the gamemaster may be directed to existing Archetype or Contact game statistics either in the **Shadowrun** (**SR**) rulebook or the **Sprawl Sites** (**SS**) gamemaster sourcebook. The gamemaster may also find hints and suggestions for handling the particular encounter.

Some adventures contain a **Legwork** section that contains information the player characters can obtain through their Contacts or through the public data nets. The gamemaster should note that **Harlequin** also contains a **Master Legwork** section with information that could be revealed any time during the multiple adventures but that is not associated exclusively with one adventure.

Some adventures also contain a **Cast Of Characters** section that includes game information and roleplaying hints for some of the major non-player characters in the adventure.

Picking Up The Pieces includes tips on wrapping up the adventure, bridging it with the later segments, and awarding Karma.

Some sections apply to the plot of **Harlequin** as a whole.

Bringing It Home acts as a master **Picking Up The Pieces** section for all the mini-adventures.

Master Legwork, as noted above, contains information relevant to more than one mini-adventure that could be researched at any time during the multiple adventures.

Getting There By Air is a short essay about airline travel in the world of **Shadowrun**. It describes travel costs and security procedures for major airlines as well as private carriers.

Running Harlequin contains notes on the master storyline, the storylines of each individual segment, and a section on Ehran the Scribe and Harlequin, the driving characters behind **Harlequin**.

At the back of the book are various play-aids and handouts to be given to the players.

PLOT OVERVIEW

This series of interrelated adventures is based on an ancient feud between two powerful Elves, Harlequin and Ehran. Harlequin has been slighted and he will have his revenge on Ehran the Scribe, the Pulitzer Prize-winning author and social theorist. This, however, will not be simple revenge, but an elaborate, symbolic ritual of destruction. Some call it The Great Game, but to Harlequin it is serious business.

Chal'han, as the ritual is known, involves the symbolic display of power over seven aspects of the target's existence:

his Physical and Spiritual being, aspects of his Past, Present, and Future, and those he Loves and Hates. By displaying this power, the challenger shows that he could have destroyed his opponent's existence, had he wished. The version of the Great Game Harlequin has chosen to play is *Chal'han che*. This challenge will leave the defender unharmed, but with his honor and prestige in tatters. The deadly version is known as *chal'han se* and usually results in the death of the defender.

The trick is that the defender does not know which version is being played.

The strictures of *chal'han* require both the challenger and the defender to act through intermediaries, known affectionately as "pawns," until the final moves. These pawns must also remain ignorant of their involvement in the Game. The player characters are Harlequin's pawns.

From the runners' point of view, what links each of the mini-adventures is the need to acquire an item in one adventure and then leave it behind in the current adventure. Each "item" is the symbolic representation of one of the previously mentioned aspects of Ehran's life, and by acquiring it, Harlequin fulfills an aspect of the Ritual.

In the opening adventure, **Physical**, the runners obtain the original hand-written manuscript of Ehran's next book, *Mankind Revealed*. They also inject a virus into the computer system of the company that intends to publish the book. The virus signals the beginning of *chal'han*, and the manuscript becomes the link to the next adventure.

In **Hates**, the runners leave behind an envelope containing (unknown to them) the title page of Ehran's manuscript. They also must get the six left-ear tips of the leaders of the Association Para-Nobilis, enemies of Ehran's pet policlub, the Young Elven Technologists.

In **Past**, the runners travel to Bavaria to acquire a rare medieval treatise on magic. In its place they leave a refrigerated case containing (again, unknown to them) the six ear-tips of the APN leaders.

In **Loves**, the runners deal directly with the Young Elven Technologists, acquiring and utilizing some back-door codes that YET deckers have installed in the systems of some prominent Seattle corporations. During the raid they also leave behind a sealed envelope containing the frontispiece of the tome stolen in the previous adventure.

Next is **Counterstroke**, where Ehran shows his anger at Harlequin's invocation of the Great Game. He threatens Harlequin's pawns—the runners—but he is bound by the Ritual not to harm them. The runners, of course, do not know this.

In **Spiritual**, the runners travel to Amazonia and the headwaters of the Amazon River. There, they steal a rare flower from a small plantation and leave behind an optical-chip copy of a fragment of the back-door program used by the YET.

In **Future**, the runners travel to Columbia, Missouri, UCAS, for a kidnapping. Their target is Ehran's hidden daughter and the final link Harlequin needs for the Ritual. In her place, the runners leave the flower.

Present is the climactic chapter where the final move of the Game is invoked and all hell breaks loose. An error occurs during the final ritual sending, and Harlequin sends the runners to determine Ehran's fate. Because this version of the Great Game is not supposed to lead to the death of one's opponent, Harlequin will lose the challenge if Ehran should die.

PHYSICAL

"Perish the universe, so long as I have my revenge."
—Cyrano De Bergerac, *La Morte d'Agrippine* (1653)

INTRODUCTION

Physical is the first mini-adventure in the **Harlequin** saga and deals with the Physical component of the *chal'han*. The target is Sylvan Information, a hypermedia publisher with exclusive rights to Ehran's books. The firm is currently editing and converting Ehran's latest work, *Mankind Revealed*, to a hypermedia format. The players team is hired to fulfill the Physical component of the *chal'han* by using a computer virus to delete the manuscript from Sylvan's computer and by stealing Ehran's unpublished manuscript.

Unless they make some major blunders, getting in and then out again with the document should make picking up this nuyen a breeze. It is what the adventure sets up for future **Harlequin** runs that is important.

SET IT UP

TELL IT TO THEM STRAIGHT

The last run was a thrill a minute; mages, miniguns, and mayhem. The word on the street is that you people are hot; a flare dazzling all who behold you. That isn't a rep someone living in the shadows necessarily wants, however. It means too many wannabes looking for you to prove how tough they are. Too many Lone Star cops who see you as their ride to a cushy administrative job down at headquarters. Time to go low-profile again, chummers. Time to carry off some jobs that show the fixers you know how to blend into the shadows. Time to take something simple. Something you can pull off with elegance and style rather than with an Assault Cannon and a GMC Banshee.

This message from a fixer seems to offer just such a chance. A fellow named Morlock will be waiting at midnight in the penthouse at Laubenstein Plaza at Sixth Avenue and Pike Street. Morlock is a Dwarf known for handling contracts for Mr. Johnsons who want services rendered in the most discreet manner.

Laubenstein Plaza is in downtown Seattle. One of the best hotels in the city, it sits in the heart of the shopping district, close to the harbor, with a great view of the Sound by day. You trek into town, arriving at 23:47 hours. That gives you a few minutes to look around.

The tower is 15 stories tall, with so many little balconies bulging from its circular walls that it looks like a purple sea cucumber. The lobby is high-ceilinged and plushly carpeted. To your left is a huge, old reception desk occupying a quarter of the room, complete with two Knight Errant security guards and a desk clerk. To your right is a bar and the room known as the Laubenstein Gallery.

The rest of the lobby is filled with overstuffed chairs and couches. A waitress in purple tights and a bodyshirt with plunging neckline strolls about taking drink orders. Some geriatric, sleepy-time music is piped in through hidden speakers. This late at night, the lobby is empty of all but a few suits looking for an opening line the waitress hasn't heard a thousand times before.

The night clerk tells you that Mr. Morlock has taken the whole top floor, and that you can go on up. He hands you a magkey for Elevator Three. You find the elevator and insert the key. The doors open to reveal four very large and very belligerent Orks staring you in the face.

"Hey chummer!" bellows one. "You ain't needed here! Go on back to the Barrens where you belong!"

BEHIND THE SCENES

This adventure works best if it starts just after the player characters have successfully completed a major run. If the gamemaster has worked with these runners before, he should take a few minutes to praise them effusively for their earlier accomplishments. Try to single out each player character for some special commendation. Let it be known that the word on the street is that this particular group is hot. Everyone and his little dog knows who the runners are. If the gamemaster has not worked with this group of runners before, he should build them up in general terms.

Being hot is two sides of the coin. On the positive side, the better the team's reputation, the more likely choice, high-paying jobs will come their way. On the downside, high reps mean that the government, corporate, or underworld powers-that-be will consider the group a threat and take action. Fixers do not like to hire runners who don't blend into the shadows well, and jobs can dry up. Emphasize this reality to the group, informing them that a few low-noise operations can help keep their reps intact with the fixers but keep them out of the limelight.

The encounter with the Orks on the elevator is a simple test. Morlock has set it up to gauge the group's resourcefulness in a crisis. He wants to see if the runners can work their way out of a tight spot without relying on automatic weapons. The Orks are really in his employ. Their orders are to hassle the runners, but not make it impossible to get through.

The thugs are equipped as below.

ORK THUGS

B	Q	S	C	I	W	E	M	R	Armor
3	3	4	4	4	6	—	3	2/1

Dice Pools: Defense (Armed) 4, Defense (Unarmed) 4, Dodge 3
Skills: Armed Combat 4, Firearms 4, Unarmed Combat 2
Gear: Sap (4M2 Stun)

Because the Orks have orders to let the party through if the runners show any initiative or imagination at all, the gamemaster should not have much difficulty roleplaying this situation to a successful conclusion. A few of the possibilities are:

1. The player characters attempt to talk and bribe their way through. Have a character make an Etiquette (Street) (5) Test. Any success indicates that the Orks can be bribed. Start their price at ¥5,000 nuyen. For each additional success, reduce the price by ¥1,000 nuyen.

2. The players arrange a diversion (fire, alarm, phone call, decoy, and so on) Make an Intelligence (5) Test for the character who thought it up. Any successes and the Orks will "fall for it" and go thundering off, allowing the runners to slip by and into Morlock's room.

3. Bluff the Orks out of the way. Make an Opposed Charisma Test with the Ork leader. If the player character wins, the Orks back down with a surly sort of grace. If the player character loses, the situation will devolve into a fight.

If all else fails, the players will have to fight their way through. If a brawl starts, the Orks will fight for three combat rounds, then break and run. That is, unless they manage to trash the runners in three turns or less. If the characters get themselves all beaten up, Morlock will be there when they awaken. Take the opportunity to lecture the players on the virtues of subtlety. Because the fight takes place near the elevator, the Orks will not be able to get more than four men into combat for the first two combat rounds.

Good roleplayers may find any number of other ways to get through this situation. Any imaginative solution will do, the cleverer the better. Once the team has bypassed the Orks, Morlock opens the door and invites them into his suite. Go to **Sign the Deal**.

SIGN THE DEAL

TELL IT TO THEM STRAIGHT

The Orks weren't that much of a problem. They were jander and bluster types who folded fast when faced with people who know which end of a monofilament whip to hold. But the…person…beckoning you into the room is something else.

He looks like a cross between a hump-backed Dwarf and a dour. His skin color might best be described as death white. As if that weren't enough, his clothes are purple satin trimmed with white and black lace!

"Gentlemen. I am J.P. Morlock. Please come in."

The Dwarf ambles into the apartment and you follow him. The air reeks with the smell of jasmine and stale sweat. Your host motions you to seats. He pours out wine and passes around a plate of what looks like real paté. He takes out a twisted cheroot and lights it.

"I represent parties looking to acquire some property. A literary work by Ehran the Scribe is to be published by Sylvan Information in the near future. My employers do not wish that work to see the light of day, but they cannot afford to be implicated in any theft. And that is where you come in, my friends. My contacts report that you may be the finest shadowrunners in this sprawling city. The mission I offer has two objectives. The first is to penetrate the Sylvan offices here in the city and get Ehran's manuscript. Being a bit archaic, Ehran has written the manuscript by hand, so it will be easy to identify. Second, you must penetrate the Sylvan computer mainframe and leave behind a virus in the datastore that contains electronic copies of the work. It is a simple viral program, which I will supply. Once activated, it will wipe out the information as well as plant some red herrings for anyone who may investigate.

"For a variety of reasons, the SAN access to the Sylvan system is very secure. I would most strongly recommend entering the system from within the physical building.

"Time is of the essence, so you will have only one week to accomplish this run. "

If the players team was able to get by the Ork guards without a fight, read this:

"Payment will be ¥5,000 nuyen each upon acceptance and ¥5,000 each upon delivery. I am adding an additional ¥2,000 nuyen as compensation for leaving intact any data not related to this run. Grubbing for extraneous data can jeopardize the operation. But you do seem to know how to accomplish your job with a minimum of force and I respect that.

"Your payment will be rendered in full once the manuscript is delivered to me.

"Are there any questions?"

If the runners were unable to get by the Ork guards without fighting, read them this:

"Payment is ¥3,000 nuyen each upon acceptance and ¥3,000 each upon delivery. I am adding an additional ¥1,000 nuyen as compensation for leaving alone any data not related to the run. I do not appreciate my runners freelancing on my time. It makes me look bad to my employers. Keep that in mind. Greedy runners don't always live so long.

"I *will* know if any extraneous Sylvan data appears on the open market. I won't allow people who cannot follow instructions to jeopardize my professionalism. In such a case, I shall take action.

"Are there any questions?"

BEHIND THE SCENES

Once the player characters have gotten past the Orks, Morlock leads them into his suite and plies them with wine and delicacies. The gamemaster should roleplay Morlock as an offensively rich version of Mick Jagger. If the runners attacked the Orks, Morlock shows only disdain. If they bluffed their way past the Orks, Morlock will treat them with the respect due professionals.

If the player characters negotiate the price with Morlock, make an Opposed Negotiation Test. For each net success that the player achieves, increase final payment by ¥500 nuyen for each player. If the team fought the Orks, increase the final payment by ¥250 nuyen each for each net success.

If the players have questions, the gamemaster/Morlock should answer them without revealing any more information than has been given above. The virus they are planting contains a program (see below) with a harmless message. The manuscript, which is about several hundred handwritten pages, will probably be in a safe in an editor's office. Morlock might suggest that Ehran probably chose to work with an Elven editor at Sylvan, but he might be wrong in that assumption. There is no backup for the team. They will be on their own.

GO ON IN

TELL IT TO THEM STRAIGHT

Sylvan Information headquarters is in the eastern part of the Bellevue District, a nice part of town where everyone has a SIN and unemployment is low (hah!). Bellevue is where many of Seattle's wealthiest have their estates. Though some Lone Star vehicles are always on patrol in the streets, most of the security is private and does not call attention to itself.

The Sylvan headquarters sits in the center of its own little landscaped park. Beautiful lawns surround the building, with walnut, oak, apple, and cherry trees dotting the grassy expanse. In the northeast corner of the grounds is an artificial lake holding three small islands linked by bridges. Beneath the surface, huge fish swim lazily back and forth, glittering gold, orange, and white.

The Sylvan building is three stories tall and faces south. It is roughly cruciform in shape, with each wing extending some 30 meters from the central foyer.

The second and third stories do not extend out over the arms of the cross, but rise up directly above the center of the building. On the south side is the main entrance, where two security guards sit in the glass-enclosed foyer during the day. At night the building is locked up, empty except for the caretaker who generally remains in his own quarters.

On the north side of the building a wide road leads to a loading dock and employees entrance. Off to the west is an underground parking area for employees only.

The loading dock doors are made of light-grade steel and are locked at night.

BEHIND THE SCENES

The shadowrunners must penetrate the building, locate the manuscript, download their virus, and escape. They may choose from any number of ways to gain access, but it probably should be done at night. More than 100 people are present inside the building by day, making illegal access difficult.

Possible means of access include the front doors, the rear doors, the windows on the ground floor of the east and west wings, and through the underground garage or barghest tunnel. All entrances are protected by maglocks and burglar alarms.

SYLVAN INFORMATION MAP KEY

ENTRANCE (A)

Entry is from the south through two double glass doors watched over by two uniformed guards. The guards are ordinary rent-a-cops, armed only with AZ-150 Super Stun Batons. (Use the **Corporate Security Guard** p. 165, **Shadowrun**.) They wear no armor.

Each desk has a PANICBUTTON for summoning a carful of heavily armed Lone Star Security men within three minutes. After 7:00 P.M. there are no guards.

The Reception Area

Three receptionists sit at a semi-circular desk that divides the waiting room from the main lobby. The waiting room is filled with plush chairs and couches done in lovely shades of Lincoln green and Arizona brown. The carpet is a thick-pile shag of deep maroon dappled with silver leaves in a seemingly random

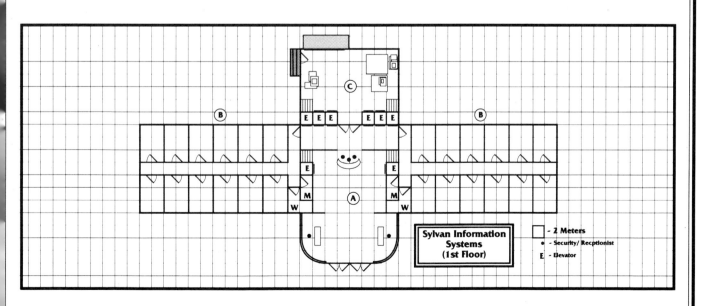

Sylvan Information Systems (1st Floor)

☐ - 2 Meters
● - Security/ Receptionist
E - Elevator

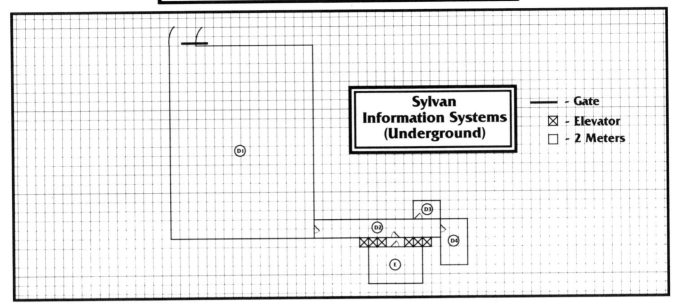

Sylvan
Information Systems
(Underground)

——— - Gate
⊠ - Elevator
☐ - 2 Meters

pattern. The receptionists have intercoms, telephones, and voice-activated terminals linking back to the main computer in the basement. They can provide coffee or tea upon demand from a low refreshment center behind the main desk.

Lobby

Dominating the lobby are stairs, elevators, and a pair of swinging doors leading to the loading and storage area. There are eight elevators total. The six on the north wall only go down to the underground area. The two on the south wall go up as well as down. The two stairways on the south wall also go up, while those on the north only go down. To the west is the Simsense Junior Editors Work Area. To the east is the Hard Media Junior Editors Work Area. The floor in the lobby is not carpeted, but is tiled with thousands of tiny ebony and ivory pieces.

JUNIOR EDITOR WORK AREAS (B)

There are two sections where Sylvan's junior editors work. Each section is identical. There are twelve cubicles in each work area, each one approximately three meters wide by six meters long.

Each cubicle contains one desk, two chairs, a filing cabinet, and a computer work station complete with fax, modem, monitor, printer, and data jack ports. In these cubicles various low-level sararimen work on Sylvan's everyday publishing projects.

These computer units are able to access the Sylvan computer system. A decker could jack in from any one of them, and either upload or download to the mainframe in the basement.

Each work area also contains one rest room, labeled M for Men and W for Women on the map.

LOADING DOCK (C)

Though Sylvan Information does not ship product, per se, it still needs a cargo area for its daily requirements.

Office furniture, computer hardware, supplies for the staff restaurant on the third floor, and other miscellaneous goods arrive occasionally and must be transported into the building without disrupting business. Such material comes in through the back door. A pair of guards with the same equipment as the front-door guards watches the area, allowing only company employees or authorized personnel access to the building.

A few pallets full of supplies to be unloaded sit here and there on the smooth concrete floor.

Employees who park underground enter the building through the six elevators that open both front and back between the lobby and the loading area.

UNDERGROUND (D)

A runner should not have to enter these areas, but in case one does, here is the description.

Parking Garage (D1)

The parking area is about 3.5 meters below the surface of the park above it. Entry is via a wide ramp leading up to the road to the back door. At night, a light steel gate rolls into place from the side and is maglocked shut to close off the ramp.

During the day it is generally about half-full.

Corridor (D2)

A four-meter wide hallway leads from the parking garage eastward to the barghest kennel and caretaker's quarters.

Along the south wall of the tunnel are six elevators that take employees up to the first floor. Security is weak here, with only the caretaker to watch the tunnel; he is not always present.

In the center of the south wall is a heavy steel door with a coded electronic lock (Maglock 5). It leads into the main computer room.

Caretaker's Quarters (D3)

The Caretaker/Kennelmaster lives in a one-room apartment near his beloved barghest hounds. It is his main job to feed and exercise them, setting them loose in the park at night and bringing them in before dawn. His quarters are furnished with a bed, stove, refrigerator, simsense player, and commode.

For the Kennelmaster, use the **Street Cop**, p. 171, **Shadowrun**.

Kennel (D4)

By day, the guard barghests are kept in a kennel at the east end of the underground corridor. The kennel has room for six hounds, but only four are presently being kept.

On the north side of the kennel, a narrow tunnel rises up to ground level to where a door is concealed near the side of the loading dock. After sundown, the caretaker can electronically open both upper and lower doors to allow the animals to get out for their nightly stint of guard duty.

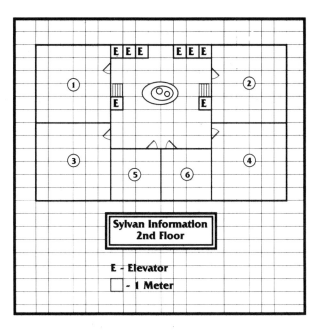

**Sylvan Information
2nd Floor**

E - Elevator
☐ - 1 Meter

MAIN COMPUTER ROOM (E)

Filled with mainframes and a few readout and input devices, the main computer room is kept at the freezing point by powerful refrigeration units because the computers work better in the cold. The north wall is all glass and shows an interior corridor running the width of the room, between the glass wall and the heavy doors that guard the entrance.

Computer techs usually do all their input and control work via terminals located in this corridor. A few light jackets hang on a coat rack at one end.

Sylvan uses the Sony-Cray 10000 mainframe, featuring sealed internal architecture and remote terminal access and maintenance facilities.

SECOND FLOOR

The second floor is where the bigwigs have their offices. All access is via elevators and stairs on the south wall. In the center of the area is a circular receptionist's desk. This receptionist deals only with people important enough to reach this level.

On this floor are two large offices and four smaller ones. All are substantially larger than the work cubicles down below. These offices belong to the following people, listed by order of importance:

1. Malachi Morgan, President and C.E.O. of Sylvan Information
2. Ngon Dinh Sum, Vice President and Director of Sylvan Information
3. Elrand Gylgalad, First Senior Editor, an Elf
4. Mark Fathom, Second Senior Editor
5. Sylvia Green, Third Senior Editor, an Elf
6. Mei Lei Fujiwara, Fourth Senior Editor

Each personage has his/her own office. Thick carpets, huge, old mahogany desks, and powerful, stand-alone computer stations mark the perquisites of rank. These computers are fully capable of working without using the mainframes in the basement.

In addition to the fancy furniture, each office contains a wall safe or a floor safe hidden behind false paneling somewhere near the desk. Those vaults store various important papers; that of CEO Morgan keeps half a million nuyen.

The gamemaster may place any documentation, paperwork, and/or money that he wishes inside these safes. The important thing is that Ehran's handwritten manuscript is in Sylvia Green's safe.

OPENING THE SAFES

These safes are the old-fashioned kind that do not lock magnetically or electronically. The best mechanical locks that money can buy keep these babies closed.

How can the players open these safes? A shaped thermite charge would work. Or someone with an appropriate Special Skill could do it with three or more successes against a Target Number 5. Or the characters could search out the combinations in Sylvan's Miscellaneous Files.

Gamemaster's Note: Inside Morgan's safe is a sheet of paper with the combinations to all the other safes, and a brief list of their contents. If the players crack Morgan's safe, they will learn that the document they want is in Green's safe, and the combination is 5L, 8R, 18L.

SYLVAN SECURITY

Other than general paranoia, Sylvan has no reason to suspect an attack. Security is light, consisting mainly of various alarms built into the building. Should an alarm sound, Lone Star is supposed to come quick and provide all the security needed.

The four company guards are normal Humans armed with stun batons. They come on duty every morning at seven and go off duty at seven in the evening. Use the **Corporate Security Guard** p. 165, **SR**, but swap Armed Combat for Unarmed Combat. Most Sylvan personnel are gone by four in the afternoon, though occasionally a junior editor will work late until six. No company personnel except executives and senior editors are allowed in the building after six in the evening.

Four barghests patrol the park grounds at night. The chance of meeting one is 1 in 6 (roll 1D6) for each game turn that one spends out on the grounds with them. These hounds have a fear-inducing sonic howl, and their bite is definitely worse than their bark. If they encounter an intruder, they will attack with intent to kill, and their howling will summon the other dogs. One more dog will arrive each combat turn until all four are in the fray. (The barghest is described on page 179 of the **SR** rules.)

The whole complex is surrounded by a three-meter-high electrified fence. Touching it without shielding results in a character suffering a 5M4 electric shock.

It is not easy to say how to play the raid on Sylvan. In general, the gamemaster should make the players come up with a plan of attack. If the plan seems brilliant, and likely to work, let it. If the plan is clumsy and lacks finesse, dump a carload of Lone Star goons on them. A vital part of this run is what the runners do on the computer. If the decker manages a successful run, give him all the information he needs to find the manuscript and escape. If he fails even to get online or is chewed up by the IC, don't give him anything.

HACKING SYLVAN

BEHIND THE SCENES

The computer system map for Sylvan Information Systems shows only a tiny bit of its complexity. There are 24 I/O terminals in the junior editors' cubicles. There are 6 independent computer modules networked to the system on the second floor of the Sylvan building with their own I/O nodes. There are innumerable files, some of which contain information vital to the players team.

SIS SYSTEM MAP

Sylvan Information Systems has spent an exorbitant amount of money sculpting the architecture of their computer system to appear as a primeval forest. Each individual file appears as a tree, with information stored on the leaves. Each subprocessor unit appears to the decker as a hexagonal stone tower guarded by knights in armor (IC). Each I/O port looks like a humble cottage. The SAN are drawbridges crossing the data streams flowing through it all. The CPU is a complete castle.

All authorized users have Elven personas.

From the outside, the Sylvan Information Systems construct appears as a simple system, a multi-hued, angular geometric form in the standard UMS (Universal Matrix Specifications) imagery. Once inside, however…

SAN #9206 (24-1209), (Red-8, Barrier 6, Blaster 5, Trace And Report 6): Once the user crosses the threshold (gets past the IC), the sculpted imagery begins. Suddenly, he is standing on an old wooden drawbridge crossing a stream (datapath) teeming with fish (data bundles). Ahead of him lies a forest primeval and a path.

SPU-1 (Red-5, Access 5, Killer 4, Trace And Report 5): Like the other SPUs in this system, this appears as a hexagonal tower set in a clearing. At its entrance sits an Elven knight resplendent in finery. He is the Access Program. A fox (Trace and Report) that looks more like a small dog sleeps at his feet.

Within the tower, the decker will find three more doorways, each leading to a path that heads off into the woods.

There is also a small stairway leading up into the tower. On that level, a series of short corridors lead off to a group of reflecting pools and crystals representing the various security control systems.

DS-1 (Green-5, Scramble 5): The corridor (datapath) leading to this node opens into a small medieval library with various tomes on shelves and piled about. The Scramble manifests as the archaic written words in the books. The information in these files is not particularly relevant to the run, and consists mainly of time records and personnel files.

I/O-1 (Orange-5, Access 1): This appears as a simple crystal ball. Sylvan security relies on the IC in the various important nodes rather than placing heavy-duty IC in their I/O nodes. The terminal this node represents is located in the security office.

SN-1 (Green-5): Appearing as a small reflecting pool, this node actually controls the internal and external security cameras at Sylvan. They all display into the security center.

SPU-2 (Green-5, Access 1): This tower has no guardian, but the grounds around it are in pristine condition. It is, of course, the building systems processor.

DS-2 (Green-5): Again a simple library, this one containing files of parts requisitions, maintenance schedules, and the like.

I/O-2 (Green-5): This terminal, physically located in the building maintenance office, is used to control the slave nodes attached to the building systems processor. It, too, appears as a crystal ball.

SN-2 (Green-5): This node controls the elevators in the building. It appears as an abacus.

SN-3 (Green-5): This node controls the exterior and interior locks for the building. It appears as a collection of locks and keys.

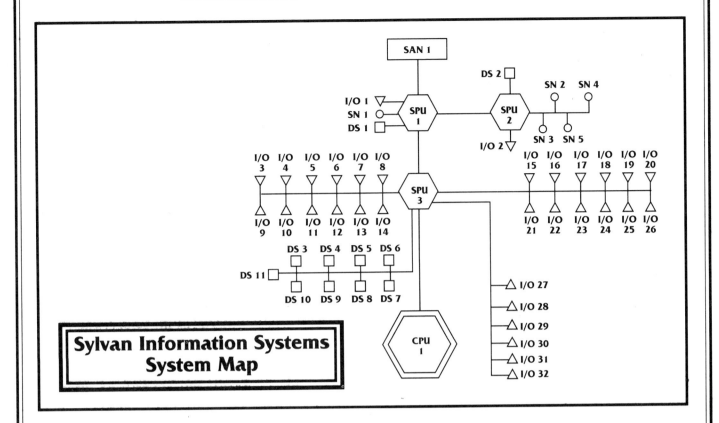

**Sylvan Information Systems
System Map**

SN-4 (Green-5): This node controls the heat sensors and fire systems in the building. It appears as a small, unlit brazier and tending utensils.

SN-5 (Green-5): This node controls the building's environment (heating and A/C). It appears as a "DiVinci"-style contraption routing cold and warm air as needed.

SPU-3 (Green-5, Access 2, Killer 3): The editorial processor again appears as the hexagonal tower, but this time it is "guarded" by a scribe seated at a desk. On that desk are many huge volumes identifying all those who are allowed access to the tower.

DS- 3-11 (Green-5, Scramble 4): These datastores are accessible to the entire editorial staff, junior and senior editors alike. It is here that the important Sylvan files will be found. They appear as library rooms.

I/O 3-26 (Green-5): These 24 I/O terminals are located in the junior editors' area on the first floor. Like the other I/O nodes in this system, they appear as crystal balls.

I/O 27-32 (Green-5): The six VIPs of the company, including the Senior Editors, use these terminals.

I/O 27	Mei Lei Fujiwara
I/O 28	Sylvia Green
I/O 29	Mark Fathom
I/O 30	Elrand Gylgalad
I/O 31	Ngon Dinh Sum
I/O 32	Malachi Morgan

CPU-1 (Red-8, Access 5, Black IC 6, Trace And Report 6): The CPU appears as a large castle guarded by a humanoid black Dragon who lurks in the ramparts atop the castle walls. The Access program manifests as numerous Elven knights lining the path to the castle.

JACKING IN

Once the shadowrunners are inside the Sylvan building, they can jack into the computer system from any of 30 different points. Of the gray and black IC encountered inside the Sylvan system, each variety of IC appears as a different beast or pack of beasts.

Gray IC

Blaster IC will appear as 1D4 + 1 coyotes. Coyotes nip and nibble at their foes, but major damage, that is, dumping the decker's persona and frying his deck, is done by howling after their victims have been subdued.

Killer IC will appear as 1D3 wolverines. Wolverines simply shred the personas, stunning the decker and his hitchhikers if it succeeds.

Trace IC takes the form of a fox. The fox does not fight, but instead darts off into the woods. Follow the normal Trace rules from the **Shadowrun** rules.

Black IC

Black IC appears as one vaguely humanoid black Dragon. (Imagine a Dragon of Human configuration, but complete with tail and vestigial wings.) It has ebony-black scales on its back and head, shading to a dark, cloudy gray on the inner sides of limbs and torso. The black Dragon also behaves like a magician, capable of fireballs and other offensive spellcasting. The black Dragon merely wants to kill any unauthorized intruder in the Sylvan Forest.

EXPLORING THE SYLVAN SYSTEM

The shadowrunners must enter the Sylvan system through the SAN, an I/O node in a junior editor's cubicle, or through an I/O node in one of the second-floor offices.

They will seem to be in a forest while inside the system. The forest teems with life; birds flit from tree to tree, squirrels run and leap, clouds of insects hover over small pools of water, frogs hop, snakes slither.

Talk it up good. Most of these actions represent the normal ebb and flow of electronic communication within the system.

Other systems show such minutiae as walls of light or swiftly changing letters and numbers. Have a blue jay dive-bomb the group or have gnats bite at their faces. Go ahead and make them nervous, but only the four creatures described above are actually hostile. To really rattle the characters, have a bear come up alongside them on a parallel path or let them spot a sasquatch watching them through a thicket of leaves.

Searching Files

The Sylvan system contains hundreds of files. They are grouped into nine categories. Though almost any file might be worth a few hundred or thousand nuyen on the street to the right people, only a couple deserve special consideration. If the players can find the important ones, give them extra Karma Points at the adventure's conclusion. The file types are:

1. Music (DS-3)
2. Simsense (DS-4)
3. Dynabooks (DS-5)
4. Graphic Publications (DS-6)
5. Administrative (DS-7)
6. Personnel (DS-8)
7. Artists (DS-9)
8. Restricted (DS-10)
9. Miscellaneous (DS-11)

Important files that can be located include:

File 6-001 contains the records of Malachi Morgan; File 6-002 covers Ngon Dinh Sum; 6-003 covers Elrand Gylgalad; 6-004 covers Mark Fathom; 6-005 covers Sylvia Green; 6-006 covers Mei Lei Fujiwara. Each file is linked to its corresponding file in section 9 showing safe combinations (ex: 6-005 links to 9-205). The gamemaster can put anything he wants into the other editors' safes, as the only really important one is Sylvia Green's.

File 8-007 is large, about 240 Mp. It contains generations of genealogical and biomedical data on dozens of families. The oldest piece of information in the file is dated 1834. The file is structured in an elaborate data base, with each family's records occupying one block of data. All the blocks contain a final entry stating "Surveillance Terminated" and listing a date ranging from 14 months to 40 years ago. Each family/data block seems to be focused on a single individual or closely related members of a group. If an investigating character makes a successful Perception (10) Test, he will notice that all surveillance and monitoring stops at the point where a medical report indicates a serious illness or when the subject(s) in question reach their late thirties or early forties.

If a full search of the data is made, it will become obvious that one data block has been deleted. If the decker (or another programmer) makes a successful Computer (12) Test, he can learn the information given on the Success Table below.

Successes	Result
1	The information was deleted as part of a normal system command. The only other obtainable information is that the data block was part of a regional subset for the Midwest.
2	As above, plus enough flags and pointers remaining in other data blocks to indicate that the primary focus of the block was a female apparently in her late twenties.
3	As above, plus the investigating character finds the remains of a tag linking this data block to external monitoring programs within the system. In other words, as information was inserted into this block, it was echoed to somewhere else in the system.
4+	As above, plus the character discovers that the file was deleted but never closed, as were the others in the file.

File 9-201 contains the combination for the safe in the CEO's office on the second floor. Files 9-202 through 9-206 contain the combinations for the other safes. The important one is 9-205, Sylvia Green, who has the handwritten manuscript in her safe.

The Viral Program

This viral program is a sophisticated piece of work. If a decker (or anyone else) attempts to analyze it, he will find that, in its current state, it is compressed. When activated, the program apparently decompresses and goes to work. In its current form, it takes up 20 Mp of space in the decker's cyberdeck. It takes two turns to decompress.

A successful Computer (or appropriate Special Skill or Concentration/Specialization) (15) Test will reveal that the program first burrows deep within the system, then appears a day or so later as a high-resolution image of a Renaissance-period rapier on all the terminals in the system. That's it. Well, that and the fact that it hunts down and erases all copies of *Mankind Revealed* in the system.

Note also that to plant the viral program, it is only necessary to reach a datastore, perform a system function within the node, and release the program's icon, which appears as a harmless little bunny. It will promptly burrow into the forest floor, then disappear until time to announce itself. There will be no other effect for the decker to perceive.

If he attempts to copy the program, he will discover that in six days it has activated itself and is beginning to occupy, at 10 Mp per hour, whatever memory-storage system the file is in, destroying any files currently in residence. The only way to get rid of the virus is to erase the memory completely. Attempting to transfer files from the affected memory will drag the virus with them.

Penetrating the Castle

Entering the CPU is unnecessary. The black Dragon guarding the one approach, plus the numerous Elven knights in silver armor around its front gate will probably discourage the players from even trying. If they do force their way in, assume that a fox (Trace and Report) has been dispatched to locate the decker.

If Lone Star security gets into the picture, count on at least three cars with two men in each. If the mission goes haywire, the runners might be able to fight their way past these guys and escape. (Use the **Street Cop**, p. 171, **SR,** if necessary. Arm them appropriately.)

PICKING UP THE PIECES

AFTER THE RUN

If everything has gone successfully, the runners now have Ehran's manuscript and they have planted the virus. They will get away from Sylvan Information Systems the same way they came in. When they set up their next meeting with Morlock to collect the rest of their fee and to turn over the manuscript, they will have no difficulty getting into the rooftop suite at Tower 801 to meet him.

If the players blew it at any stage in the preceding scenario, the most likely outcome is for them to wake up either in a Lone Star holding cell or in a hospital. Lone Star will hold them for a couple of weeks, questioning them repeatedly. Providing the runners do not further incriminate themselves, the cops will eventually turn them out on the streets. If the characters end up in a hospital, they will get out when their wounds heal, hitting the streets poorer but no wiser. The advance that Morlock gave them should cover most of their medical bills.

If the adventure has failed but the gamemaster would like to play on, he could assume that Morlock later hired some other shadowrunners who succeeded in obtaining and delivering the manuscript to him. He simply passes the papers to the next Mr. Johnson when it seems appropriate to run the next mini-adventure in the **Harlequin** story.

MANKIND REVEALED

If any runner takes the time to read *Mankind Revealed,* he will discover several things. First, Ehran has terrible handwriting. Second, he has written the book in English. Third, it reads like so much neo-philosophical trash. The most anyone can figure out is that the book predicts a future where all mankind lives happily and in harmony. It'll sell millions.

AWARDING KARMA

This run is the kind the runners should be skilled at pulling off by now. If not, they definitely should be looking for another line of work.

The team should receive the following Karma Points for the run:

Successfully retrieving the manuscript	3 pts
Successfully planting the virus	2 pts
Acquiring the genealogy file*	1 pt

*The gamemaster should award the point, but not reveal why.

Individual Karma should be awarded as per the rules on page 160 of **Shadowrun**.

HATES

"The Association Para-Nobilis was founded in 2040. Its purpose is to protect *Homo Nobilis*, the Elves so much in danger from today's society. During the riots of 2039, a total 4,739 Elves were killed. An Elf is killed every day in the Seattle streets purely because of Human fear and prejudice. The Association Para-Nobilis was founded to show that in this place, at this time, Humans can stand beside their Elven brethren, helping them to be all they were truly intended to be."

—From a pamphlet distributed by the Association Para-Nobilis, Seattle, 2051

INTRODUCTION

The above excerpt from a flyer distributed in many of Seattle's lower schools earlier this year is a direct quotation from the Association Para-Nobilis constitution and represents the highest hopes and principles of APN founder, Leo Ridgeworth. Ridgeworth's death in 2043 forever changed the course of his former organization. The circumstances surrounding the monorail accident that took his life were suspicious, but no one could ever prove foul play. Aaron Mitchell, former secretary to Ridgeworth, took over the 27-member group.

Convinced that Ridgeworth's death was murder, Mitchell trained the 27 APN members as soldiers and launched a small covert "war" to destroy the group's enemies. Many of the organization's opponents died, but only six APN members survived. After several months, Mitchell (now known as Xeric) called a halt to the violence and began a recruitment drive to rebuild the APN. It was not long before membership began to swell.

The group's current membership is at about 300 members. Most do no more than attend the weekly meetings and pass out literature, but the Council of Elders (consisting of the six survivors of the "war") live and breathe the ancient Elven stories, which they attempt to pass on to the other APN members. In the last two years, the APN has been aggressively promoting a return-to-nature philosophy as the ideal way of life for Elves. Their fanatic belief extends to terrorist attacks on anyone, Elven or not, who opposes their ideas. Indeed, the APN and the Young Elven Technologists have often butted heads. The leaders of the APN are certain a YET attack is imminent and they are prepared for it. This is the situation as the runners come on the scene.

WETWORK

TELL IT TO THEM STRAIGHT

You receive a standard telecom call requesting a meeting at Takuri's, one of the nicer restaurants in downtown Seattle. The caller, a pleasant-voiced woman, identifies herself as Charlie. She says she wants to discuss doing business with you.

When you arrive, Takuri's is fairly full, but the dim lighting prevents you from identifying anyone (or anyone from identifying you). The headwaiter, a big Japanese in classic kimono, smiles slightly when you ask for Charlie. He nods and conducts you to a door that looks like the entrance to a coat closet. Instead, it opens into a small, private dining room where three people are waiting.

The middle person is Charlie Tarrow, a woman just starting to lose her natural good looks. Not even cybernetics and cosmetics can give her the beauty that once needed no prompting.

To her left is Wyrd, a Human male, probably a razor. His eyes flick quickly over each of you before settling on the group's leader. Wyrd wears his red hair in a high-top fade, and from the looks of it, more than nature and static electricity are holding it up. He's dressed in Trés Chic synth leathers.

The third, Trey, is young, no more than 18. Unlike the other two, he's not used to this sort of thing. Everything about him shows it, from his crisply new lined coat to his quick, careless motions. His blond hair is slicked back, giving him the look of a refugee from an old vampire movie. The only one of the three who is visibly armed, he carries a Streetline Special in a quick-release shoulder holster.

Charlie is the old-fashioned type; she'll order and eat dinner before discussing business. You don't object because this is a great opportunity to eat something besides SushiSoy, and she's paying. When everyone has had their fill, Charlie asks Trey to stand watch outside, then begins to explain the particulars of the run.

"Maybe you've heard of the group known as the Association Para-Nobilis? The public knows them as proponents of the Elven ideal, but my client has a somewhat different view." At this point, Charlie tosses the leader of your group an envelope. Inside are some old-fashioned photographs, the kind very few people know how to sabotage anymore. They are photos of Elves who have been murdered, and the cause of death is always an archaic weapon such as a sword, bow, and so on.

"The APN has been killing Elves who don't believe in their 'Elven ideal' concept of skipping through meadows while playing a fragging lute. My client wants them eliminated. He's offering ¥20,000 nuyen, plus certain bonuses that I will explain in a moment."

"The APN headquarters building is near the Renraku Arcology—in its shadow would be more accurate. The target of the run are the six core members of the APN who live at the headquarters. It'll be tough, but I believe you can do it without bringing the Renraku Reds down on your heads.

"I spoke of bonuses earlier. The first is for dropping this off." (She holds up a sealed envelope.) "You are to leave this on the lap of the APN leader, who I like to call Xeric the Mad. This part of the run is worth an extra ¥2,500 nuyen."

"The second bonus is for a bit of head-hunting. The APN is composed almost entirely of posers, Elf wannabees who've had surgery and/or wear false ear tips to look more like Elves. My client wants the false left ear tip of each APN core member, for a further bonus of ¥3,000 nuyen per tip. These bonuses bring the combined total for the job to approximately ¥40,000 nuyen, which should be more than enough for a night's work. Actually, my client cares little for the final condition of the APN, as long as they are shut down, the six ear tips are collected, and the envelope delivered. Well, posers?"

BEHIND THE SCENES

She leans back in the chair to let the runners discuss it among themselves. She expects them to accept the princely sum, but can go up another 10 percent if necessary. She claims total ignorance of the meaning behind the conditions to the run. In fact, about the only thing she knows is why she's calling the runners "posers." (They're posing as shadowrunners. A private joke between herself and Wyrd.)

The run has no deadline, but, obviously, the sooner it's done, the sooner the runners get paid. Charlie offers ¥5,000 nuyen as an advance payment, which is negotiable up to ¥10,000 more if the runners really need it. Of course, if they need the money that bad, they had better not be negotiating for a high price. If the runners need additional firepower, she will arrange it, for a ¥500 nuyen service charge. Wyrd and Trey are the two she trusts most; Wyrd because of long experience, and Trey because he's too loyal to try anything. Either will require a full share of the payment for the job.

Charlie Tarrow and Wyrd were shadowrunners before the term was popular. A network of fixers that they thought had fallen apart 20 years ago has contacted them to arrange this job. They're uncomfortable because far too many people know they're involved.

Intelligent runners will probably try to get more information about the APN and its base of operations before they go in there to geek the core members. There are three main ways to find out more about the APN and its headquarters: The runners can get the floor plans of the building if they think to check with the Public Works works records (the original plans, at least; it *was* a city building years ago). They can interrogate a non-core member of the APN or go to a meeting themselves (assuming they have a non-Elf willing to dress in the requisite phony ears, hair, and leather leggings). Finally, they can try to get info on the streets, but that is the most dangerous and the least reliable method.

Note that if the runners somehow open the sealed envelope, they will find it contains the manuscript title page of Ehran's *Mankind Revealed*.

DEPARTMENT OF PUBLIC WORKS (SHIAWASE CORPORATION)

The Public Works' staff is upset with these runners trying to get information from them. "They don't have authorization, they aren't law enforcement or corp employees, and they walked into *my* office carrying *guns*!" After the runners have heard lectures from a couple of employees on the wisdom of bringing *guns* into *their* office, someone will ask them what they want. That's the start of a whole other problem. "*What* building? Oh, that building. Well, it's not a current city structure, so we wouldn't have the plans." What they aren't saying is that the original plans *would* be in the Archive section. If any of the runners really starts trying to communicate, someone will take pity on the group and mention it.

The Public Works Archive Hall once was an underground nuclear shelter, and still retains the concrete walls, the bare light bulbs, and the screech of rodents in the dark. To get there is a simple matter of finding the entrance in the building's sub-basement behind the door marked MEN and then descending 14 flights of stairs. Roughly 150 meters wide by 40 meters long by 5 meters high, the room is filled with files dating back to presidential election results from 1900. In one corner is Harriet's office, which contains an old, overstuffed easy chair, an even older TV, and of course, a computer terminal linked into the modern filing system that is overloaded with current data.

Harriet is in charge of the Archive Office. As she'll tell anyone she meets, she's 88 and has run the office for the last 47 years. She's a little bit deaf, but is pleasant and the only person in the city who might possibly be able to help the runners. About 35 years ago, the city tried to computerize all the information here, but soon after they finished, the virus hit and trashed all the records. When Shiawase Corporation won the contract to administer Seattle's Public Works Department, they tried to fire Harriet. What they soon learned, however, was that the department could not function without her.

Harriet is just under a meter and a half tall, weighs 36 kilos, and looks as if the ceiling fan could blow her away. She normally wears a flowered sun dress and reading glasses and needs a step ladder to reach the top shelves. She'll immediately drop everything to help the "nice young people."

Harriet is a little bit senile, but can provide some good information. About two weeks ago, a YET member stopped in, also looking for the plans to the APN headquarters in preparation for a raid. If the runners treat her well, she could also connect them with a powerful ally in her daughter, Kerry.

The most charming runner, if there is one, should make a Charisma (4) Test.

Successes	Result
0	Harriet finds the plans after three hours of looking through the files and having the big, strong runners move stacks of paper for her. Give the runners a copy of the map, but don't tell them about the sealed doors.
1	Harriet finds the plans in about two hours, then mentions that someone else was here looking for the same plans about two weeks ago.
2	The other person looking for the plans was an Elf who looked like a samurai. Harriet also offers the runners some Aunt Sara's Baked Brownies.
3+	Harriet finds an update of the plans, which mentions that an elevator to the basement was installed (draw it on the map). She also offers to introduce her daughter to one of the runners.

INTERROGATION/INFILTRATION

There are two ways to approach Interrogation/Infiltration. Either the runners will have to corner a current member of the APN and question him about the organization, or they can sneak one of their own into a meeting. Either method presents problems.

Interrogation

The APN, in addition to its weekly Thursday night meetings, keeps a reception area open so anyone can stop in and talk. The runners could either stop an APN member on his way home from a meeting or wait for a member leaving with literature for some of the area schools. (Use the **Human Pedestrian Contact**, p. 116, **Sprawl Sites**.)

The information they can get, however, is limited. Unless by sheer chance they manage to grab one of the six core members of the group, they probably will get no more than the plans of the first floor. (Most fringe members never leave the first-floor assembly area).

Infiltration

This method is slightly better than the other, but not much. The APN's weekly Thursday night meetings sponsor talks by members on subjects as diverse as: "The Role of Elves in Modern Society," "The Humanis Threat," "Thwarting Misguided Metahumans," and so on. Because APN members are all Elf posers, a real Elf might have a problem passing himself off as a poser. If discovered, he will be either honored or attacked, depending on his reputation.

If he's a "worthy" Elf (one who wanders around with swords and bows, rides an animal, and so on), they will all want to be like him. If he's a standard street samurai with wires and cyber-everything, they'll be a bit upset. A Human would have an easier time posing as a poser-Elf member, but might find it annoying to wear false ears, fake fur clothing, and a sword.

Infiltration will yield the floor plans of the first floor, and also show the runners how the senior APN members look and dress. (Important clues if their mission is to kill them.) The runners will also hear a lecture on "The APN and Its Role in Today's World," a two-hour diatribe lauding the organization.

STREET CONTACTS

The APN has some corp backing. Any snitch or gander-girl knows that so the runners won't have to roll any dice to find that out. All they need do is ask. Only two groups on the street will dare oppose the organization. One is the Young Elven Technologists, the Elven group that calls for Elves to work and live in the modern world without sugar coating or complaint. The other is Sceptre Productions, a media outfit that lost a video crew five months ago. The runners will have to approach one of these two groups before they'll get anything but doubledrek and jetwash.

Young Elven Technologists

The runners will be able to contact the Young Elven Technologists fairly easily, but YET members will only say, "The Young Elven Technologists believe in the ability of *Homo Nobilis* to exist and prosper in the world without resort to stereotypes that may be eons-old but are still inaccurate. In this, we are diametrically opposed to the Association Para-Nobilis, and attempt to combat their misconceptions as always: through logical, reasoned debate."

Sceptre Productions

The runners may have better luck with Sceptre. When they call Sceptre, they are referred to a woman who tells them that a crew was lost several months ago near the Aztechnology pyramid. This is the only information she will release unless the runners can pique her interest by mentioning either the information Harriet Taylor gave them or the photos Charlie Tarrow gave them. Otherwise, her response is simply "No comment." If they mention their information, however, she invites them to meet her later that evening to exchange data, giving the team an address in a high-class part of town.

The address belongs to a townhouse in the corp sector, a two-story luxury affair that probably costs someone a good 30 grand a month. City records list the townhouse's owners as Sceptre Productions and its current inhabitant as Kerry Taylor, a freelance reporter noted for embarrassing corps and runners alike with stories of their human-rights violations.

A dark-haired woman in her early thirties, Kerry is the daughter of Harriet Taylor. The Sceptre video crew lost five months ago was led by her "significant other," and she's out for blood.

Kerry explains that the lost crew consisted of four people assigned to monitor the APN after Sceptre heard rumors that APN members might be murdering Elves. The crew's bodies were found only by chance the night after a bloodbath in a computer club owned and patronized by Elves. A still-functioning wristphone led DocWagon to the corpses, which were buried in a meter of ceracrete. Three days later, Taylor quit her job and volunteered to expose the APN for Sceptre.

For once, Kerry doesn't care whether or not she gets a story, as long as this association of "Elf-protectors" gets nuked. If she has to ally with the runners to do it, she will. As she explains to the group, their kind of "white magic" the world can do without.

Kerry is not all that she seems, but she is careful not to reveal her magical talents unless absolutely necessary. She considers her magical abilities a convenient ace in the hole. On the other hand, she will reveal all that she knows about the APN's inner circle, including their descriptions and photos.

Kerry has been on this crusade for four months, harassing the APN until they are certain she's connected with their YET enemies. Indeed, the APN has scheduled Kerry's swan song for this very night. About an hour after the runners arrive at the townhouse, APN spies decide that the runners are part of the conspiracy. There will be four more APN members than runners present, with Erendahl watching outside. His intent is not to engage, but instead to see just how tough these new minions of the YET are. After the fight (assuming the runners win), he will leave, reporting to the Council of Elders that the runners are formidable, and advising that the Council hire mercs or runners of their own.

THE RAID

TELL IT TO THEM STRAIGHT

When Charlie said the APN headquarters was in the shadow of the Renraku Arcology, she wasn't kidding. The Arcology has a technologically advanced system that routes sunlight (what there is in Seattle) into the depths of the building to illuminate the inner parks and residence levels. Some of the light is also bounced to the far side of the building to illuminate those parts of downtown Seattle that would literally be in the Arcology's shadow most of the day. Regardless, the APN headquarters lies in a shadow, an apparent design flaw.

By evening, the display lights of the Arcology cast a diffuse glow over the area, keeping the building well-lit. The time of greatest darkness and deepest shadow? Just after dawn.

BEHIND THE SCENES

The headquarters of the Association Para-Nobilis is an old two-story building. It is home to 19 APN members and has up to two dozen cycles chained to the rack at any one time. Because the runners should be trying to avoid wholesale slaughter and trying to avoid attracting the attention of the Renraku Security forces, a quiet raid during the early morning hours stands the best chance of success. Statistics are given for entry during these hours.

The ground floor consists of the APN's main meeting rooms. Weekly Thursday meetings are held in the garage that once housed city vehicles, and several other rooms serve as smaller meeting rooms where the Council of Elders confers or briefs its closest followers. Because large trucks were once garaged on the ground floor, the ceiling is more than four meters high. Fierelle lives on this floor, but that is not common knowledge.

The second floor contains the sleeping quarters for most APN members who actually live here. In addition, standard APN procedure calls for the members to set up at prepared defense points on the second floor, should it ever become necessary to defend the Councilors. Also on the second floor is Xeric's office, where he keeps the APN's records on countless stacks of paper, with not a terminal in sight.

The basement is the most difficult of the three floors to reach, as it is accessible only by the ladder or the cargo elevator from the first floor. The basement is used for storage as well as for weapons practice. Thiran the Weapons Master usually sleeps down here rather than submit to the scrutiny of the rest of the APN. Also down here is an animal that is the symbol of the APN: a horse surgically altered to look like a unicorn.

The APN is expecting the Young Elven Technologists to make a hit on them soon, so temporary watches have been set. At any one time, there are at least four posers awake and armed. In addition, if an alarm is raised or heavy weapons fired, Lone Star will be called in (responding in 2D6 minutes) to investigate both the APN and any runners caught on the premises.

RUNNING THE RAID

As in **Physical,** the events of this mini-adventure are straightforward. Yet that is exactly why it is almost impossible to predict what approach the runners will take for the raid. They could opt for subtlety or just as easily choose the "in-through-the-front-door-gun-ablaze" approach. Or anything in between.

As the player characters make their plans, the gamemaster must pay close attention, all the while deciding where to position APN members and what other events may occur during the raid. Ultimately, the raid will be resolved through flat-out combat, and the gamemaster may have to wait till then for many of his decisions. He may even *want* to wait till then so he can factor in the current situation.

GROUND FLOOR

Elevator Room (1)

On the walls of this room are ancient posters singing the joys of being a member of the Seattle Fire Department. The room is otherwise empty. One of the room's two light switches is next to the door and the other is on the wall opposite.

If anyone examines the floor closely, he will notice the cut-out of the elevator in the northeast section of the room. The light switch opposite the door controls the elevator. When it is up (as it is currently), the elevator is here on the ground floor.

Storage Room (2)

This is a storage room for tools APN members use to repair their bikes and other items around the headquarters. The door on the north wall leading to the elevator room is larger than normal; two meters high by two meters wide.

Video Room (3)

This is where the APN keeps most of its audio-visual equipment, old as it may be. Amid the clutter of old slide projectors, video-disk players, and so on is a ladder leading down through the floor.

Meeting Room (4)

The main meeting room of the APN has floor-to-ceiling wall murals depicting scenes from the works of Tolkien and other fantasy authors. Hanging between the murals are samples of ancient Elven weaponry (swords, bows, and such), but they are fakes. On the north side of the room is a raised dais with a projector screen, several chairs, and a podium. Facing the dais are rows of folding wood chairs.

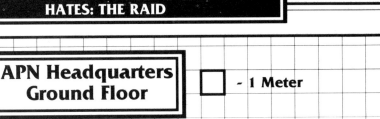

**APN Headquarters
Ground Floor**

☐ - 1 Meter

If an alarm has already been raised, four APN members will be set up on the east side of the room, defending the entrance to Room (2). One will be armed with a Uzi III. Their goal is to delay any invaders and possibly lead them to believe that the upper-level access is in Room (2). If no alarm has been raised, the room is empty.

Admissions Office (5)

A small admissions office, this room has a window facing out on Area (6) for reception purposes. Next to the phone on the desk in the center of the room is a small white button. This white button is a silent alarm switch that activates a beeper in the rooms of the councilors and the main bunkroom. At least one person is always here, sitting in the dark and trying not to panic and hit the button. Because of several false alarms, Xeric will call the office to check up on the guard anytime the alarm is activated. Only if he gets no answer or if the guard on duty verifies the alarm will Xeric raise the alert. If the alarm has already been raised, there will be three people here, armed and wearing Armor Vests with Plates.

Lounge (6)

This small lounge area has a vidscreen on the east wall, with a couch facing it.

If the alarm has not been raised, a seven-year-old girl is sleeping quietly on the couch. If questioned, she can provide the runners with the location of the "Red Woman's" bedroom at the end of the hall (Room 11). If the alarm has been raised, she will be under the couch.

The girl is not involved with the APN. She only sneaks in here every so often with the unofficial approval of Fierelle. When questioned by a sympathetic runner, little Maria may talk about the "Red Woman's" questions, mainly concerning the ethics of killing someone to preserve his purity. Of course, the little girl will not phrase it that way.

Propaganda Room (7)

This small room contains multiple racks of APN pamphlets, statistics, and studies. Whether or not the alarm has been raised, the room is empty.

Office (8)

This office is where Xeric does his indoctrinations of new "converts" to the APN. In a glass case at the front of the room is a quill pen that has been bronzed. A small plate identifies it as once having been used by the Elven sage Xeric. The only other item of interest is an Ares Predator II in a side drawer of the desk.

Another white alarm button is in the knee well of the desk. The room is empty, whether or not the alarm has been raised.

Bedroom (9)

This is the bedroom of Blaine Deathedge. Decorated in shades of black and gray, it resembles a war museum almost as much as it does a cemetery. The walls are festooned with various types of lethal hardware, from an AVM to an original Bowie knife. Almost any type of weapon can be found in here. A military cot in the corner has a panel of red and green alarm lights facing the head.

If an alarm has not been raised, there is a 50-percent chance that Deathedge will be awake and meditating here. If the alarm has been raised, he will wait inside with his HK227 (explosive ammo) until it is evident that the attackers are elsewhere. Then he will leave the room, find whatever flunkies are left alive, and attempt to assault the rear of the invading force.

Bathroom (10)

Once an institutional facility, this bathroom has been refitted with a tub to make it a private bathroom.

If the alarm has not been raised, there is a one-in-six chance that an APN member is leaving the room as the runners arrive. If the alarm has been raised, the room is empty.

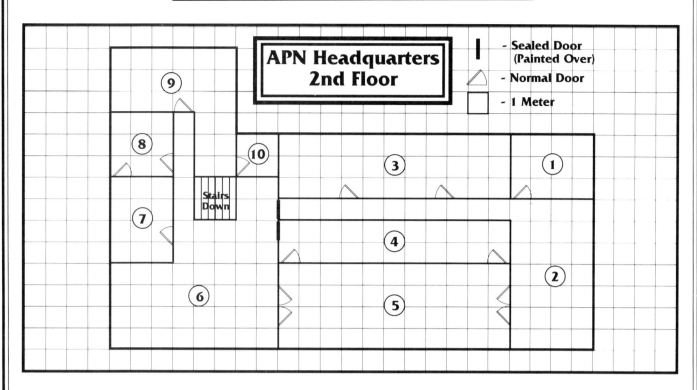

**APN Headquarters
2nd Floor**

| - Sealed Door (Painted Over)
△ - Normal Door
□ - 1 Meter

Red Woman's Bedroom (11)

On duty outside this room is a guard armed not only with the standard Ares Crusader of the APN, but also with a Uzi III. Inside, the large room looks like a blood-red version of an Arabian Nights tale. Sitting among the red veils, red bedclothing, red walls, and red carpets is a woman dressed entirely in red. She is awake and watching you from a bed in the corner.

For several weeks, Fierelle has wondered about the morality of killing Metahumans to preserve their purity, and is slowly starting to realize that something is not quite right. The fact that little Maria in the lounge thinks it's murder does not help.

When the alarm is raised, Fierelle will simply remain here, wondering whether she has the right to kill anymore. Because of this, her instinctive reaction will be to talk, not shoot. If the runners take the time to speak to her calmly, they might well get her to help, or at least not hinder them. If asked, she will give up the cosmetic ear tips she wears. Of course, if little Maria is still with the runners, having her run across the room screaming, "Don't hurt the Red Woman" may also be an incentive.

SECOND FLOOR

Bedroom (1)

This is Allair Shadowdeath's room. Photographs of well-known media and vid stars are pinned to the walls. The subjects of the photos invariably have blood-red circles drawn around them. Underneath the bed in the corner is a pile of rubbish. On top of it is a balding man with pointed ears who wears a long, flowing black robe.

Because Allair has no combat abilities, whether or not the alarm has been raised, he is here asleep. If the runners wake him, he immediately claims to be the "Great and Powerful Mage of Death" and demands that they kneel before him. The BTL chip in his chipjack makes him say this and believe it, too.

Workroom (2)

This looks like a magician's workroom from a bad horror sim, and that's about what it is. A workbench on one side of the room holds beakers that, upon closer examination, prove to contain different Sloppy Soy mixes.

If there is not yet an alarm, one guard is here, cursing and wishing he had drawn duty in one of the other two guardposts. If the alarm has been raised, there will be four men, excluding Allair, behind the overturned workbench. If the runners have broken through the sealed door by the stair, they will manage to come in behind the guards. If not, the guards are considered to have Cover. The four guards are armed with the standard weapons. Allair has an HK227.

Storeroom (3)

This old storeroom contains video equipment worth about ¥30,000 nuyen, as well as three AVMs. The room is unguarded.

The AVMs are not currently functional, but an armorer could repair them for about ¥5,000 nuyen. If anyone takes the time to look, it will be immediately obvious that the missiles will explode if fired, doing 4S4 damage to anything within four meters.

Bathroom (4)

This is a communal bathroom for the resident male members of APN in the building. The eastern half has shower stalls facing sinks, and the western half bathroom stalls.

If no alarm has been raised, there will be 1D6 – 3 members present. If the alarm has been raised, it will be empty.

Bunkroom (5)

This bunkroom holds the beds for most of the male members of the APN. The 13 beds are arranged in rows along both walls. A footlocker is at the base of each bed.

Every other footlocker contains an Ares Crusader Machine Pistol among the clothing and toiletries. If the alarm has not been raised, there will be 3D6 APN members here. If it has been raised, no one is present.

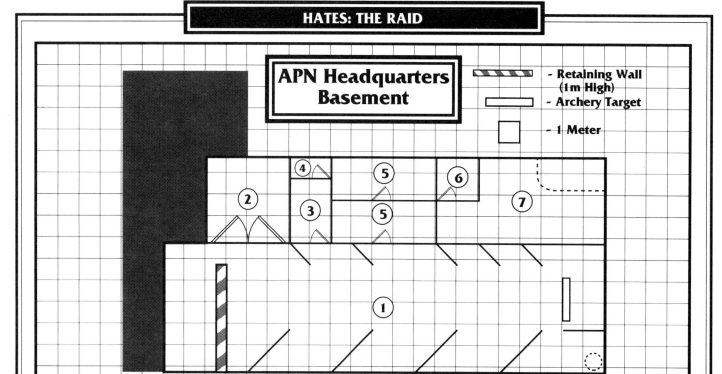

APN Headquarters Basement

- Retaining Wall (1m High)
- Archery Target
- 1 Meter

Main Lounge (6)

This is the main lounge area of the APN, also used for briefings when APN members go out on strike missions. The trivid on the wall opposite the stairs is currently tuned to a documentary about Eastern Dragons. The three couches in front of it are empty.

If no alarm has been raised, the single guard here is asleep, slumped on the couch nearest the trivid. If the alarm has been raised, the four armed guards will be crouched behind the couches, giving them Cover against anyone coming up the stairs.

Bedroom (7)

This bedroom contains the beds for the four female APN members who live at the headquarters. Pinups of good-looking male Elves (some in classical garb, some not) adorn the walls.

If no alarm has been raised, three APN members are asleep here. If it has been raised, no one is here.

Bathroom (8)

This is the bathroom for bedroom (7). It is a small, privately outfitted facility instead of the institutional model the men get.

The room is empty.

Bedroom (9)

This is the bedroom of Xeric the Mad. It is expensively outfitted in a Japanese rice-paper motif. Xeric's bed is a mat lying in the northwest corner, with desktop lamps surrounding it.

If the alarm has not been raised, Xeric is in here asleep. If it has been raised, he will have joined the guards protecting Allair in Workroom (2), and this room will be empty.

Plan Room (10)

This small room has a Maglock 10 on the door. Inside are APN contingency plans to wipe out almost every high-tech group of Elves in the area.

If the alarm on this room is not deactivated, an explosion will destroy the papers when the door is opened (and raise the alarm if it hasn't been done already).

BASEMENT

Archery Test Range (1)

Thiran uses this test range to teach APN members how to shoot. Projections from each wall (in addition to providing nifty cover for shadowrunners) help protect the archers from shrapnel. (Thiran's been trying to perfect these explosive arrows, y'see).

If the alarm has been raised, there will be six APN members down here, all set up to fire at anyone coming down the hall from the direction of either the elevator or the ladder. After three combat turns, Thiran and Erendahl will come out and add their HK227s to the fray. If no alarm has been raised, no one is here.

Stable (2)

This section of the basement smells of horses. It has been turned into an impromptu stable to house a unicorn. The stall is filthy, as is the water trough and grain basin.

The unicorn is actually a horse modified for the APN by a veterinary surgeon, and so is worth almost nothing.

Armory (3)

This is the APN's main armory, where are stored their heavy weapons when not in use. Uzis and HKs share the walls with grenade bandoliers and two missile launchers. There is no ammunition for any of these weapons, however.

Though APN leaders profess a back-to-nature philosophy, they understand the value of modern firepower.

Ammunition Room (4)

The door to the ammunition room is protected by a retina scanner, keyed to either Thiran or Erendahl. Cases of grenades are piled on the floor next to clips of ammunition and three HEP missiles. On a rack on the far wall sit twelve arrows with explosive heads. (They don't work yet, and will blow up in someone's face!)

This room is empty, either because the alarm has not been raised or because everyone is too busy to load most of the heavy guns.

Bedroom (5)

Thiran's bedroom. The small outer room is piled high with sports magazines describing the latest advances in UrbanBrawl and Thai kick boxing. In the inner bedroom, Thiran and Erendahl are talking over their next raid. At the sound of anything unusual (gamemaster option), they will come out shooting to kill.

Thiran and Erandahl are each armed at all times with an Ares Predator II heavy pistol. Thiran also likes flash grenades, and usually has six or seven on his person.

Bathroom (6)

This is a small bathroom for use by people undergoing combat practice down here. In the mornings, Erendahl and Thiran shower in the first-floor bathroom.

Elevator (7)

This is the bottom of the elevator that goes to Room 1 on the ground floor. The machinery is underneath the bottom of the shaft (it is actually a hydraulic lift instead of an elevator), but is very noisy when used. An alarm button is next to the light switch by the door.

If no alarm is raised, and the runners come down via elevator, the single guard here will hit the alarm button as he goes to alert Thiran and Erendahl. If the alarm has already been raised, the room is empty.

CAST OF CHARACTERS

The six members of the APN's inner council are each involved for different reasons. Xeric believes he has been divinely chosen to save the Elves from themselves. His fanatical outlook gives the APN its fire and inspiration.

Allair is the most pitiful of the inner core group. He was a brilliant scientist before BTL chips took his mind "far into the dark caverns of truth." Now he wanders around believing himself an evil mage, killing those he once hoped to save.

Blaine Deathedge is the APN's enforcer. Always dressed in black, he does not care whether it's little old ladies the APN wants to geek, as long as he gets to kill some of them. His closest companion is Thiran, the APN's weapons master, who treats his body like a chopping block on which others may shatter their swords.

Erendahl joined the APN to mock Lone Star and to geek runners, not to preserve the Elven ideal. He will take any chance to hurt and embarrass runners, so long as his 'stick isn't thrown out.

The last core member of the APN is Fierelle. Like Allair, she has been an APN member for so long she's forgotten her real name. Fierelle has more seniority than Xeric, but she is under the sway of his charisma. She will probably "die for the good of the cause" as soon as Xeric figures out that she's starting NOT to see things his way.

ALLAIR

Core APN member.

The most scientifically inclined member of the organization, Allair originally built the alarm system that protects the headquarters. Shortly after that, he began to work on illegal simsense chips to give the other APN members "Elven" philosophy. He currently believes he's a necromancer, and tries to act the part. Actually, he's a scientist, as described on p. 108, **Sprawl Sites**, (Simsense Specialty).

APN MEMBER

The typical APN member is slightly nuts, and actually believes that the actions of the APN are aiding Elves everywhere. Despite this, the members are worldly wise and fairly capable opposition. Use the **Elf Poser-Gang Member**, p. 110, **Sprawl Sites**, for guards and such. Other members use the standard **Pedestrian**, p. 116 of the same book.

CHARLIE TARROW

"Charlie-Horse," as some people still call her, helped found the fine old fixer traditions in the early 2030s. After a long and danger-spattered career, she left with Wyrd and retired. She's only back in action now because the offer came through channels she thought extinct for decades. Use the standard **Fixer**, p. 167, **Shadowrun**, with +2 on all skills.

DEATHEDGE

Core APN member.

Deathedge is the great mystery. The biggest and most deadly of the APN core members, he dresses in black and uses any weapons necessary to complete a job. These include missiles, grenades, and other people. Use the **Street Samurai**, p. 46, **Shadowrun**.

ERENDAHL

Core APN member.

Probably the closest of the APN's Council of Elders to a "classic" Elf in physical makeup, Erendahl is tall, blond, and exceptionally good-looking. He's in this more because of the fun he has confusing cops and runners than because of any financial benefits or the desire to help others. Use the **Former Tribal Warrior**, p. 103, **Sprawl Sites**, but give him Projectile Combat Skill instead of Etiquette (Tribal).

FIERELLE THE RED

Core APN member.

Fierelle started all this to help people, and lost her mind in the Great Purge after Ridgeworth's death. She constantly wears and surrounds herself with red as a reminder of the dead Elves she has been unable to help. Fierelle is probably the only member of the Council of Elders who could be persuaded that the APN is wrong, should the runners actually take time to speak with her. Fierelle uses the **Combat Mage**, p. 98, **Sprawl Sites**.

HARRIET TAYLOR

Harriet Taylor is a small, elderly woman with the mutant power to make people feel good (just kidding). Harriet tries to mother most people, and they usually let her succeed. Harriet uses the **Pedestrian**, p. 116, **Sprawl Sites**.

KERRY TAYLOR

Kerry is Harriet's only daughter, and has a reputation for being a hard-nosed investigative reporter. She blew the whistle on the Telamr Elven Slavery ring and has written articles about the covert corp wars in Africa. In all this, she never had time for herself, and a friend is dead because of it. In her vengeance, Kerry will use the **Former Wage Mage** Archetype (Healer Orientation), p. 38, **Shadowrun**. Her apartment can be found under Large Residence, p. 34, **Sprawl Sites**.

THIRAN

Core APN member.

The APN's master-at-arms, Thiran is an expert in medieval combat, but more suited to frontal hack-and-slash than subtle thrust and parry combat. Numerous fights have left him dozens of scars so that his face looks like a fright mask and the rest of his body is not much better. Use the **Former Tribal Warrior**, p. 103, **Sprawl Sites**, but give him a sword in place of the Beretta.

TREY

A student of Charlie's, Trey Wilson is 16, brash, and totally ignorant of subtlety. Use the **Corporate Security Guard**, p. 165, **Shadowrun**.

WYRD

A hermetic mage of many years' experience, Wyrd is here only to safeguard Charlie while she tries to figure out what's going on. Wyrd uses the **Combat Mage**, p. 98, **Sprawl Sites**.

XERIC THE MAD

Core APN member.

Xeric (Aaron Mitchell) really is mad. He is the one who came up with most of the APN's current strategy, and believes that he alone can save the Elves. The scary thing is that when he starts talking, other people start to believe it as well. Use the **Bodyguard**, p. 97, **Sprawl Sites**.

PICKING UP THE PIECES

Charlie will be waiting for the runners at a prearranged location, ready to take possession of the ear tips and to pay the runners their due.

KARMA AWARDS

TEAM KARMA

Dropping·videodisc in Xeric's lap	1 pt
For every three ear tips	1 pt
Saving/Protecting the little girl	1 pt
Allowing Fierelle to try to atone for her actions	1 pt
Killing the little girl by mistake	−2 pts

INDIVIDUAL KARMA

Award per the guidelines, p. 160 of the **Shadowrun** rules.

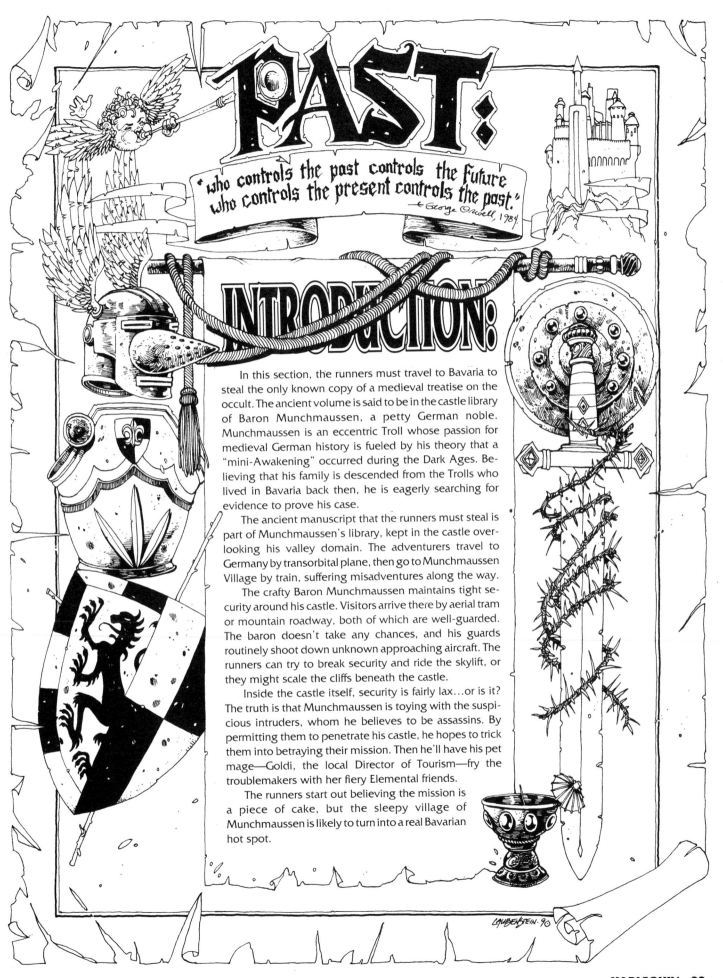

PAST:

"who controls the past controls the future
who controls the present controls the past."
— George Orwell, 1984

INTRODUCTION:

In this section, the runners must travel to Bavaria to steal the only known copy of a medieval treatise on the occult. The ancient volume is said to be in the castle library of Baron Munchmaussen, a petty German noble. Munchmaussen is an eccentric Troll whose passion for medieval German history is fueled by his theory that a "mini-Awakening" occurred during the Dark Ages. Believing that his family is descended from the Trolls who lived in Bavaria back then, he is eagerly searching for evidence to prove his case.

The ancient manuscript that the runners must steal is part of Munchmaussen's library, kept in the castle overlooking his valley domain. The adventurers travel to Germany by transorbital plane, then go to Munchmaussen Village by train, suffering misadventures along the way.

The crafty Baron Munchmaussen maintains tight security around his castle. Visitors arrive there by aerial tram or mountain roadway, both of which are well-guarded. The baron doesn't take any chances, and his guards routinely shoot down unknown approaching aircraft. The runners can try to break security and ride the skylift, or they might scale the cliffs beneath the castle.

Inside the castle itself, security is fairly lax…or is it? The truth is that Munchmaussen is toying with the suspicious intruders, whom he believes to be assassins. By permitting them to penetrate his castle, he hopes to trick them into betraying their mission. Then he'll have his pet mage—Goldi, the local Director of Tourism—fry the troublemakers with her fiery Elemental friends.

The runners start out believing the mission is a piece of cake, but the sleepy village of Munchmaussen is likely to turn into a real Bavarian hot spot.

PIECE OF CAKE

TELL IT TO THEM STRAIGHT

THE INVITATION

You're minding your own beeswax when the trio of hired musclemen saunters into the bar, waving your pix around and saying they have to speak with you. Walturr the barkeep is an old pal who used to do some shadowrunning himself before the Seoul Men had him hardwired to the counter. He motions you into the back room, then calls the strangers over to speak with him.

The back room is like many others of its kind, decorated with faded posters of bosomy German blondes and yesterday's sport stars, all clutching foaming mugs. You check your escape route, then put your ear to the door to hear what you can—which is nothing.

After the bar girl comes to call you out again, you see the strangers sprawled unconscious on the tavern floor, unbloodied but quite motionless. Walturr has their personal effects in his hands. "You know them dreks?" he asks.

You shake your head. The barkeep tosses you a small, sealed envelope with your name elaborately scripted in kaleidoscopic ink. "I think it's for you." Inside the envelope is a white card, laser-engraved with abstract filigree and scripted in the same dizzy ink as your name on the outside. It reads:

The Place: After
The Time: Nine Tonight
The Reason: A Job Offer

Well, well. Work is work, and anyone worth working for should have known what would happen to amateurs like these three who come poking around after you. In fact, it was probably part of a test. Probably, you've passed.

THE MEET

It takes a moment of access to learn just what and where "After" is. You were expecting a restaurant or another bar—the name just isn't corporate—and you aren't far off the mark. After is a private club, exclusive but not too pricey, with a reputation for being snobbishly liberal. It's located in downtown Seattle, several blocks from the University of Washington campus.

You arrive at the appointed time, descending the substreet-level stairs to rap on the oak door. Apparently you're expected, for the maître d' ushers you in.

The place looks like a bomb hit it, but then you see that's actually the decorative motif. Little nooks for meeting and dining are nestled within "craters" in the floor, and rubble is strewn around for effect. The chairs and tables are deformed, as though partially melted, but the flowing forms remain usable. The smell of ozone is sharp in the air, and the lighting is dim except for the blinding flashes of simulated nuclear detonations.

Arcing wires protrude from shattered walls, contributing their crackle and sparks to the club's eerie ambience. Not many people are present. Most are huddled in small groups within the crater nooks, discussing politics or philosophy with manic ardor.

"If you please, be seated," says the lone figure seated at the table to which you are conducted. Her breathless accent is definitely French, especially the way she trills her r's. Two pointed Elven ears protrude from her elegantly coifed golden hair. However, her neo-European-cut business suit (and the two goons watching intently from an adjacent nook) mark her as corp.

"I enjoyed the way you received my invitation," she says, displaying a pleasure that seems genuine. "You've come highly recommended, and I have no doubt the job I have for you will be one of the easiest you've ever been offered.

"First, you are to make a pickup. There is a certain book that is 'overdue,' and you shall collect it for us.

"Second, you are to make a delivery, but it's to the same place as the first. The object to be delivered is a simple valise, locked tight and quite harmless.

"The fact that you will be required to journey overseas should be no problem for seasoned runners like you. All travel arrangements have been made, and I can provide complete information about your destination."

BEHIND THE SCENES

Ms…er…Mr. Johnson often handles transatlantic missions, but has no idea that the current one does not involve the usual political intrigues or espionage. (If she knew what was in the valise, she might be horrified.)

Once the runners accept the job, she begins to give them details of the mission.

THE CASTLE

The travel arrangements will take the runners by transorbital flight to Berlin, then by bullet and conventional train to Munchmaussen, a tiny hamlet on the eastern fringes of Bavaria. To keep from raising anyone's suspicions, the runners are to leave unusual equipment behind. Once in Bavaria, everything will be provided. During the journey, the characters should pretend to be ordinary tourists.

The target of the break-in and delivery is the castle in the German village of Schloss Munchmaussen. Mr. Johnson provides a complete map to the castle grounds (see p. 43), but cannot supply floor plans for the individual buildings. The medieval home of the Baron Munchmaussen is set atop a mountain cliff and visitors arrive there via aerial tramway this time of year. Low-flying vehicles are strictly prohibited within the baron's domain.

THE TOME

The ancient book is believed to be kept in the baron's personal library on an upper floor of the castle's keep. It is a medieval manuscript, nearly 15 centimeters thick, bound between wooden covers that are 30 centimeters square. Despite the tome's sturdy construction and great weight, age has made it delicate. Mr Johnson urges the runners to bring it back in mint condition.

The runners will recognize the book in two ways. First, the cover is engraved with the title, *Pandemonicus Faustus*, and below that with the subtitle, *Collectanea Occultica*. Second, the frontispiece depicts the archdemon Asmodeus. The illustration uses a long-lost monastic art that makes the blood-red ink appear to be wet.

THE VALISE

Ms. Johnson shows the gray valise to the team, but does not give it to them. Instead, she promises to have it pre-checked onto their flight as part of their luggage.

The aluminum satchel is only 20 centimeters by 25 centimeters, but is heavy for its size. Bright red markings declare it to contain perishable medical supplies. A tiny digital readout embedded in the handle reads "250" (the temperature of the interior of the valise, in degrees Kelvin or absolute). Valves in the bottom of the case occasionally leak small amounts of a cold, cloudy vapor, which quickly dissipate. The valise is securely locked.

This refrigerated container holds the collection of "Elven" ears the runners obtained in the previous adventure, but don't tell them that.

The flight departs at six in the morning, and is the only one scheduled to Berlin for several days. If the runners decide to investigate Baron Munchmaussen before they leave Seattle, have them try a Sociology, Neo-Europe (4) Test. (Current, accurate information on foreign politics is hard to get.) Consult the following Success Table to see what they learn.

Successes	Result
0	Baron Munchmaussen rules the tiny Bavarian domain of Munchmaussen, which consists of a single valley. His castle overlooks the Village Munchmaussen.
1 – 2	The baron was once a big spender, a jet-setter known from the Riviera to the Alps. He has not been seen about in recent years, having apparently become a recluse in his castle. He is a Troll.
3+	Munchmaussen is crafty as a fox, say his enemies. He has managed to stay out of the politics that keep his nation in turmoil, and is said to keep a tight rein on his subjects.

THE MONEY

Johnson is prepared to offer the runners ¥40,000 nuyen each for the run, ¥10,000 nuyen now and the rest on delivery of the tome. Use the standard Negotiation rules from **Shadowrun** if the runners decide to try to get more for the job.

WHAT GOES UP

TELL IT TO THEM STRAIGHT

The shuttle is a Mitsubishi Skyclimber, one of the new, fuel-efficient transorbitals. The shark-tooth emblem of Luftlande Airlines painted on the sides gives the passenger plane an oddly predatory look.

Less than 40 passengers are on this flight, leaving the shuttle half-empty. Your assigned seats are just behind the first-class section, next to one of the air-steward stations.

There are four seats in each row, separated by a narrow aisle. Each chair is an individual light acceleration couch. The strapping-in procedure involves so many webs and buckles that even you are slightly intimidated. A tray arm is built into the seat, and includes a video display and an input jack.

You take note of the following passengers:

•A short woman, dressed entirely in white and gray skins, who takes a seat just behind you. Her broad face has an Oriental agelessness, but she speaks English without a trace of accent. She looks alertly about the cabin, constantly fingering the various animal icons on a leather thong about her neck.

•Three elderly Japanese, their hair close-cropped and their business suits of nondescript cut, are seated in first class. When one of them steps into second class looking for a steward, you see the glint of steel between his wrist and the black briefcase cuffed to his arm.

•Toward the rear of the plane, a green-haired young woman appears to be singing, but you hear no sound. On second glance, you see that she's wearing a sonic damper. Noticing your attention, she blushes prettily and smiles.

•Two couples board the shuttle together, taking seats several rows behind you. They are clean-cut and the language they speak sounds like German. They behave affectionately toward one another.

•A frazzled middle-aged woman comes down the aisle, leading a young Ork child by the hand. You suspect the little boy has recently Awakened, as he seems to be ashamed of his appearance. One of the passengers points at the child and says something to his companions, who burst out laughing.

At last, the hatches are closed and the shuttle is ready for takeoff. The air stewards demonstrate the use of the emergency evac suits and the reentry cushions, then the pilot welcomes you onboard:

"This is Luftlande Flight 613, and I am Kapitan Georg Willems. We'll be taking off precisely on schedule this morning, arriving in Berlin in the late morning hours. I am pleased to report that the Tempelhof International Airport is no longer experiencing the difficulties reported in the morning news, and we are assured of a secure landing. Thank you for flying Luftlande. We hope you enjoy the flight."

The "No Smoking/Chipping" and "Fasten seat belts" signs come on.

Liftoff is much the same as for conventional jet flights, though it takes the craft a much longer roll to go airborne. The cabin remains at a noticeable incline throughout the early stages of flight, as the jet engines labor to propel the plane into ever-higher regions of the atmosphere. The chair's terminal relieves some of the tedium of the flight, allowing you to tie in directly (through satellite) with entertainment and news broadcasts.

In time, the intercom bell rings. "This is Kapitan Willems. We are about to be begin the final climb to suborbital altitude. Please fasten your seat belts and extinguish all smoking materials. Air stewards, take your positions."

Shortly afterward, a tremor shakes the shuttle as the boosters engage, lifting the vehicle toward space. Through the small portholes, you see the sky dim from pale blue to midnight black and stars become visible against the ebony background. A layer of fleecy clouds dropping snow over northern Canada hides the earth's surface from view.

At last, the boosters cut off, and the shuttle coasts toward apogee. With the thrust gone, the apparent gravity also fades. One of the Japanese businessmen cries out sharply in distress and bolts for the rest room. The lady behind you also looks a little pale, and then pulls something from one of her leather pouches and swallows it.

Suddenly, there's an explosion, and dense, acrid smoke fills the cabin. "Hijack! We're being hijacked!" someone screams.

BEHIND THE SCENES

Be sure to enforce all the usual airport security procedures and restrictions (see **Getting There by Air**, p. 144), especially the anti-augmentation restraints. Luftlande uses remote-activation shaped-charge bracelets, and shows passengers a graphic video of what might happen to those who break its rules.

Use the narrative material given above to make the plane flight real, moving through it swiftly or slowly, depending on how interested your players seem.

Body Tests are required at two points during the initial flight: shortly after take-off, Target Number 3, and after the boosters cut off, Target Number 4. If a character scores no successes, he or she becomes nauseated, suffering a –1 penalty to all target numbers until back on the ground (if nauseated after take-off) or back to near-normal gravity (if nauseated in zero-gee).

WHAT IS GOING ON

Mistakes happen. In this case, agents of the Eagle's Union of Destiny, a pro-imperial German policlub, were monitoring Mr. Johnson's meeting with the runners. Knowing that Mr. Johnson's jobs are often performed for French (and therefore anti-German, at least from their point of view) interests, the EUD has jumped to the conclusion that the runners are their enemies. Go figure.

The Germans—Klaus, Fritz, Mikki, and Hildi—have set off a smoke-impaction bomb. Visibility is reduced to one meter, and anyone conducting vigorous physical activity (such as combat) must make a Body (5) Test to avoid a wracking cough (losing all actions for one turn).

Amid the confusion, Klaus, Fritz, and Mikki (use the **Gang Member** stats, p. 39, **Shadowrun**, but give them spurs instead of hand razors) plan to assault the runners and execute them, then plant evidence that implicates them as the nonexistent hijackers. Meanwhile, Hildi (**Decker**, p. 34, **Shadowrun**) has jacked into the shuttle's computer system, and is attempting to disarm the restraints on her compatriots. What she has discovered, however, is that she cannot deactivate only some of them; she must deactivate them all. Deciding to risk it, she does. So long as Hildi is operating her deck, the restraints remain inactive. But what the four Germans don't know might kill them. It is possible to determine whether a bracelet is activated or deactivated only by close examination, so don't tell the players the status of their characters' bracelets unless they actually ask.

The only weapons the Germans have are their spurs. For victory, they are counting on the element of surprise and the hope that their victims will be too afraid to risk using their own anti-augmentation devices.

ABOUT ZERO GRAVITY

There are two ways to move around the cabin at apogee: flying and crawling.

Crawling is the easiest, and entails pulling oneself along using any available handholds, be they seat backs, luggage compartment handles, other passengers, and so on. A character can move a number of meters equal to half his Quickness. At the end of each turn of crawling, the character must make a

Quickness (4) Test. If he scores no successes, he loses his grip and starts to fly in a random direction.

Flying is what a character does when he launches himself from Point A toward Point B without benefit of intervening handholds. The number of meters traveled per turn equals the runner's Strength. A Quickness (6) Test is required to launch properly; if the character scores no successes, he flies off in a random direction. While flying, a runner cannot change his direction of travel (unless he can grab something), but can change his facing with a successful Quickness (7) Test. To land properly (i.e., feet first), a character must pass a Quickness (5) Test; a bad landing results in a 2M1 wound.

Fighting in zero-gee is also difficult. Apply a +2 penalty to all Target Numbers for thrown-weapon and missile attacks. Characters attacking or hit in melee combat must make a Quickness (7) Test at the end of the turn. If they score no successes, the characters fly away in a random direction.

IF THE RUNNERS NEED HELP

The gamemaster may bring in any or all of the following non-player characters, especially if the runners befriended them during the flight.

•The woman in sealskins is an Eskimo shaman. Use the **Shaman** (Deceiver), p. 44, **Shadowrun**, for her stats. She might use the Chaos spell to distract everyone.

•The elderly Japanese "businessmen" are actually high-powered freelancers. Use the **Former Company Man**, p. 37, **Shadowrun**, for them. They might force their way down the aisle, subduing anyone who challenges them. They are wearing restraints, but will fight without engaging their cyberware.

•The green-haired young lady is actually a Sky Marshal working for Luftlande. Use the **Street Cop**, p. 171, **Shadowrun**. Her augmentation restraints are dummies, and she has a concealed Net Gun (see **Street Samurai Catalog**, p. 72).

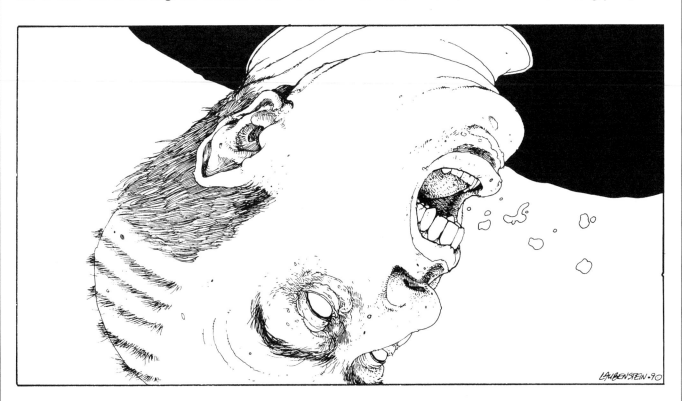

SPEEDING BULLETS

TELL IT TO THEM STRAIGHT

The descent into the atmosphere is uneventful. The jets kick on, guiding the shuttle into the approach for Berlin's Tempelhof International Airport. Black smoke boils up from the horizon, but there is no sign of active combat in the city.

When you land, German security police demand to sequester the passengers for questioning, but the pretty Sky Marshal vouches for you. An airport limo conducts you to Neustadt Station, where you board the bullet train for Munich.

A train steward greets you (in English) and shepherds you through disembarkation. Seven teams of customs agents, representing each of the German states through which you will pass on your way to Munich, inspect you and your belongings, stamp your papers ("real" paper, nothing electronic), and exact their fees (incorporated in your train ticket). Again, augmentation restraints are required (see p. 144, Taser models, this time).

The bullet train is shark-nosed and gray, looking like a worm of technology rather than a passenger vehicle. Twin-mount cannon barrels protrude from cupolas mounted on every fourth car, situated to fire to both sides as well as overhead. Obviously, this train runs on time.

Whisper-quiet at speeds greater than several hundred kilometers per hour, the bullet train swiftly and efficiently deposits you in Munich, where you change trains. Another English-speaking steward takes custody of your team as well as another North American group: a flashily dressed Easterner, his female companion, and their three hunting hounds.

"Pleased t'meecha," says the man, baring his teeth in an enormous smile. "Name's Hardrow. This is Sheila. We're dog trainers." He leans closer. "These Germans are pushovers for hunting dogs. Especially man-killers. But we don't do any of that cyberstuff. Our dogs are strictly pure, no scything claws or venom glands. So what're you doing over here?"

Soot-streaked and bullet-scarred, this train is no bullet. Indeed, it looks like it might have been in service a few decades longer than some of the medieval ruins you see. The other passengers are German, farmers and factory hands, by the looks of them. This time there is no customs check (nor any security procedure) before pulling out of the station.

You soon find out why. Fifteen minutes after leaving the station, the train stops at a village, where a customs agent and a dozen soldiers board. The conductor shows them through, instructing you to produce your papers for inspection. Twenty minutes later, the train is underway once again.

In the next three hours, the train crosses four more borders and undergoes four more inspections. The conductor is increasingly exasperated and snappish, especially with foreigners who don't understand his Bavarian dialect.

Once more, the train slows down for a customs check. With their unbuttoned uniforms, blood- and food-stained clothing, and unwashed, unshaven faces, these soldiers look particularly disreputable. No customs agent boards with them.

The conductor looks more harried than usual as he fetches paperwork for the "inspectors." Thumbing through your travel documents, a soldier grunts, then demands something in thickly accented German. The conductor shrugs, turns to you, and says something else in German.

Obviously, something is wrong.

BEHIND THE SCENES

The local baron is little more than a brigand, and has sent his soldiers to extract booty from the train and its passengers. The troops (Use the **Merc**, p. 40, **Shadowrun**, but arm them with Steyr AUG-CSL assault rifles, p. 53, **Street Samurai Catalog**.) enjoy their role, and are not above stealing what they want and tormenting the helpless. There are three soldiers in the runners' car, and nine others elsewhere on the train.

The other problem facing the characters is language. Here, as well as later in the adventure, all the German NPCs speak Bavarian dialect, a +2 Target away from ordinary German. The only character who can translate is Sheila the dog trainer, and she gets the interpretation wrong half the time.

The soldiers first insist that something is amiss with one of the runner's papers. Then they demand that a fine be paid, suggesting that one character's personal belongings would make a nice donation. Meanwhile, another soldier starts shouting at a farmer couple, firing several rounds through the roof of the compartment to impress them.

FURTHER COMPLICATIONS

Because players are prone to take action, the runners will probably try to fight the soldiers, who are likely to outclass them—in weapons, if not in abilities. At the appropriate moment, the gamemaster may read the following:

The rattle of automatic gunfire is heard, coming from a distance. A train window shatters, and a smoking metal canister lands in the aisle of the runners' car. Grunting and shouting, the soldiers shoot out the windows on one side of the train, then kneel in firing positions behind the openings. You cough and gasp as you breathe in the bluish vapors from the grenade.

"Heavens to Betsy!" shouts Hardrow, the other dog trainer. "What's going on?"

The conductor, lying in the aisle, looks up. "Putsch," he says, then points a finger against his head and pulls an imaginary trigger. He winces.

"Pooch?" says Hardrow, puzzled. Then he lurches to his feet. "They're killing our dogs, honey. I've got to get to the baggage compartment!"

The conductor tries to explain to the dog trainer that a rebellion ("putsch") is in progress. The newly arriving soldiers (use **Ork Mercenary**, p. 41, **Shadowrun**) are here to liberate the train, but they are more concerned with gaining possession of the vehicle than safeguarding the passengers' lives.

The four liberators are driving a Krupp Komet. This German panzer is a licensed version of the GMC Banshee, but smaller and less armored (4) than the American model. It is also less well-armed, equipped with one heavy cannon and a grenade launcher, a water cannon in the turret, and two surveillance/decoy drones.

The attackers use their cannon to keep the enemy soldiers quiet, also doing collateral damage around and to the player characters. Eventually, they board the train and try to seize it, landing on top of the car in which the player characters are riding.

The defending soldiers fire on the panzer until it becomes obvious their assault rifles are not damaging it. Then they hold their fire, waiting to battle the boarders in the train car. Their grim code of honor forces them to fight to the death. Because they are unfamiliar with trains, it does not occur to them to man the exposed cupola guns (twin autocannons) at the rear of this compartment.

Meanwhile, Hardrow is forcing his way to the rear of the car. This is double-deadly: the attackers mistake the move for an attempt to man the cupola guns, and the defenders don't want any civilians doing anything. In either case, he is likely to get himself killed unless the runners step in.

Meanwhile, the train begins to move, the engineer hoping to escape across the border, which is only five minutes' away. The liberators cannot cross the border without provoking war with the neighboring baron.

THE RUNNERS' OPTIONS

The players can react to this encounter in three ways:

If they simply sit still, they'll have some uncomfortable moments when the liberators board the train. Bullets will fly everywhere, but the player characters will probably live through it.

If the runners take this opportunity to turn on the brigands, they can probably surprise them, knock them out, and seize their weapons (while the liberators continue to fire, of course). Afterward, the players must decide whether to fight the boarders as well, or surrender to them.

Lastly, the runners could side with the original troops against the new arrivals. Having noticed that the cupolas were unmanned, the liberators cease to pay attention to them. If a character can get up there and surprise the panzer with a burst at close range, that should be enough to scare off the would-be

WELCOME, CHUMLICHEN!

TELL IT TO THEM STRAIGHT

At last, the old diesel-burner chugs into Munchmaussen Valley, a remote and picturesque locale. Staring out the windows, you see peasants wearing the lederhosen and long skirts of two centuries ago, working in the field side by side with the latest cybertractors.

Directly ahead is the lovely village of Munchmaussen, dominated by its medieval church and town hall. You are amazed to see no sign of modern civilization: no aerials, no neon- or laser-glitz, and no graffiti. Village women water their flower boxes in picture-postcard fashion, while old men whittle and puff on long-stemmed pipes. The scent of baking apples fills the air.

Above it all rises Schloss Munchmaussen, perched on the heights of the valley's largest alp ("our very own Matterhorn," gushes the tourist brochip). The mountaintop and its cliffs are snow-covered, though the weather is warm in the lower valley. A deceptively thin-looking cable links the castle to the valley below. You watch as a tram ascends to the castle.

At the village's train platform, the local tourism director boards with the usual passel of soldiers and customs agents. She calls you by name, looking around questioningly, then approaches when she spots you nodding. "Welcome, chumlichen (German for chummers)! My name is Goldi," she says in slightly accented English. "I'm here to welcome you to Munchmaussen. All your luggage has arrived, and your accommodations are waiting for you."

BEHIND THE SCENES

Munchmaussen isn't quite the paradise it seems. The baron's police and bureaucrats tightly regulate life in the village, keeping a close watch on suspicious visitors. Tourism is the lifeblood of this remote town, however, and so the baron's agents must use tact in investigating strangers.

As Munchmaussen's Director of Tourism, Goldi Schonbosom welcomes visitors, arranges sports tournaments and hotel dances, conducts driving tours (no rental vehicles are available in Munchmaussen), and acts as a kindly friend. In her secret identity as Baron Munchmaussen's chief of intelligence, she also keeps an eye on strangers, quizzing them about their vacation plans, then using her intuition to detect spies and infiltrators. Given the intrigues of modern Germany, her talents (and her spells) are constantly called into play. Use the **Former Wage Mage** (Fighter), p. 38, **Shadowrun**, but raise Goldi's Charisma to 4. Note that she keeps her magical abilities secret.

Questions that might trip up the runners:

"You are mountaineers, jawohl?" (She has seen their luggage.)

"What an interesting item! Is one of you a doctor?" (If she sees the valise.)

"I understand that crime is severe where you come from." (She doesn't know where the runners are from, and is fishing for information.)

"Such a mess in Berlin. Did you pass through there?" (Goldi is hoping the characters might reveal their political leanings when discussing this subject.)

She continues to ask probing questions, cunningly concealed in general conversation, while helping the runners collect their luggage and check in at the youth hostel (see below).

As Goldi gets ready to leave, make a secret Opposed Intelligence Test for her and the player character who has been doing most of the talking, but reduce the player character's Target Number to 3 or 4 if the runner has done a good job of roleplaying.

If Goldi scores the most net successes, she becomes suspicious of the runners and forces herself on them for the day as a tour guide. Otherwise, her suspicions are not aroused (yet), and she lets them explore Munchmaussen on their own.

VILLAGE MUNCHMAUSSEN

There are no more than 40 structures in the entire village, with the following major buildings.

St. Gretchen's

This ancient Gothic structure is a functioning church. Unknown to the baron and his minions, it is also the center of the feeble local resistance movement. If the runners need help against Baron Munchmaussen, or if they just need a place to rest and heal after the adventure, Father Braun might help them.

Munchmaussen Town Hall

Another old structure, this building is crowded with the bureaucrats and functionaries who administer Baron Munchmaussen's realm. Here is where comprehensive records, both on paper and in datastores, are kept on every resident.

Hotels

These modest resorts, generally boasting less than 20 rooms, pride themselves on elegance. The housemen are in livery, the maids in spotless white, and every dinner is a chef's masterpiece. Prices are steep, naturally.

Youth Hostel

The establishment where the runners lodge is for traveling students and others on a limited budget. Guests bunk six to a room. There are a minimal number of staff, for the laundry and kitchen are automated.

Shops

The main street of Munchmaussen is lined with small craft shops, each with its own meister in residence. Their specialties are proclaimed boldly on old-fashioned carved signs: pipes, clocks, sausages, jewelry, clockwork toys, and Bavarian costumes.

LUGGAGE

The runners will probably want to inspect their baggage (shipped directly to Munchmaussen by Mr. Johnson) when Goldi is not around, or her suspicions really will be aroused. When they do so, they find the following assorted contents:

Crate #1, labeled "Open First":
- Ares Predators with silencer*
- Standard ammunition (10 clips for pistol)
- Defiance Super Shock (Taser)
- Taser Cartridges (4 magazines of 4)
- Knives*
- Micro-Transceivers*
- White Noise Generator
- Bug Scanner
- Maglock Passkeys x 2
- Respirators x 2
- Valise

Crate #2:
- Armor Jackets*
- Snowsuits (full-body, no protection, 2.25 kg)
- Climbing boots (1.4 kg)*
- Backpack*
- Survival Kit*
- Low-Light Goggles*
- Medkit
- Stimulant Patches (4) x 12
- Tranq Patches (2) x 12

Crate #3:
- Heckler & Koch HK227-S (SMG with integral silencer)*
- Explosive Rounds (10 clips for SMG)
- Stun Rounds (5 clips for SMG)
- Flechette Rounds (3 clips for SMG)
- Standard ammunition (5 clips for SMG)
- Grenade Launcher (mounts under SMG)
- Smoke Grenades (2 magazines of 6)
- Missile Launcher (with 4 anti-vehicle missiles)

Crate #4:
- Grapple Gun, with attached rappelling gear
- Stealth Grapple Line (200 meters)
- Catalyst Stick (for stealth grapple line)

Uncrated:
- Climbing Gear x 2
- Snowshoes*
- Rope (100 meters)

* [one per player character]

The players should be overjoyed to find some equipment items present and chagrined to find others missing. At some point, they must begin to figure out how to bring all this stuff into the castle with them. For that matter, how are they going to get it out of the youth hostel without being spotted?

Mr. Johnson included Smartgun Adapters for those characters able to use them.

When the runners are ready to assess Schloss Munchmaussen, proceed to the next section, **Tough Schloss**.

TOUGH SCHLOSS

TELL IT TO THEM STRAIGHT

An explosion shatters the tranquillity of Munchmaussen. Looking into the sky, you see a feathery white trace from a launched missile linking the ramparts of the schloss with a dark smudge of smoke overhead.

"Testing the baron's defenses," volunteers a villager, one of a crowd apparently gathered to watch the spectacle. He gives you a friendly smile—or is it a leer? "Every week, Graf Eisenstein sends his spy drone, and Graf Munchmaussen always shoots it down. Paranoid about the skies, our baron is."

BEHIND THE SCENES

Sooner or later, the runners will be ready to tackle Schloss Munchmaussen and to "check out" the ancient volume. What happens next depends on how they decide to break in and whether or not they get caught.

The only "wrong" way to break into the castle is to try to fly in, for Munchmaussen has plenty of missiles. The three practical ways to enter the schloss are described below.

THE MOUNTAIN ROAD

This seven-kilometer drive seems more like 20, due to the frequent switchbacks. Heavy snowdrifts and the winter's rockfalls make this route impassable for most vehicles. On foot, it's a two-day hike to the castle, and the runners must be constantly alert for aerial patrols by surveillance drones (every one to six hours). Escaping their notice requires an Opposed Test of the runners' best Stealth Skill against the drone's Perception of 3. Adjust the Target Numbers by +2 for poor visibility.

SKYLIFT

Two tram cars suspended from a stout cable and controlled by the castle's archaic computer system travel between the mountain fortress and the valley. The almost-reliable machinery resides in one of the castle's towers.

The valley tram station, on the outskirts of town, is manned by two policemen at all times (use the **Detective**, p. 35, **Shadowrun**, for all village cops). There are no controls here. Everything is operated from the schloss.

Each car seats a dozen people, has a sliding door on either side, and is connected to the cable by a steel bracket. The two cars are always at opposite points on the run, that is, if one is at the castle, the other is in the village.

The runners might be able to sneak into the castle with bureaucrats and servants reporting for their shifts. With proper disguises, getting past the local cops isn't difficult. The castle's security team, however, is harder to fool. Play it by ear, depending on what the runners try.

Another way to enter the castle using the skylift is to get control of the tram through the Matrix (see below), ride it to the schloss, and hope to bypass security there.

An interesting variation is to ride on top of the tram, holding onto the steel bracket. The high winds and extreme cold make this difficult, calling for separate Body, Strength, and Willpower Tests, each at a Target Number 5. Those who fail will slide off unless someone saves them or unless everyone is roped together.

THE CLIFF

The third way to enter Schloss Munchmaussen is to scale the cliff. There are four different faces that must be climbed. To determine the target number for each face, the gamemaster rolls 1D6 and adds 2 to the result. For each hour the runners spend scouting the face, the gamemaster rolls again. If he rolls a number lower than the target, the characters have found an easier path.

To climb each face, at least one of the characters must make it to the top, requiring an Athletics (5) Test and an hour. If the test fails, he has a climbing accident. Roll 1D6 and consult the table below.

Die Roll	Result
1 – 2	Climber is delayed; add one hour to his time and have him try the Athletics Test again.
3 – 4	Climber potentially suffers minor injury (3M1), but may try a Body Resistance Test to reduce the damage.
5	Climber potentially suffers major injury (4S2), but may try a Resistance Test.
6	Climber falls to his death unless he succeeds at an Athletics (5) Test. (O.K., so maybe near death. It's the gamemaster's decision.)

Once the first character has reached the top and set a rope, other characters can follow with only an Athletics (4) Test and a half-hour of climbing. Weaklings can be trussed up and hauled to the top from above, but this takes an hour and tires those doing the lifting (–1 penalty to further success tests).

The runners must watch for patrols (every one to six hours) by surveillance drones.

GETTING CAUGHT

Baron Munchmaussen and his Director of Tourism are crafty folks. If they detect the runners, all they will do is put the guard captains on alert. Rather than kill the runners immediately,

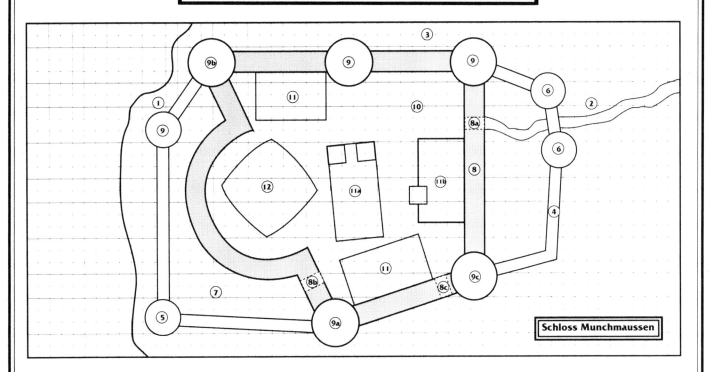

Schloss Munchmaussen

Munchmaussen wants to find out what they are up to. Therefore, the guards are instructed to "play dead" if shot at, to surrender when possible, and to cooperate with the intruders without making them suspicious.

If the guards are not on alert, they resist intruders with their usual zeal. For stats on the castle guards, use a mix of the **Former Company Man**, **Merc**, and **Ork Mercenary**, all found in the **Shadowrun** rulebook (pp. 37, 40, 41, respectively).

CASTLE MAP KEY

The Cliff (1)
This is a sheer drop leading to the valley below.
Mountain Road (2)
As described above. In the summer, this is the primary supply route for the schloss.
Rough Ground (3)
The terrain is so rough that running is nearly impossible (one-quarter normal rate; Dexterity (4) Test every turn not to fall down).
Outer Walls (4)
These stone walls are 7 meters high, topped with crenelations and a covered rampart. Floodlights and security cameras are mounted every 20 meters, and a pair of guards walk the walls every hour.
Tram (5)
The skylift cars enter through a two-story opening cut in the side of this 15-meter tower. The lower chambers contain the machinery for operating the tram. Visitors enter the castle by following the covered ramparts to the security checkpoint (Tower 9e).
Gatehouse (6)
These twin towers flank the castle's major entryway, which has been locked shut with an iron portcullis for most of the winter. There are five guards on duty here, plus five more asleep in the north tower barracks.

Garden (7)
In the summer, this is the baron's favorite picnic area. At the moment, it is covered with unmelted winter snow.
Main Wall (8)
This wall stands 20 meters tall, and is the boundary of the castle proper. In all other respects, it is identical to the outer walls. There are three openings: an archway (8a; always open) leading to the gatehouse, a gate (8b; latched but not locked) to the garden, and the ancient "sortie gate" to the south (8c; rusted shut).
Towers (9)
There are two sizes of towers in the schloss. The smaller are only five stories high, while the larger ones are eight stories tall. All are topped with steep, conical roofs. There is a single, barred window on every level.

Because they are cold and drafty, the towers are generally uninhabited and used for storage. The exceptions are: the security checkpoint (9a) where arriving workers are processed and four guards are on duty at all times; the drone launch tower (9b), manned by two security personnel; and the main barracks (9c), where ten guards are off-duty at any given time.
Courtyard (10)
Four vehicles are parked on the cobblestones: Three Volksedanz (a European import version of the Ford Americar) and a Mitsubishi Nightsky. Two guards make the rounds hourly.
Administration Buildings (11)
These structures house the bureaucrats who administer the baron's dominions, as well as their voluminous files (paper and computer). All are four-story wooden buildings with steep roofs. One is a remodeled church with twin bell towers (11a); another (11b) also has a modest tower.
The Keep (12)
This four-story, crenelated blockhouse is detailed in **Tome Sweet Tome**, below. The roof is steep and surrounded with ramparts.

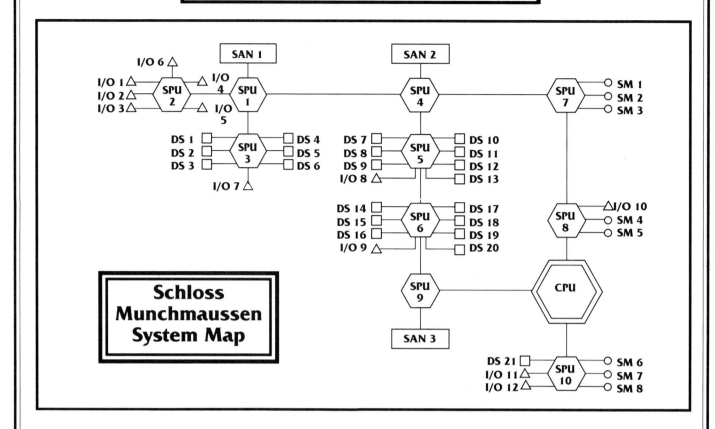

SCHLOSS MUNCHMAUSSEN SYSTEM MAP

CPU = Central Processing Unit
DS = Datastore
I/O = Input/Output Port
SAN = System Access Node
SM = Slave Module
SPU = Sub-processor

SAN-1: The unlisted number for Munchmaussen's Town Hall. Orange-4. Access 5.
SPU-1. Data routing for town government only. Orange-6.
SPU-2. Town security. Orange-5. Access 8.
   I/O-1 through 3. Concealed surveillance cameras in the larger rooms of hotels and homes of influential citizens. Orange-5.
   I/O-4 through 6. Concealed surveillance cameras in shops, streets, youth hostel. Green-3.
SPU-3. Public Control Office (Munchmaussen Town Hall). Orange-6. Access 4.
   I/O-7. Terminals. Green-4.
   DS-1 through 6. Dossiers on citizens of the barony, current and past investigations, the town's public records, and so forth. Green-7.
SAN-2: The unlisted number for Munchmaussen Castle. Orange-8. Access 4.
SPU-4. Data routing for the castle. Red-5. Tar Baby 4.
SPU-5. Government bureaucracy. Green-4. Trace 6.
   I/O-8. Terminals. Orange-4.
   DS-7 through 13. Governmental records. Red-9.
SPU-6. Senior bureaucracy. Orange-4. Blaster 6.

   I/O-9. Terminals. Orange-5.
   DS-14 through 17. Financial accounts of the barony. Orange-7.
   DS-18 through 20. Personnel records, including "secret" personnel such as Goldi Schonbosom. Orange-6.
SPU-7. Environmental Control. Green-7.
   SM-1. Electricity. Green-7. Black IC 4.
   SM-2. Heating/air conditioning. Orange-5.
   SM-3. Skylift machinery. Green-6.
SPU-8. Castle security. Orange-8. Access 8.
   I/O-10. Security cameras, concealed throughout the castle. Red-7. Access 1.
   SM-4. Security cameras (movement, focus, and so forth). Orange-7. Barrier 10.
   SM-5. Maglocks on doors, elevators. Green-5.
SAN-3: Another unlisted number for Schloss Munchmaussen, known only to the baron and his closest associates. Red-5. Black IC 4.
SPU-9. Data routing for the baron. Orange-8. Trapped IC (Blaster 5 hidden as Access 3).
CPU. Red-11. Killer 2.
SPU-10. Baron Munchmaussen's personal subprocessor. Red-6. Black IC 5.
   I/O-11. Security cameras, in castle and town. Orange-6.
   I/O-12. Terminal in inner library. Orange-6.
   DS-21. Baron's private records. Orange-6.
   SM-6. Master override for maglocks on doors, elevators. Red-6. Access 5.
   SM-7. Master override on security cameras (castle). Orange-5.
   SM-8. Master override on electricity. Red-7. Tar Pit 3. All RTGs in Bavaria are Code Green-3.

TOME SWEET TOME

TELL IT TO THEM STRAIGHT

When the runners enter the library:

You enter a comfortable, old-fashioned study, warmed by a blazing fire and filled with shelves of books, the old-fashioned kind, with real pages. An ancient globe stands in one corner, an antique book stand on one side of the fireplace, and a primitive stone statuette on a pedestal beside the door. A priceless cut-glass chandelier hangs from the ceiling.

Gamemaster's Note: Goldi may be present. See notes below.

When the runners investigate the bookstand:

Lying on top of the old bookstand is a volume of even greater apparent age. The book is thick, with wooden covers held shut by a bronze clasp. The cover is engraved with the title, *Pandemonicus Faustus*, and the subtitle, *Collectanea Occultica*. There is, however, no sign of the frontispiece depicting Asmodeus. A closer study of the book will reveal to even the most uninformed that this tome is a replica.

BEHIND THE SCENES

MUNCHMAUSSEN'S SECURITY

There are three possible levels of security in the keep: Lax, Vigilant, and Full Alert.

Lax

Baron Munchmaussen is unaware of any threat. The guards in the keep expect to be warned of intruders by the other guards and electronic systems, and are less than fully alert. When alerted, however, they shoot to kill.

The baron follows his usual routine: office work during the day, dinner and chitchat with close friends, then a few laps in the pool and to bed. He'll spend a few early morning hours (he suffers from insomnia) in the basement gallery, finding comfort in his archaeological treasures. Goldi is not on the castle grounds.

Vigilant

If the runners unpacked their equipment in the youth hostel and didn't deactivate the hidden security cameras, Baron Munchmaussen is aware that suspicious strangers are in his valley. If Goldi has become suspicious of the runners, she also tips off the Baron.

In either case, the Baron has issued a general warning to the keep's guards. They are to allow intruders into the Baron's private rooms, so that Munchmaussen can learn what these individuals want and then deal with them personally. Without an alert for a specific time, however, the guards remain less than fully alert.

The Baron wanders in and out of his secret security post (15a), checking the camera network to make sure the "assassins" are under surveillance. Goldi is summoned to the castle (Room 10a), does her conjuring in the Great Hall, and then keeps watch over her fiery friends (in the fireplace) in the library.

Full Alert

The runners have been detected approaching the schloss. The guards are fully alert, but have been instructed to "play dead" if shot at and to otherwise cooperate with the intruders. Baron Munchmaussen is in the secret security post, and Goldi is in the closet (a one-way mirror in a portrait allows her to keep eye contact with her fiery minions in the library fireplace and to throw spells into the room).

THE BOOK

If the runners remember everything Mr. Johnson told them, they will realize the volume in the library is a replica. The original book, normally kept in the basement gallery, is currently lying open on top of a coffee table in the baron's quarters. He's been reading it.

WHAT SHOULD HAPPEN

Munchmaussen's plan is to let the runners betray their goal, after which he can call in his guards. He thinks the valise is a bomb and that the player characters are "Yankee hitmen" hired by his enemies to kill him.

The runners will be allowed to break into the castle to reach the library, where they examine the replica tome, betraying their mission. Suddenly, the baron steps into the room with a sinister chuckle. "So that's all you were looking for, *nicht war?* I am so disappointed."

When the runners attack the baron, he fights back, counting on Goldi's two Fire Elementals (Force 4) to even the odds. He has also summoned the keep guards, who should arrive quickly from the other floors.

If the players are on the ball, they may surprise Munchmaussen before he is ready to spring his trap. If captured, he tries to learn the runners' mission before attempting an escape. Similarly, if Goldi is discovered in the library, she waits until the characters betray their goal before she calls her Elementals to attack. (Any runner who makes a successful Intelligence (4) Test will think to inspect the fireplace and spot the lizard-like feet of the Elementals through the flames.)

Goldi avoids casting her magic in any obvious manner, hoping to keep her identity as a mage a secret. She prefers to strike victims from behind with her Mana Bolt, but resorts to Sleep if the runners seem to be getting an upper hand. She is not creative with the Elementals, simply ordering them to attack the characters without damaging the library's contents. Their primary tactic is to Engulf, and they Project Flame only when nothing precious is in the line of fire. They will avoid using Flame Aura because of the risk of setting the room on fire; the keep has no fire sprinklers.

The baron and his minions are especially careful about the valise, which they believe to be a bomb. The Elementals are ordered not to attack the intruders in any way that would risk setting off the explosive. When the baron or his guards try to hack open the box, they discover the refrigerated Elven ears.

Remember that Goldi, the Baron, the guards, and the Elementals all communicate with one another in Bavarian German.

ABOUT THE BARON

Baron Munchmaussen is a sick Troll, afflicted with a painful rheumatism that has caused him to abandon his former lifestyle of constant excess and frequent travel. It is his unconscious longing for death that makes him take ever greater risks, including toying with suspected spies and assassins.

For his statistics, use the **Troll Bouncer**, p. 173, **Shadowrun**. The baron speaks several languages elegantly, including his native German (with or without a Bavarian accent) and English, and is a student of Sociology (3) as well as Etiquette (Jet Set). The baron dresses in medieval fashion suitable for a German noble.

With his passion for medieval history, Munchmaussen believes he has uncovered evidence that Trolls inhabited Bavaria in the middle Dark Ages. The tome is worth more to him than life itself because he believes it substantiates his claims.

The baron is not consciously suicidal, however. If it is obvious that he cannot retain his book, Munchmaussen will seek to escape, with the intention of chasing the runners down at a later time and place of his own choosing.

AFTERMATH

If the players are lucky, their characters nab the tome and escape in the baron's own Hughes Airstar (see **Brown Hall**, below). Even if less lucky, they will be temporarily safe from Munchmaussen's revenge if they can escape from his valley. The journey back to Seattle should be pleasant enough, unless the gamemaster wishes to devise complications.

Should the runners fail get the book in their first attempt and wish to try again, or if they are captured by the baron, they may need the help of some local NPCs. Father Braun of the Munchmaussen Underground (see **Welcome, Chumlichen!**) may prove very useful.

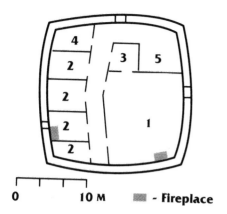

0   10 M   ▨ - Fireplace

FIRST FLOOR

Reception Hall (1)

This large chamber, lavishly decorated in medieval style, is the first line of protection for the baron. Polite but efficient functionaries verify the identities of all who enter. Except for the trio of desks for the bureaucrats, the room is furnished with antique chairs and writing tables for the comfort of those who wait here.

Offices (2)

These four rooms are the cubicles of the baron's senior bureaucrats. At night, the offices are locked.

Security Post (3)

A pair of security guards (use the **Ork Mercenary**, p. 41, **Shadowrun**) are always present.

Restroom (4)

Decorated with polished brass and antique porcelain fit for a throne room.

Elevator Landing (5)

A small but modern elevator (six-person capacity) has replaced the staircase that once spiraled here.

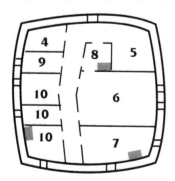

SECOND FLOOR

Dining Hall (6)

The seven-meter long obsidian dining table dominates this stylish room. A suit of armor stands in one corner and a Chinese vase in another. In the early evening, the baron often dines with his close associates here.

Antler Hall (7)

After dinner, the baron's guests adjourn to this casual smoking room, which is hung with hunting trophies and scenes of the arctic.

Kitchen (8)

This kitchen is a miniaturized marvel of modern technology, enabling two cooks to perform the work of six. Dumb waiters link the room with the bar on the next floor.

Cloakroom (9)

Guests' coats and other possessions are stored here by the chief butler. An intrusion alarm silently alerts the security post on the top floor if thieves enter.

Guest Rooms (10)

These rooms are unoccupied, unless the gamemaster wishes to add his own twist to this adventure.

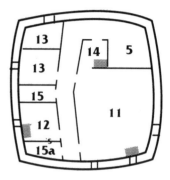

THIRD FLOOR

Great Hall (11)

Formerly used by the baron for his famous entertainments, the maglocked recreation room has an abandoned look to it. A temporary wooden stage, erected for a rock concert five years ago, has never been torn down.

A Rating 4 Conjuring Circle (Fire Elemental) is concealed beneath a tarp spread across the floor. If the baron has summoned Goldi, she has already conjured her Elementals. In such case, the room reeks of smoke and the center of the tarp is fire-scorched.

Library (12)

The baron's greatest treasures are said to be housed in this room, including the medieval text which the runners are after. See **The Tome**, p. 35.

Baron's Chambers (13)

The baron's living quarters include a bedchamber and small living room. An enormous portrait of the first baron of Munchmaussen hangs over the hexagonal bed.

Bar (14)

When the baron used to entertain, his servants catered his parties from this nook. Dumb waiters link it to the kitchen on the floor below. The room is still well-stocked with many varieties of expensive liquors.

Closets (15)

These rooms are used for mundane storage (cleaning supplies, laundry bags, vacuum cleaners) by the staff. The exception is 15a. Though labeled as a closet, it is actually Baron Munchmaussen's secret security chamber, linked to the library by a concealed door. None of the closets are monitored by the castle's security camera network.

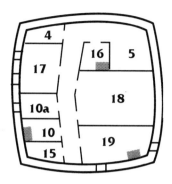

FOURTH FLOOR

Servants' Room (16)

The maids and butlers of the keep use this room for relaxation. Besides video equipment and a modest snack bar, nothing much of note is here. If the runners have been undetected so far and think to borrow some of the clean uniforms available here, the security guards will be less likely to notice their intrusion.

Chapel (17)

This Rococo chapel was constructed during the early eighteenth century, and nearly every available centimeter is covered with frescoes, oil paintings, ornaments, and stucco figures. The baron will not allow his guards to take any action that would damage this historical treasure.

Brown Hall (18)

The security cameras show a room in the throes of reconstruction, but it is a false view. The doors are stoutly maglocked, and only the baron has the key, which he wears on a golden chain around his neck. The roof folds back and the floor elevates, allowing exit for the baron's Hughes Airstar (with collapsible rotors), his ultimate escape route. Hey, we said he was paranoid, right?

Security Center (19)

The other on-duty members of the keep's security team are posted here. Two watch the monitors constantly, and two others leave here every half-hour to make the rounds. The guards are lax unless the baron has them on alert.

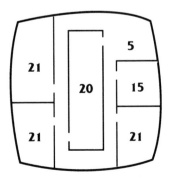

BASEMENT LEVEL ONE

Blue Gallery (20)

This chamber has been turned into a museum of the middle Dark Ages, and is hung with many ancient and macabre items: runic bibles illustrated with demons, broken swords engraved with twisted characters, and tapestries that appear oddly out of focus.

Vaults (21)

Stuffed with unwanted furniture and decorations from other periods in the castle's history, these rooms might produce a few gem-studded gewgaws if the runners look hard enough.

BASEMENT LEVEL TWO

Pool (22)

Baron Munchmaussen swims four laps every night before turning in. Because the water is very warm, the air is misty (three meters visibility).

Weight Room (23)

An open doorway leads into this chamber, which is filled with exercise and bodybuilding equipment. At the gamemaster's discretion, one or more off-duty security guards might be working out here.

Gym (24)

A boxing ring sits at the center of this small room. In former years, Baron Munchmaussen delighted in challenging his guards to bouts. His growing disability now prevents him from enjoying this pleasure.

Steam Room (25)

The baron spends much time here, for the warmth and humidity ease his pain. Visibility is reduced to one meter because of the clouds of steam.

Fungarium (26)

The baron indulges in a form of gardening that can only be called eccentric. He uses this room to raise exotic fungus and molds in glass containers. If any containers are opened, a vile smell spreads throughout the basement.

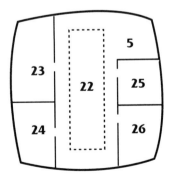

PICKING UP THE PIECES

It should be obvious by now that this particular segment has its tongue firmly planted in its cheek. It is certainly possible to run **Past** in a serious and straight manner, but, hey, don't ya think the runners deserve a little bit of weird every so often?

Because the opposition in this segment could be a little too powerful, the gamemaster may want to balance each encounter individually. An easy method is to penalize the opposition's Initiative by some constant value, thus giving the runners the advantage.

RUNNING FOR THE BORDER

The runners have a number of options for getting clear of Schloss Munchmaussen, and the gamemaster must be ready to deal with the various contingencies, just in case. It could be an easy stroll out or just as crazy as the trip in.

Johnson will be waiting for them when they get back to Seattle, money ready and looking to take possession of the tome. She will, mysteriously, also know full details of what occurred at Schloss Munchmaussen.

ASSIGNING KARMA

TEAM KARMA

Surviving the run	1pt
Acquiring the real tome	1pt
Bringing back the false tome	– 2pt
Properly leaving the valise	1pt

INDIVIDUAL KARMA

Assign individual Karma per the Individual Karma rules on p.160, **Shadowrun**.

LOVES

"Of all that is written, I love only what a person hath written with his blood. Write with blood, and thou wilt find that blood is spirit."
—**Nietzsche,** ***Thus Spoke Zarathustra***

INTRODUCTION

It is now time to incriminate the Young Elven Technologists. (Don't feel too sorry for them. They've had it coming for awhile.) It seems that some bright financial software designers who work for Sylvan Information and who also happen to be Young Elven Technologists have been leaving imperceptible back doors in their programs. Once Sylvan Information installs one of these packages for its client, the policlub is able to use the program's back door to siphon funds whenever necessary.

Harlequin has become aware of all this through other shadowruns made against Ehran (after all, the player characters are not the only act in town). He now wants to frame Ehran's precious policlub for computer piracy, enjoying the subtle irony of hoisting Ehran with his own petard.

PARTY TIME!

TELL IT TO THEM STRAIGHT

Puyallup Barrens is far from the chrome and neon wonder of Seattle, but still close enough to fall under its shadow. For the past 20 minutes, your team has been sitting in sober silence as a fixer of your acquaintance, Sandii (no last name, no flashy handle, just Sandii…) confidently weaves her Chevy Vanguard through the dense Thursday night traffic. The closest thing to conversation is her occasional, off-color remark about the driving habits of Seattle's night owls. Even these cease as you reach the outskirts of Puyallup, where the traffic thins to a trickle. People living in such squalor have little use for something that they can't eat in a pinch; even the family dog may have its place on the menu.

You remember how, earlier this evening, Sandii slid into a seat at your favorite table at the Club Penumbra, saying, "This is your lucky night. You're all invited to a party."

In the deafening confines of the nightclub, you almost didn't hear her say "…in Puyallup."

Before you could protest that the Barrens is no place for man, beast, or anything in between, Sandii flashed one of her patented smiles. Light danced off her stainless steel razor-teeth (rumored to be a "gift" from a dissatisfied oyabun with no tolerance for failure). Her fingers are, however, all present and accounted for. (At least they seem to be her fingers…).

"This is strictly a business call," she said, slapping an envelope bulging with nuyen on the table. "I told Johnson you wouldn't go that far out of town without getting something for your trouble. Here's ¥250 nuyen for each of you just to listen to his tune."

Greed is a terrible habit. You make a mental note to try to kick the habit someday.

Your reverie is interrupted as Sandii brings her big van to a stop in front of a large, two-story building. You can feel the vibration of the thunderous music emanating from within its brick walls. If the windows were not already boarded up, you are certain the driving force of synthi-bass would have shattered the glass. Through the pitched skylight, pulsating light casts an eerie orange and magenta glow over the building. In the faint illumination, you can read the words "Fire Station 118" etched into one of the building's cornerstones, but you know the place hasn't served that purpose since before the Awakening…

"End of the line, chummers," Sandii says. "Johnson will meet you inside. He said to wander around, enjoy the party, and he'll meet you at some point tonight. Did I tell you that he doesn't want you packing artillery? Everyone gets scanned at the door. I guess these Elves are kind of touchy about little things like that.

"You can leave your gear here, 'cause I'll be waiting for you just up the street."

When Mr. Johnson contacts the runners, he will lead them to a relatively quiet corner to speak with them. Read the following:

"His voice is smooth, cultured, and has a distinctive Elven accent, almost the antithesis of the person to whom it belongs. The speaker is Elven, but he could pass for a misshapen Human or perhaps a good-looking Ork. Thin pink lines of scar tissue criss cross his scalp, cutting through his close-cropped hair like roads on a dark map. His craggy face could have been hewn from a piece of quartz. His mouth, however, is slightly undersize and unable to contain his stunning set of gold-capped teeth.

He glances about before continuing, "I have a task requiring persons with your special talents.

"My real name and the organization I represent are unimportant. All you need to know is that the Young Elven Technologists have committed a number of atrocities that have, thus far, gone unpunished. With your help, I intend to rectify this injustice.

"First, located somewhere in the computer system on these premises, the Young Elven Technologists have a datastore containing a number of back-door passcodes to the systems of some very influential institutions. You must obtain two copies of these passcodes.

"Second, one copy must be delivered to the private suite used by Ehran the Scribe when he visits. His next visit is scheduled for this Saturday. Along with the passcode, you must also leave a sealed missive that our mutual acquaintance, Ms. Sandii, is currently holding.

"Third, you must make a very quick Matrix run against Dassurn Securities and Investments. This is where the other copy of the passcodes may prove beneficial. The branch office at LTG # 3206 (52-7229) employs SAN software that can be circumvented using one of the passcodes. All you have to do is determine which passcode to use. Once inside Dassurn's system, go to the Liquidations subprocessor. When you get to this SPU, execute the program that Ms. Sandii gives you; it will handle the rest. When it's finished, get out.

"The run must take place no later than tomorrow night. The Young Elven Technologists have no meetings scheduled until Ehran's arrival on Saturday, so only a skeleton crew should be present. More important, Dassurn Securities and Investments audits all its branch offices on Monday morning. This will leave the Young Elven Technologists in a precarious position, with no time for a cover-up.

"Under no circumstance should you deviate from this plan or attempt any facet of this run from beyond these walls. Deck into the Technologists' system from inside this building, then go directly to Dassurn. For reasons best kept secret, all paths must lead directly to the Young Elven Technologists' doorstep…especially if things sour.

"When you have completed the run, our Ms. Sandii will meet you at Club Penumbra. She will take possession of the passcodes in exchange for a sum of ¥40,000 nuyen each."

Mr. Johnson's eyes dart left, then right, while he reaches into his pocket. He sets down a credstick for each of you, "I am prepared to pay ¥4,000 nuyen in advance."

Gamemaster's Note: If the team balks at Mr. Johnson's generous offer, have the leader of the team make an Opposed Negotiation Test against Johnson. Assume that Johnson's Willpower is 7 and his Negotiation Skill is 7 as well. Each success indicates Mr. Johnson's willingness to increase his offer by ¥750 nuyen. If no successes are scored, Johnson's offer is firm.

Read the following to the team immediately after they come to terms with Johnson:

Before you can learn any further details from Johnson, your attention is drawn to a major scuffle near the front door. From the corner of your eye, you see three Trolls, Ares MP-LMGs in hand, heading toward the door.

Above the noise of the crowd, you hear a shrill voice: "I tell ya, I am Lee Gorbin!"

BEHIND THE SCENES

Mr. Johnson has invited the shadowrunners to meet him at a party being thrown by the Young Elven Technologists. Like most policlubs, the YET occasionally sponsors events to attract the youth in their area. Along with the music, dancing, and simsense, the young people also get a little exposure to the club's political and social views. Those showing even the slightest interest are invited to other activities by friendly policlub members who always seem happy to see them. Many eventually become members of the policlub.

Because various policlubs are in competition for these potential recruits, the potential for violence at one of these social functions is high. It is common for members of one policlub to crash another club's party. Tonight security is very tight, particularly because the Association Para-Nobilis, the YET's fiercest rival, has been making noises about the Young Elven Technologists openly attacking them. Before allowing the player characters to enter the building, the doorman scans them electronically with a Detek-It™ Hand Wand. The gamemaster makes a Perception Test, 5 dice, for each item a shadowrunner tries to smuggle past the doorman; the item's Concealability Rating is the Target Number. If he detects something, the doorman will politely ask the character to surrender the item(s) until he leaves. Those who check in their weapons and armor are allowed inside; those who refuse are not.

If the runners attempt to force their way past the doorman, they will encounter an amazingly injudicious display of force. Within 1D6 turns of an altercation, three Trolls (use the **Troll Street Samurai**, p. 108, **Street Samurai Catalog**) arrive to restore order. If the gamemaster is handling things properly, that should be enough to cool the runners' heels. If not, a strike force of six Elven bruisers (use **Elven Poser-Gang Member**, p. 110, **Sprawl Sites**) and two **Elven Hitmen** (p. 166, **Shadowrun**), each armed with an Ares Predator with Smartgun Adapter and two extra clips, arrive 2D6 turns after the last Troll falls.

Adding to the mayhem, 40-odd party-goers begin a mad rush for the exits at the first sign of major trouble (such as gunfire). Needless to say, a number of innocent and not-so-innocent bystanders will get hurt in the hysteria that follows.

To get inside the hall, Mr. Johnson arranged for a member of the Young Elven Technologists to be temporarily "delayed" and took his place at the party. Several Elves present will remember talking to Gorbin, and the doorman knows that he had let him in earlier this evening. The sudden appearance of a second Lee Gorbin sets off a scuffle between the doorman and the real Lee.

Characters who investigate may be surprised to discover that the protesting Elf is the twin of their Mr. Johnson! As they wait to see what happens next, an Elf named Alex Manke steps in and orders the three Trolls to look for the other Lee Gorbin, then he spirits the newcomer down to the basement.

While the characters are putting two and two together, they find that their Mr. Johnson has vanished. Johnson is nobody's fool, and has beat a hasty retreat...somehow. He's just gone. It doesn't take a genius to figure out that the shadowrunners are in for a long night if anyone fingers them as being the last people to see the first Lee Gorbin. The most intelligent thing to do is get out of the building and into Sandii's van as fast as possible.

Once they're free and clear, and presumably safe, Sandii will give the runners the chip containing Johnson's program and a wax-sealed envelope, the one they are supposed to leave on Ehran's desk.

About the worst thing that can happen is for the characters to instigate trouble before they meet with Mr. Johnson. If this happens, Johnson will leave the meeting hall and give them their mission briefing when the runners return to Sandii's van. Of course, Johnson will also reduce the amount he is willing to pay the shadowrunners by ¥3,000 nuyen each. Getting him to increase this figure requires a successful Opposed Negotiation Test, with each extra success adding ¥500 nuyen to his offer.

If caught on the premises after the appearance of the real Lee Gorbin blows Mr. Johnson's cover, the player characters will be detained for 2D6 + 2 hours (during which the characters could be preparing for the upcoming shadowrun or getting some sack-time). On the other hand, perhaps they can convince the Head of Security that they know nothing (by making a successful Opposed Negotiation Test against him).

Who is Mr. Johnson, the imposter Lee Gorbin? Well, it might be Harlequin come to meet the runners who've been doing his dirty work, but then again, it might not. We're not saying.

POLICLUB GROUND FLOOR MAP KEY

For a "normal" description of this level, see page 58.

Lounge (1)

Couches and recliners line the eastern wall, near the simsense entertainment center, while the center of the room is taken up by two-meter-long conference tables and wooden benches. At any one time, there will be 20 or more people in this room, eating, drinking, gossiping, and checking out the latest simsense releases.

Dining Area (2)

This room contains a row of buffet tables filled with trays of food. Not just stuffers, but real food! Along the east wall, a bar has been set up to serve punch or more potent drink. There will be 1D6 + 2 people in this room helping themselves to food and drinks.

Kitchen (3)

This room is self-explanatory. There are 1D6 food servers preparing additional plates for the buffet. A bathroom occupies the northwest corner. The rear exit to the building is locked and bolted.

Solarium (4)

Stepping into this room for the first time is like stepping into a dream-park; trees, shrubbery, and grass are the decor. Wooden benches line the east and west walls. Along the south wall, a mini-mono musician is performing on a small stage. The central clearing is filled with 3D6 + 6 barefoot dancers moving to the blaring music created by the mini-mono's wild gyrations, each muscle contraction causing a specific note to sound or light to flash.

The skylight, approximately 15 meters overhead, is visible from the solarium floor. A hydroponic light system is integrated with the skylight's metal support frame to provide "sunlight" when natural lighting is unavailable. Approximately six meters above the ground, partially concealed by tree branches, are two catwalks accessible from the second floor's **Commons Area (1)**. Two guards are positioned on each catwalk. Along the northwest wall is a staircase leading to the second floor and basement levels. Two YET members stand guard over it. A small storage closet containing garden equipment and plant food is in the northwest corner of the room.

When a character leaves the solarium, he must make an Unresisted Willpower Test against a Target Number equal to the number of minutes he or she was in the room. If the test fails, the character suffers disorientation, ringing ears, R.E.M. (rapid eye movement), and deafness similar to the effects of a Force 3 Chaos spell (see **Shadowrun**, page 95) which persists for 1D6 minutes.

ENCOUNTERS

Paying attention is the hallmark of a good shadowrunner, or at least an old shadowrunner. If the players believe this is just an unusual place to meet their prospective employer, they are dead wrong. Johnson's shadowrun will bring them back to this very site, and this social gathering has given them the perfect opportunity to reconnoiter the site firsthand.

After the characters have wandered around a bit, the gamemaster should use one or more of the following encounters to spice things up. All may be run, but the encounters need not occur in any specific order.

Circulating

Every half hour, a character is able to eavesdrop on a conversation. Each time, the gamemaster rolls 2D6 and consults the following Success Table to determine what is overheard. In all instances, the character is not involved in the discussion and unable to question the speaker, and the subject is not brought up again.

Successes	Result
2	"I don't like the idea of our club being open to non-Elves…no matter what Ehran and all the other big shots think."
3	"These guys really know how to throw a party. I don't know about you, but if I can join them, I will. It sure beats eating gutter scraps and sleeping in a cardboard box."
4	"Who invited the Trolls?"
5	"I've got some really great nyborg at my place if you wanna cut outta here."
6	"These Elves must be loaded! Did you see that spread?"
7	"I'm telling ya, Lee, a lot of those APN got geeked and are blaming us for it." (**Gamemaster's Note:** The character who overhears this conversation will later recognize "Lee" as Mr. Johnson when he eventually contacts the shadowrunners.)
8	"Hello, my name is Johnson." (**Gamemaster's Note:** See **Meeting the Mister** below.)
9	"If the Association Para-Nobilis tries anything funny, we've got more than enough manpower—or should I say Trollpower?—to deal with them."
10	"You can git yer hand off my lady or spend the rest of yer life having people call ya Lefty."
11	"Excuse me, Mister Troll, sir, but you're standing on my foot."
12	"Mercurial? I can git ya a bootleg chip of the time she played Underground 93."

Dance With Me

The recruiting methods employed by the Young Elven Technologists are not much different from those of other policlubs. However, this policlub is particularly interested in having deckers join their ranks.

Any decker who walks the walk and talks the talk is approached by an attractive member of the opposite sex who will ask for the next dance. (Use the stats of the **Simsense Star**, p. 118, **Sprawl Sites**.) The lonely and the desperate easily fall prey to policlubs when a recruiter turns on the charm. Getting "close" to a prospective tyro is their business. Getting away from the recruiter, who will do practically anything to gain the decker's confidence, is extremely difficult.

If the character wants to use the opportunity to learn about the Young Elven Technologists, he makes an Opposed Negotiation Test against the recruiter. The following table shows the number of net successes the player character needs to obtain various bits of information. We'll be nice and assume the YET recruiter can pry no information out of the iron-jawed decker. Each success level should include the information from the lower success levels.

Successes	Result
1	"Our ultimate goal is to shatter the myths about Elves. We can only do this through reeducating not only those who perpetuate the Elven stereotype, but the entire world. To do so, we need people who are sensitive to the unique problems of our race…we need people like you."
2	"We aren't a policlub, we have real representation. In fact, our chairman is Ehran the Scribe. You know, the guy who won a Pulitzer Prize for *Mankind Ascendant*. Right! He writes all our literature and brochures. He even stays here when he's in town. It's not the Ritz, but he's got his own private suite upstairs. In fact, he's coming to our youth meeting this Saturday. If you want to give me your address and phone number, I'd be glad to give you a call and swing by on my way in to pick you up."
3	"Believe me, any decker who's a member of the Young Elven Technologists can write his own meal ticket. Deckers are just about the most important people in our organization. How else can we get our message out to the world? You can't send everybody a letter, but you can reach them through the Matrix. That's where it does the most good. Hey, maybe I could show you our computer room? Of course, we can't go in or anything, but we could take a peek at the facilities through the glass."

Gamemaster's Note: If the decker takes the recruiter up on the offer, she will take him downstairs to show him the computer room, but alas, nothing else.

Party Animal

"Hey chummer! Why don't ya watch where yer goin'!"

Accidents do happen, and unfortunately, the first character to get a drink from the bar has managed to elbow one of the Troll Street Samurai that YET hired to beef up security.

If the character makes a successful Opposed Negotiation Test against the Troll, no harm is done. Otherwise, the Troll will take a big swing at him. Before things can get out of hand, another Troll appears and restrains the first.

If the character is still conscious, the second Troll will demand that the first one apologize. He will do so, but only grudgingly, before heading off down the stairs to the basement.

Lancelot Windtree

The majority of the Elves have gone out of their way to refute the physical Elven stereotype, with one exception: Lancelot Windtree. A peripheral member of Ehran's entourage, Windtree fancies himself far more important than he truly his. A whiny, arrogant, racist Elf, Windtree is handsome and he knows it. The only person who measures up to his standards is Ehran, and Windtree's manner lets everyone know it.

Present at the party only because Ehran demanded it, Windtree wears his boredom and bigotry like a badge. His presence is definitely notable, and one the runners will remember later.

Lancelot is handsome and elegant, with thin features and silver hair. He wears a loose-fitting tunic and trousers that are woven from natural fibers and obviously expensive. Slung over his back is an ornamental sword of fine craftsmanship.

Point Windtree out to the runners, they'll meet him again in **Counterstroke**.

RUNNING THE SHADOWS

BEHIND THE SCENES

The gamemaster should let the players decide how they spend their time before starting their shadowrun against the Young Elven Technologists. They might choose to scout out the building and its immediate vicinity, they might want to check with their Contacts (see **Legwork** in this section and the Mmaster Legwork section later on), or even have a look from Astral Space.

ASTRAL SCOUTING

With a name like Young Elven Technologists, a runner might suspect that the group has a magical "chink" in their armor. Ehran the Scribe, however, is not so blind as to ignore the spiritual protection of his precious policlub.

When Ehran is away from the meeting hall, which is most of the time, it is extremely vulnerable to astral scouting. Only the Administrative Offices and Ehran's private suite are guarded by Force 8 Wards (see p. 69, **The Grimoire**). Everything else is an open book to an astral traveler.

When Ehran is in town, he brings along his entourage, and trust us, that means trouble. The player characters can count their lucky stars that Ehran is still out of town when the shadowrun takes place.

YET HALL MAP KEY

BASIC PLAN

The exterior walls of the Young Elven Technologists' meeting hall are constructed of Normal Brick (Barrier Rating 6). The upper windows have been filled in with the same brick facing, but the ground floor windows are merely boarded up (Barrier Rating 1). The rusted remains of blow-torched iron supports dot the north and east walls, where fire escapes were once located.

Interior walls and doors are Normal Wood (Barrier Rating 1), except for those in the Solarium, which are Normal Construction Plastic (Barrier Rating 4) unless otherwise noted.

Security camera positions are noted on the individual maps. They have a 45-degree angle of vision and are connected to monitors in **Main Security**, located in the basement.

EXTERIOR GROUNDS

The area surrounding the meeting hall is clear of all debris (the policlub takes pride in the hall's appearance, which is a stark contrast to the neighborhood in which it is located. Exterior lights, in protective wire baskets, and security cameras are mounted on the four corners of the building.

Victims of vandalism, the cameras are no longer functional. During the day, this is obvious from the street to anyone making a Perception (5) Test; under less than optimum conditions, the

gamemaster should use the Visibility Table, p. 66, **Shadowrun**, to modify the Target Number.

During the evening, the lights illuminate the grounds in a five-meter radius. The lights cannot be damaged by thrown rocks or objects because of their protective cages. However, a sniper could damage them (+6 to the normal Target Number).

THE ROOF

Helipad (1)

The helipad consists of a raised platform standing two meters above the rooftop. A short flight of steps leads down to the actual roof. The helipad platform forms a housing for the air-conditioning plant underneath (Barrier Rating 3).

Staircase (2)

The door to the shack accessing the staircase is bolted shut from the inside. The door is made of Normal Steel Sheeting (Barrier Rating 6) and cannot be opened from the outside.

The staircase connecting the roof to the second floor was removed when the Young Elven Technologists renovated the building. Its "floor" is made of Normal Construction Plastic (Barrier Rating 4).

Skylight (3)

The skylight consists of several dozen sheets of Normal Armor Glass (Barrier Rating 2).

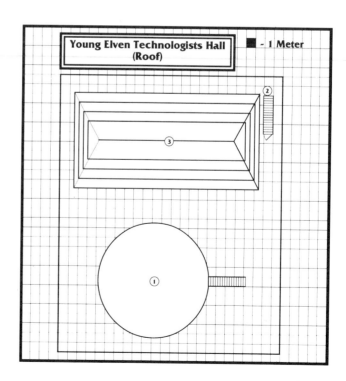

Young Elven Technologists Hall
(Roof)

■ - 1 Meter

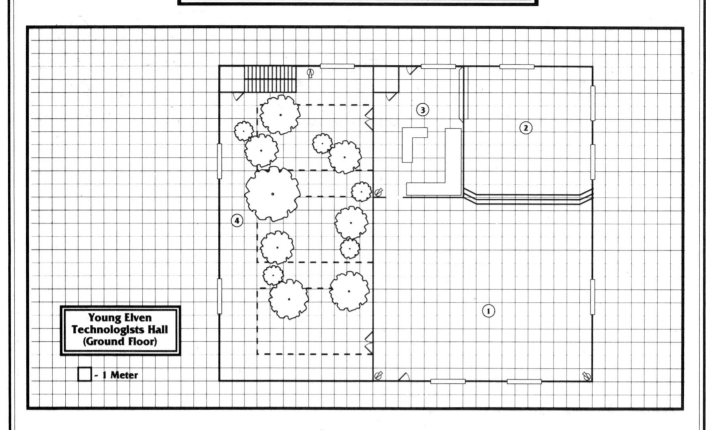

Young Elven
Technologists Hall
(Ground Floor)

☐ - 1 Meter

GROUND FLOOR

Lounge Area (1)

This area is filled with couches, recliners, chairs, coffee tables, and an entertainment center. The room is often used for informal meetings and gatherings.

If the shadowrun takes place in the early evening, the front door will be unlocked and there will 1D6 + 3 policlub members present (use the **Elf Poser-Gang Member** Contact, p. 110, **Sprawl Sites**). Two of the Elves are plugged into the simsense; the others are just sitting around shooting the bull.

After 11:00 P.M., this room is dark and empty; the front door is maglocked, Rating 3.

Dining Area (2)

This room is used as an eating area for policlub members. It contains a large table surrounded with chairs. Regardless of when the shadowrun takes place, the room is empty. However, the table still has plates of food left over from the party.

Kitchen (3)

This room is used for food preparation. A bathroom occupies the northwest corner. The back door is maglocked, Rating 5.

Solarium (4)

Stepping into this room for the first time is like stepping into a dream-park; trees, shrubbery, and grass are the decor. Rows of wooden benches are set in the center of this room for formal meetings of the Young Elven Technologists.

Approximately six meters above the ground and partially concealed by tree branches are two catwalks accessible from the second floor. Another ten meters or so above the catwalks is the skylight. A hydroponic light system is integrated with the skylight's metal support frame to provide "sunlight" when natural lighting is unavailable. A staircase leading to the second floor and basement levels is located along the northwest wall. A small storage closet containing garden equipment and plant food is located in the northwest corner of the room.

This room is shrouded in yellow-green throughout the night. It is also empty.

Gamemaster's Note: If a combat occurs in the solarium, a number of the following situations need to be considered.

•The trees and shrubs provide no hard cover for cowering individuals. They do provide soft cover in the form of target number modifiers to an attacker's test to hit something behind the cover.

•Firing through the catwalk counts as Full Cover (+4 to the attack target number); firing through the flooring (Barrier Rating 8) counts as Blind Fire (+8 to the target number).

•Anyone firing upward will also have to worry about hitting the skylight in the roof. If a shot misses and the firing angle is such that the gamemaster feels the skylight would be hit, an attack against the skylight glass (Barrier Rating 2) is made. Glass taking more "boxes" of damage than its Barrier Rating shatters, raining down slivers and fragments on those unfortunate enough to be standing below. (The victim must make a Quickness (3) Test to get out of the way; those who fail make a Damage Resistance Test against 3M3 damage; Impact Armor assists. Glass shards cover the ground in a two-meter radius directly below the former pane. Henceforth, the area is considered Difficult Ground (see **Shadowrun**, p. 65) and "attacks" anyone moving through it (victim makes a Quickness (4) Test to avoid stepping on glass; those who fail make a Damage Resistance Test against 3L1 damage). If the gamemaster is feeling particularly vicious, a –2 meter movement penalty might also be applied to any character suffering a wound after moving through a glass-littered area.

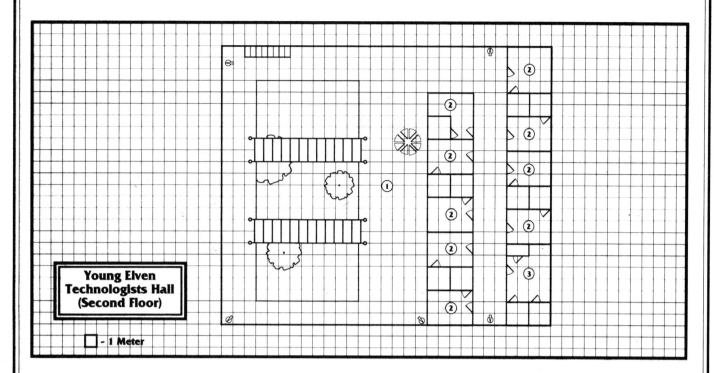

Young Elven
Technologists Hall
(Second Floor)

☐ - 1 Meter

SECOND FLOOR

Commons Area (1)

This area is open to the huge pitched skylight and solarium (see description above). The two catwalks are constructed of wood and rope (Barrier Rating 0, but provide soft cover) and are attached to metal posts on either side of the commons.

Cutting the rope requires a sharp knife and four turns. Anyone standing on the catwalk must make a Quickness (5) Test or fall to the ground, six meters below. Anyone still on the catwalk when a second rope is cut must make a Strength (4) Test to hold onto the catwalk (or else fall). If both ropes are cut from a single side, the catwalk swings down. Depending on where the character was positioned when the final rope was cut, he may crash to the ground or smash into the solarium wall.

Small Apartment (2)

These are self-contained, one-room flats used by Young Elven Technologists members who are either between apartments or visiting from out of town. Each has its own bed, dresser, clothes rack, and toilet facilities.

If the shadowrun takes place in the early evening, three of the rooms are occupied by the Troll Street Samurai hired by Alex Manke to beef up security. The rooms they have are left to the gamemaster's discretion, though Ehran's suite should remain empty.

If the shadowrun takes place later than 11:00 P.M., two additional rooms are occupied by a pair of Ehran's strong-arms, one Bodyguard and one Combat Mage (p. 97, 98, **Sprawl Sites**). They have, as always, arrived in advance of of their employer. Again, the rooms they use are unimportant, though they would probably want those adjacent to and across the hall from Ehran's Private Suite (see Room 3).

Each occupant has a maglock passkey matching his apartment's door. The locks are Rating 5.

All other rooms are maglocked and empty.

Ehran's Private Suite (3)

This is Ehran's private quarters. When he is away, the door is maglocked (Ehran has the passkey) and linked to a PANICBUTTON™ alarm (controlled by Slave Module Two (SM-2) in the computer system). A Force 10 Ward is worked into the wall decor to protect the entire suite from astral invasion. Like the other apartments, its furnishings are spartan, but it does have a small den area containing a writing desk, telephone (I/OP-1), two computer terminals (I/OP-4 and I/OP-7), and a datastore (DS-13). Most of the books on the bookshelf were written by Ehran (under his own name and under a number of pseudonyms).

Regardless of the shadowrun's timing, this room is empty. However, Ehran's strong-arms in the rooms nearby might come to investigate any noise the characters make when they are here dropping off a copy of the back-door passcodes and Johnson's envelope.

THE BASEMENT

Storage Closet (1)

A storage closet containing cleaning supplies, mops, and buckets is underneath the stairs leading up to the ground floor. The door to this closet has no lock.

Women's Room (2)
Men's Room (3)
Main Security (4)

From inside this armor-glassed station, security has a clear view of the entire main hallway. Video monitors hooked to each security camera inside and outside the building are displayed simultaneously. A central alarm can be activated from this desk with the flip of a switch. Maglocks on both sets of double doors can be opened from this desk (or through the SM-4 computer node).

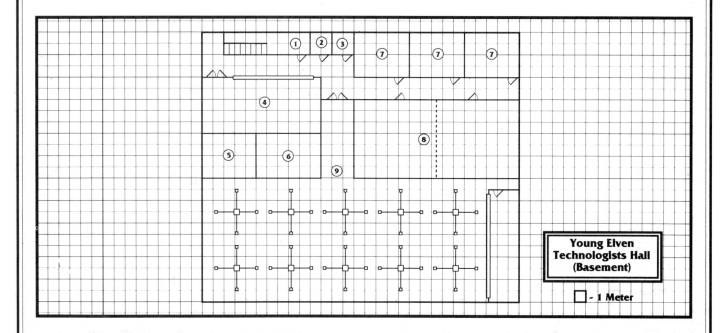

Young Elven
Technologists Hall
(Basement)

☐ - 1 Meter

If the shadowrun occurs in the early evening, six security guards will be present: three on duty, three off duty. If the run takes place after 11:00 P.M., three guards will be present, one manning the Main Security desk, the other two passing time in the Lounge.

Armory (5)

The door leading into the armory is made of Reinforced Sheet Steel (Barrier Rating 24). It may only be accessed with a passkey held by Alex Manke (or through SM-4).

The room contains a rack of four Heckler & Koch HK227 submachine guns, four Ares MP light machine guns, six Ares Predator heavy pistols, and nine Armor Jackets (three are Troll-sized). Also on the shelves are a number of boxes of ammunition for all the weapon types stored here.

Weapons are checked in and checked out to security personnel only. Note that the above inventory assumes that all available weapons are present. If any of the guards are using some of the weapons, the gamemaster should reduce the inventory accordingly.

Security Lounge (6)

This room serves as both a luncheon area and a place to kick back and relax during the long hours of sentry duty. Chances are good that the characters won't be spotted if they wander into a security camera's field because the guards are in here (it's hard to get good help these days).

Administration Offices (7)

These offices belong to the three section heads of this branch of the Young Elven Technologists: Nick Francis (Indoctrination), Patricia Stein (Recruitment), and Alex Manke (Security). All have maglocked doors accessed by their respective passkeys or through the SM-4 node.

If the shadowrun takes place in the early evening, Alex Manke occupies the first office (use the **Elven Street Samurai**, p. 104, **Sprawl Sites**). If the shadowrun takes place after 11:00 P.M., all the offices are empty.

Conference Room (8)

This room contains two large tables, each able to seat a dozen people. If necessary, the room may be split into two semi-private conference rooms, as indicated by the dotted lines.

Computer Room (9)

This cavernous area is where the hottest deckers in town get to hang out after they join the Young Elven Technologists policlub. Ehran puts them to work developing software for Sylvan Information and other corporations under his control.

The area is divided into 40 workstations. Each cubicle consists of a pair of 1.5-meter-tall partitions, a comfortable chair, a small desk, and a computer terminal. Enclosed in a sound-proof glass room (Barrier Rating 2) along the east wall is the Young Elven Technologists' Central Processing Unit.

At any one time, there will be 2D6 **Elven Deckers** (p. 36, **Shadowrun**) using the system.

ELVEN DEFENSE

The shadowrunners will have the element of surprise working for them as long as no external alert or security alarm is triggered. The Young Elven Technologists are in a tentative "state-of-preparedness" because of the recent events involving the Association Para-Nobilis, but their defense is geared toward handling something along the lines of a "frontal assault." They don't expect the APN to use subtlety (they never have in the past).

If any character moves into the path of a security camera, the gamemaster makes a 3-dice Perception (5) Test to see if the character is spotted. The gamemaster should roll the dice even when the characters are snooping around outside, just in case they look up and notice the camera. It's little jabs like these that make being a gamemaster so worthwhile.

Characters can maintain their edge through Stealth and quick, assassin-like strikes against the Young Elven Technologists. Just for the record, a surprised, dead, or unconscious figure cannot sound an alarm. If any other condition exists, the player may do whatever is necessary to keep his victim from squawking.

The reactions of the Young Elven Technologists depend on how they become aware of the shadowrunners' presence. If possible, they will try to get the drop on the characters by arranging an ambush for them in the solarium or in the commons area. If it is obvious that the runners are trying to get into the system, the deckers in the basement will start shutting down the system (takes 2D6 turns).

If the characters are just slumming around outside or up on the roof, security will try to trap them on the upper levels and force their surrender. Even if they succeed, the characters will be "saved" by the arrival of the Association Para-Nobilis Elfies (see **Crossfire**, p. 67).

If the characters get the upper hand on the Elves, the YET will retreat downstairs, where everyone gets a weapon from the Armory and joins the fray. If things really go poorly for the Young Elven Technologists, they will retreat into the computer room for a final showdown.

If things are going too smoothly for the shadowrunners, the gamemaster has the Trolls and Ehran's bodyguards as wild cards to play. If the characters are doing a room-by-room search of the second level, these guys will not sit around passively waiting for their turn to come. They will try to isolate the characters in a single room or, failing this, make them retreat back toward the commons area where security can get to them.

These guys make their living doing just this sort of thing, so the gamemaster should play them smart. They are not monsters squatting in a dungeon room waiting for a band of adventurers to swagger in and end their miserable existences.

CRACKING THE CODE

BEHIND THE SCENES

The Young Elven Technologists computer system may not be very sophisticated, but it is well-protected. Its IC has geeked more than a few brash deckers in the past few years.

Some of the hottest Elven Deckers in the Barrens may be jacked-in when the shadowrunner makes his move against the system. If the player decker sets off an external alert, an Elf decker will enter the system to investigate. Use the **Elven Decker**, p. 36, **Shadowrun**, but use the equipment described under **The Opposition**, p. 116 of the same book. If the Elfie gets trashed, smile and give the decker another five minutes (or until another alert is sounded) before two more Elf deckers enter the system. Keep doubling the number every five minutes (or every alert) until something gives.

Likewise, if the decker gets a little too flamboyant, such as using an Attack 10 Combat Utility to make crushed IC, the gamemaster should have an Elf decker witness the pyrotechnics and investigate.

On the second go-round, a team of four security brutes (use the YET Muscle Contact elsewhere in this book) will close in on the decker's real-world location in 1D6 minutes, assuming he's in the building.

YET SYSTEM MAP

CPU = Central Processing Unit
DS = Datastore
I/OP = Input/Output Port
SAN = System Access Node
SM = Slave Module
SPU = Sub-Processing Unit

CPU-1: Young Elven Technologists Central Processor. Red-3, Barrier 5, Trace and Burn 4.
  DS-13: General. Orange-3, Scramble 4, Trace and Report 3.
SAN-0: Connects to Matrix at LTG # 4206 (47-2551). Unlisted private line. Orange-3, Access 3, Trace and Dump 3.
SAN-1: Connects to Matrix at LTG # 4206 (47-1378). Unlisted private line located in Ehran's Private Suite. Orange-4, Access 4, Trace and Burn 3.
SPU-1: Data Routing. Orange-3, Access 3.
  DS-1: E-mail datastore. Orange-3, Access 3.
  DS-2: Administrative E-mail datastore. Orange-3, Access 4, Trace and Report 3. Ehran's E-mail file is also protected by a Scramble 4.
  DS-3: Routing datastore. Records of all routing requests are located here. Orange-3, Scramble 4.
  I/OP-1: Telephones located on the ground and upstairs levels. Green-3, Access 3.

I/OP-2: Telephones on the basement level. Orange-3, Access 4, Trace and Report 3.
SPU-2: Administration System. Orange-5, Barrier 4, Blaster 4.
  DS-4: General. Orange-3, Scramble 4.
  DS-5: Personnel. Dossiers compiled by Security of all active members living in the area. Includes employment records showing no less than two dozen Young Elven Technologists working for the Sylvan Information Corporation. Orange-3, Scramble 4.
  DS-6: Restricted. Contains numerous top-secret files, including a list of Sylvan Information's client names, addresses, LTG locations, and software packages purchased. If the decker cross-references with the files located in DS-13, he will be able to match the purchasers to their respective back-door passcodes. (One file at 10 Mp.) Red-3, Scramble 4, Black IC 3.
  I/OP-3: Terminals located in Administration Office. Orange-3, Access 4, Trace and Dump 4.
  I/OP-4: Terminal located in Ehran's private suite. Orange-3, Access 5, Trace and Dump 4.
SPU-3: Research and Development. Red-3, Access 4, Tar Pit 3.
  DS-7: General Records. Orange-3, Scramble 4.
  DS-8: Project Records. Sifting through these files could be extremely time-consuming. Most projects are involved with the development of financial software, though some of the newer ones are complex security programs (32 files at 60 Mp each; worthless because none are complete or documented.). Orange-4, Scramble 4, Trace and Burn 4.
  I/OP-5: Terminals located in Computer Room. Orange-3, Access 4, Trace and Dump 4.
SPU-4: Secondary Programming System. Red-3, Barrier 5, Black IC 3.
  DS-9: Archive Files. Contains a number of financial software programs, but no back-door source code. Red-3, Barrier 4, Trace and Burn 4.
  DS-10: Back-up Files. Red-3, Barrier 4, Trace and Burn 4.
SPU-5: Security. Red-3, Barrier 5, Trace and Burn 4.
  DS-11: General Records. Orange-3, Scramble 4, Killer 4.
  DS-12: Access Data. Includes a complete log of all access requests. This is where all those Trace reports are duly registered by the computer. Orange-3, Barrier 4, Killer 4.
  I/OP-6: Terminal located in Main Security. Orange-3, Access 4, Killer 4.
    SM-1: Cameras. Orange-4, Access 4, Blaster 4.
    SM-2: Alarms. Orange-4, Access 4, Trace and Report 4.
    SM-3: Exterior Door Maglocks. Orange-4, Access 4, Blaster 4.
    SM-4: Interior Door Maglocks. Orange-4, Access 4, Blaster 4.
SPU-6: Ehran's System. Red-3, Barrier 5, Trace and Dump 4.
  I/OP-7: Terminal located in Ehran's Private Suite. Orange-4, Access 5,

DS-13: Ehran's portable datastore. Located here are all the back-door utilities developed by Ehran's deckers to access Sylvan Information's client systems. If cross-referenced with the file located in DS-6, the decker will be able to match the back-door passcodes to their respective purchasers. (Six utilities at 40 Mp each). Blue-6.Trace and Dump 4.

DS-14: General. Orange-3, Scramble 4.

DS-15: Personal. Includes Ehran's appointment calendar, rough drafts of speeches, books, and articles, and so on. (Ten files at 30 Mp each) Orange-3, Barrier 5.

DS-16: Restricted. Contains several files describing Ehran's intentions for the Young Elven Technologists, plus a few oblique references to Sylvan Information. Red-3, Scramble 4, Black IC 3.

Gamemaster's Note: If the decker decides to lift unnecessary files, use the guidelines given in **Install Data Values**, p. 158, **Shadowrun**, to determine their value and size. He will be unable to find anything that will assist him or anyone else within this or any other segment of **Harlequin**.

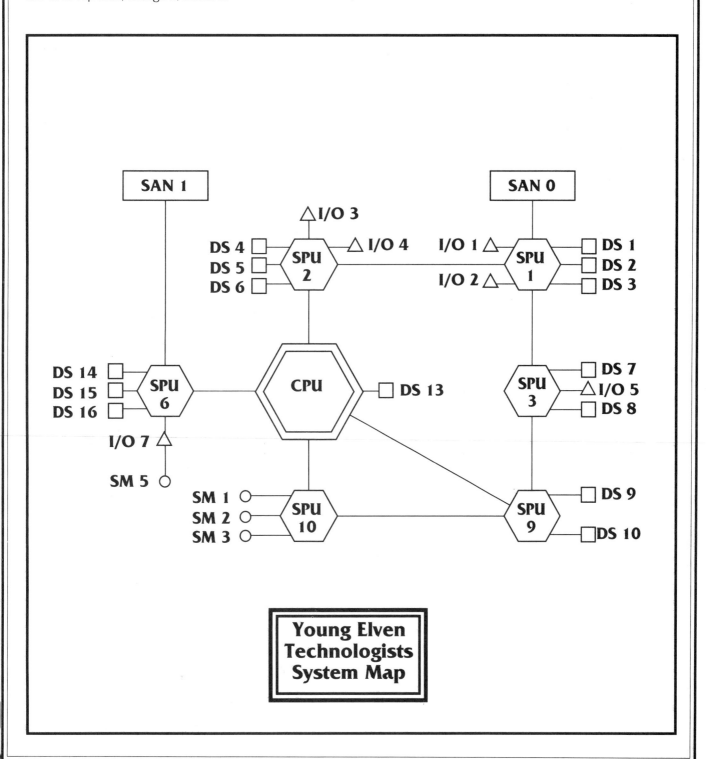

Young Elven Technologists System Map

DECKING DASSURN

TELL IT TO THEM STRAIGHT

Your fingers fly across the keyboard of your cyberdeck with a precision that comes only through practice. And you've had a lot of practice, haven't you, decker? You punch in the coordinates to Dassurn's system and thumb the power switch without skipping a beat. As reality dissolves, the glory of the Matrix unfolds before you in a coruscating latticework stretching in all directions to the Grid-horizontal.

You ride a stream of energy through the fiber-optic lines like a downhill racer, letting go the instant you reach Dassurn Securities and Investments' access node.

BEHIND THE SCENES

What happens next really depends on the decker's success or failure in his run against the Young Elven Technologists' computer system. If he was able to locate both the back-door passcode file and the Sylvan Information client list, he will have the correct passcode when he goes decking Dassurn. If he was only able to find the passcode file, the decker has a one-in-six chance of choosing the correct passcode to use against Dassurn. The gamemaster and decker each roll 1D6. If they match, the decker has the correct back door. Of course, the decker has no way of knowing this until he tries it. If he only located the Sylvan Information client list, he has no passcode to use against Dassurn; he'll just have to go in the hard way.

Read to the decker using the correct passcode:
You kick-start the passcode utility and stand back to give it room to maneuver. Milliseconds pass and you begin to wonder if Johnson wasn't selling you a bag of goods, then a tiny hole appears in the alphanumeric wall. As you watch, the gap grows larger and larger, not by destroying the wall, but by forcing the data to flow around it.

Smiling, you step through…

Gamemaster Note: Theoretically, the backdoor should lead directly to the system's CPU, but real-life isn't theory. Dassurn did not install the software in its CPU but in SPU-8 (Account Transaction Control). From here, the decker will just have to locate the Liquidations SPU normally. He does have the advantage of getting this far into the system without tripping any alarms and he has another way out of the system if things get too tight.

Read to the decker using an incorrect passcode:
With a silent prayer to the cybernetic Host of Hosts, you kick-start the passcode utility and stand back to give it room to maneuver. Your smile turns to a frown as you realize you guessed wrong. Dassurn's shimmering wall starts to break

apart, massive chunks of data flaring like meteors dissolving in the Earth's atmosphere.

You feel like a two-bit criminal who went out to buy a maglock passkey and came back with a chainsaw. Though there is definitely a hole in the system big enough for your Persona to waltz through, everybody and their cousins know you are here. So much for the subtle approach.

Steeling yourself, you step through…

Gamemaster's Note: Oh well, you can't win 'em all. The passcode burned a hole through Dassurn's system like a military icebreaker. When the decker comes through the hole, he appears in a randomly determined SPU (the gamemaster rolls 1D6 to determine the number of the SPU in which the decker begins). Any ice present in the node is gone, destroyed by the insidious back-door-turned-icebreaker. However, the decker must contend with a computer system that is already on External Alert (see **External Alerts**, p. 66).

Read to the decker not using a passcode:

Maybe it would be quicker and easier to call up a back door and let it do all of the work for you. But where is the challenge and excitement in that? Besides, who's to say the mythical back door works in the first place? You prefer to handle things in your own way because, ultimately, it comes down to a decker and his machine against the Matrix, not some "magical" shortcut that could leave you facing Black IC in the belly of a cybernetic leviathan.

DASSURN SYSTEM MAP

CPU = Central Processing Unit
DS = Datastore
I/OP = Input/Output Port
SAN = System Access Node
SPU = Sub-Processing Unit

SAN-0: Connects to Matrix at LTG # 3206 (52-7229). Listed. Orange-3, Barrier 3.
SAN-1: Connects directly to Mercantile Exchange(s). Red-3, Access 3, Black IC 3.
SAN-2: Connects only to Dassurn Securities and Investments main computer system. Green-6.
SPU-1: Customer Service. Orange-4, Access 5, Trace and Dump 4.

I/OP-1: Terminals. Orange-3, Access 3.
SPU-2: Customer Information. Orange-4, Access 5, Blaster 4.
  DS-1: General data. Orange-4, Scramble 4.
SPU-3: Secondary Customer Information. Orange-4, Barrier 5, Trace and Dump 4.
  DS-2: Archive Files. Orange-3, Access 4, Tar Pit 4.
  DS-3: Back-up Files. Orange-3, Access 3, Tar Pit 3.
  I/OP-2: Terminal. Orange-4, Access 5.
SPU-4: Liquidations. Red-4, Barrier 4, Killer 4.
  DS-4: General Files. Red-3, Scramble 4.
  I/OP-3: Terminals. Orange-4, Access 3.
SPU-5: Exchanges. Orange-4, Barrier 3.
  DS-5: General Files. Orange-4, Scramble 4.
  I/OP-4: Terminals. Orange-3, Access 3.
SPU-6: Transfers. Orange-4, Barrier 3.
  DS-6: General Files. Orange-4, Scramble 4.
  I/OP-5: Terminals. Orange-3, Access 3.
SPU-7: Purchases. Orange-4, Barrier 3, Trace and Dump 4.
  DS-7: General Files. Orange-4, Scramble 4.
  I/OP-6: Terminals. Orange-3, Access 3.
SPU-8: Account Transaction Control. Red-3, Access 3, Tar Pit 4.
  DS-8: General Files. Red-3, Barrier 3.
  I/OP-7: Terminals. Orange-4, Access 3.
SPU-9: Data Routing. Orange-4, Access 5, Trace and Report 4.
SPU-10: Accounting. Red-4, Barrier 3, Trace and Burn 4.
  DS-9: General Files. Red-3, Scramble 4.
  I/OP-8: Terminals. Orange-4, Access 3.

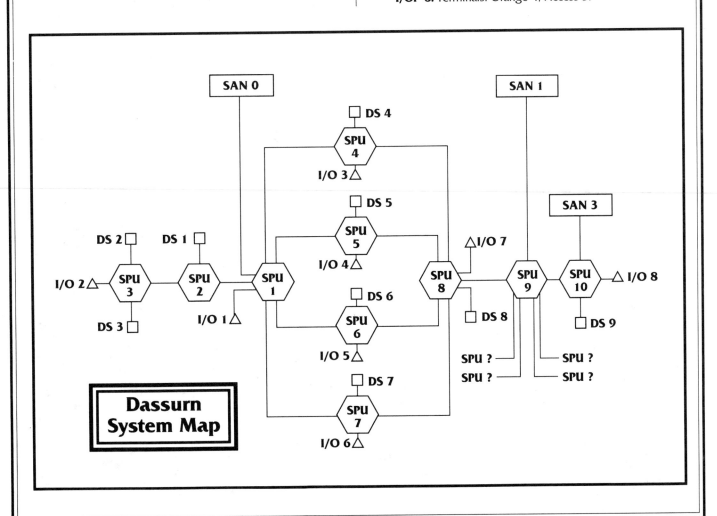

Dassurn System Map

BEYOND THE BRANCH OFFICE

The system described above is not complete. Its CPU and number of SPUs exist beyond the scope of this adventure and are left for the gamemaster to design, should the need arise.

EXTERNAL ALERTS

Under normal circumstances, Dassurn Securities and Investments maintains a number of security deckers to deal with external alerts. In the decker's favor is the fact that Dassurn's offices have restricted access during the weekends and thus maintain a smaller security force.

When an external alert is tripped, one Major League decker (use **Decker**, p. 34, **Shadowrun**) will enter the system to investigate. He will be using a Fuchi-6 with Level 1 Response Increase, and carrying Attack 6, Shield 2, and Mirrors 2. All his Persona programs are rated at 5. If he gets dumped, he will shut down the system after recovering from dump-shock.

INSIDE THE LIQUIDATIONS SPU

Once the decker reaches the Liquidations SPU (and defeats the ice located in the node), he will need three turns to run Johnson's program. After that, it's time to get out.

Read to the decker running Johnson's program:

You watch in fascination as the day-glo green alphanumeric code scrolls out into the "air" in front of you. The code is definitely Elven, the syntax like something out of a textbook, but a monster. Decompiled, it mimics a legitimate cash-out transaction, complete with retinal and cellular confirmation from a bevy of accredited phantom analysis labs. The data-flow is too fast for you to follow, a nightmare of subroutines and nested loops that hit the system from all sides, overpowering the compensator programming.

Suddenly numbers start scrolling at an unnatural rate, nuyen being transferred to Ghost knows where from the branch office's account reservoir, then its cash reserves, then tapping its credit line before reaching out across the Matrix to the home office for a little mother's milk…

You stand spellbound, unable to think, watching the program trying to siphon Dassurn dry.

The red lights are flashing now, as the boys in the home office finally get around to severing the cybernetic umbilical connecting them with their money-hungry offspring.

Somebody is extremely rich tonight, but you wouldn't want to trade places with him for all the money in his bank account right now.

Gamemaster's Note: At the same moment the decker begins his run against Dassurn, the Association Para-Nobilis begin their frontal assault against the Young Elven Technologists. All those player characters not jacked into the system should proceed to **Crossfire**, the next section.

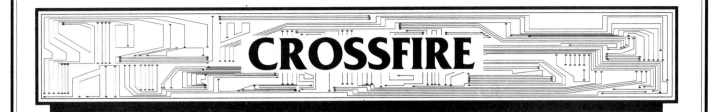

CROSSFIRE

TELL IT TO THEM STRAIGHT

An explosion rocks the building at its foundations, beating a thunderous path through the ground floor. Your feet desert you, leaving you sprawled out on the floor. From your new-found vantage point, you notice a few extra cracks in the ceiling and walls, plaster and dry wall having fallen away to reveal bare wood joists. They don't build them like this anymore.

Picking yourself up, you hear the muffled but unmistakable staccato of machine-gun fire coming from the direction of the ground-floor lounge. Apparently your Mr. Johnson isn't the only one interested in seeing the Young Elven Technologists take the big dive.

BEHIND THE SCENES

As though the shadowrunners weren't enough, now the remnants of the Association Para-Nobilis have decided to even the score with the Young Elven Technologists. Not known for their subtlety, ten APN Elfies (**Elf Poser-Gang Member**, p. 110, **Sprawl Sites**, but armed with Heckler & Koch MP-5TX submachine guns, with three extra clips, and wearing Lined Coats) have blown a hole through the south wall. The new opening is centered on where the front door used to be and is roughly four meters wide and three meters tall. They are now in the process of "sweeping" the ground floor, looking for survivors. The occasional burst of gunfire indicates that they've found yet another one.

When the shadowrunners get up enough nerve to investigate, the APN will have cleared everything east of the solarium. The Young Elven Technologists will assume positions along the stairs and wait for the APN to show their faces. The characters may or may not be able to reach the solarium without going through one of the two Elven groups, but this probably won't matter because the initial fusillade will send everyone diving for cover. Those characters brave enough to move should be able to get by when the Elves' heads are down.

GETTING OUT

At this point, a nasty gun battle between the APN and the Young Elven Technologists should occur. The gamemaster need not waste a lot of time rolling for the non-player characters, but should dramatize the results instead. What the characters do depends on the players. The best course, especially if they have completed their shadowrun objectives, is to sneak out an exit and let God sort things out. If, however, they want to hunker down behind a piece of defoliated shrubbery and shoot it out with a bunch of macho Elves with chips on their shoulders, by all means let 'em have their fun. They'll come to their senses as soon as they run out of ammunition.

UNITED ELVEN FRONT

At a particularly dramatic moment, the Elves stop shooting at each other and take active notice of the shadowrunners. At this point, all the characters who participated in the run against the Association Para-Nobilis make Perception (3) Tests.

Read to those characters who succeed at their Perception Tests:

Now that you have a chance to get a look at these newest Elven arrivals—the cut of their clothing, the hair styling, the insignia that adorns their headbands—it all looks so familiar. Then it clicks. These dandies are members of the Association Para-Nobilis, part of the group your shadowteam was hired to wetwork a short while back.

A cold shiver runs down your spine as you recognize one of the APN Elfies from across the room.

Gamemaster's Note: Those who fail the test do not recognize the Elves. They all look alike anyway. The important thing is, the Elves recognize the characters. As the Association Para-Nobilis and Young Elven Technologists negotiate a temporary truce in favor of skinning a shadowteam that has done them both dirty, the characters will probably want to beat feet out of there and out of Puyallup.

The gamemaster may resolve the chase by using the **Shadowrun** rules governing pursuit, page 64 of the basic rules. It is far easier just to have each character make a Quickness (5) Test to reach his vehicle safely. If the test fails, the character presumably stumbled over a hole or something and is subject to a long-range attack by one of the Elves. (If the characters have managed to breeze through this run with nary a scratch, have it be the Elf with the biggest, baddest weapon and a weapon Specialization to boot.) If the character survives, his next Quickness Test has a Target Number of 4, then 3, and so on, until he makes it to his vehicle or dies.

Once the runners reach their vehicle(s), they are clear of trouble...for now.

DEBUGGING

The only problem that might arise here is the characters getting killed in a prolonged gunfight. If they keep shooting, so will the Elves. If they die, they knew the risks.

If the gamemaster wants to draw out the pursuit scene, the Association Para-Nobilis arrived on Honda Vikings and the Young Elven Technologists have one Ford Americar that they keep parked out on the street. The characters will get 1D6 + 2 turns head start on the Elves. However, both Elven groups know the streets of Puyallup like the player characters know the shadows. They should have no problem making up for lost time if the gamemaster wants them to.

PICKING UP THE PIECES

If the shadowrunners have been completely successful, they will exchange the disk containing all the back-door passcodes for the agreed-upon sum. If they were only partially successful, the team will not get as much money out of the deal. Through his mysterious channels, Mr. Johnson has already heard what the characters were able to accomplish and has adjusted the amount on each credstick according to their performance.

If they failed to obtain a copy of the back-door passcodes for delivery, subtract ¥5,000 nuyen. If they failed to run Johnson's program in the Liquidations SPU, subtract ¥2,500 nuyen. If they failed to deliver the envelope and copy of the passcodes to Ehran's suite (or tampered with the wax-seal in any way), subtract ¥1,500 nuyen. If they used the wrong passcode against Dassurn and therefore left a path of destruction in their wake, subtract ¥1,000 nuyen.

If the shadowrunners also turn over a copy of the Sylvan Information client list, they will each receive a ¥1,000-nuyen bonus. If they return the program Johnson gave them to use against Dassurn Securities and Investments, they will each receive a ¥1,000-nuyen bonus; if they return it after Sandii asks for it, they will each receive ¥250 nuyen.

Aside from their payment for services rendered, the shadowrunners have also made enemies of the Association Para-Nobilis and the Young Elven Technologists. Though it is highly improbable that either of these two groups could locate the runners, the one thing past experience has proven is that it's a small world out there . . .

AWARDING KARMA

The characters are awarded karma according to the following guidelines.

GROUP KARMA

Surviving the adventure	1 pt
Using correct passcode against Dassurn	1 pt
Using wrong passcode against Dassurn	−2 pts
Running Johnson's program in Dassurn's Liquidation SPU	1 pt
Delivering envelope to Ehran's suite	2 pts
Tampering with sealed envelope	−1 pt
Delivering copy of passcodes to Ehran's suite	1 pt
Delivering copy of passcodes to Mr. Johnson	1 pt

INDIVIDUAL KARMA

As per **Shadowrun** rules, page 160.

LEGWORK

Given the shadowrun's timetable, the characters have little opportunity to conduct extensive investigations. Prior to the run, the gamemaster should allow the players to check with two of their contacts. Each time, the player must tell the gamemaster what he wants to investigate and how he will go about it.

Investigating a subject that is not found below means that no information pertinent to the adventure is available. The gamemaster may supply his own information if he wishes, including any red herrings that might waste the characters' time or lead them into trouble.

If the character investigates a subject for which he has an Appropriate Contact, the Target Number is 5. If the character does not have one of the requisite contacts, the Target Number is 10.

The number of successes listed under a subject's **Available Information** section indicates what knowledge the character gains. Higher success levels include all the information available to the lower levels.

DASSURN SECURITIES AND INVESTMENTS

For a complete business profile of Dassurn Securities and Investments, see Chapter 20 of the **Seattle Sourcebook**.
Appropriate Contacts
Any contact is appropriate. Dassurn Securities and Investments is a major international banking firm with a high profile in the Seattle business community.
Available Information
Any successful result will reveal nothing: there are no rumors to be had.

JOHNSON'S ENVELOPE

Any character who visually examines the envelope that Mr. Johnson gives the team should make a Perception (5) Test to determine what information is gleaned.

Successes	Result
1	The envelope is ordinary except for the fact that Johnson has used a wax seal rather than using the gummed adhesive flap.
2+	The faint impression of a laughing clown (or jester) head can be seen on the wax seal.

Any character who breaks the wax seal and examines the envelope's contents will discover a single sheet of paper. If the character was involved in the shadowrun against Baron Munchmaussen, he will recognize the sheet as the frontispiece of the ancient tome they snatched from the Troll not so long ago.

JOHNSON'S PROGRAM

A Computer B/R (8) Test is required to crack the compiled code of the program Johnson gave the team to run in the Dassurn's Liquidations SPU.

Successes	Result
1	The program is a sophisticated money-transfer routine.
2	The program has a number of sub-routines written into it for countering standard identification verification procedures, including retinal and cellular scans. It also appears to be a sophisticated, one-shot viral construct; use once and it's gone.
3	Once the program gets past the verification software, it "transforms" into a Revenue Service confiscation program that systematically seizes the assets of every account connected to the system.
4+	After it cleans out the accounts, the program routes the money to a specific SIN account at LTG # 5206 (19-1165).

Gamemaster's Note: It is beyond the scope and time constraints of this adventure to handle the upshot of this information. Should the characters wish to follow the trail, LTG # 5206 (19-1165) is a Tacoma bank. If a decker can reach the bank's customer account database—a dangerous undertaking—he will learn that the SIN account designated in Johnson's program belongs to none other than Ehran the Scribe!

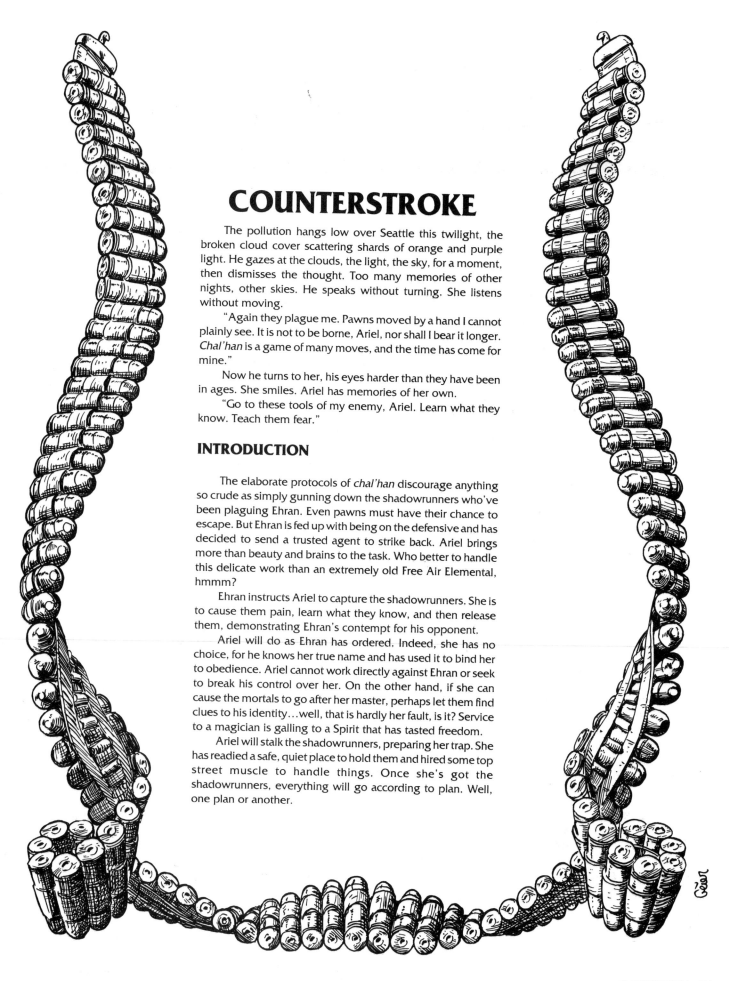

COUNTERSTROKE

The pollution hangs low over Seattle this twilight, the broken cloud cover scattering shards of orange and purple light. He gazes at the clouds, the light, the sky, for a moment, then dismisses the thought. Too many memories of other nights, other skies. He speaks without turning. She listens without moving.

"Again they plague me. Pawns moved by a hand I cannot plainly see. It is not to be borne, Ariel, nor shall I bear it longer. *Chal'han* is a game of many moves, and the time has come for mine."

Now he turns to her, his eyes harder than they have been in ages. She smiles. Ariel has memories of her own.

"Go to these tools of my enemy, Ariel. Learn what they know. Teach them fear."

INTRODUCTION

The elaborate protocols of *chal'han* discourage anything so crude as simply gunning down the shadowrunners who've been plaguing Ehran. Even pawns must have their chance to escape. But Ehran is fed up with being on the defensive and has decided to send a trusted agent to strike back. Ariel brings more than beauty and brains to the task. Who better to handle this delicate work than an extremely old Free Air Elemental, hmmm?

Ehran instructs Ariel to capture the shadowrunners. She is to cause them pain, learn what they know, and then release them, demonstrating Ehran's contempt for his opponent.

Ariel will do as Ehran has ordered. Indeed, she has no choice, for he knows her true name and has used it to bind her to obedience. Ariel cannot work directly against Ehran or seek to break his control over her. On the other hand, if she can cause the mortals to go after her master, perhaps let them find clues to his identity…well, that is hardly her fault, is it? Service to a magician is galling to a Spirit that has tasted freedom.

Ariel will stalk the shadowrunners, preparing her trap. She has readied a safe, quiet place to hold them and hired some top street muscle to handle things. Once she's got the shadowrunners, everything will go according to plan. Well, one plan or another.

WALK IN THE PARK

TELL IT TO THEM STRAIGHT

It's been a little slow lately, and so when Mr. Johnson shows up, waving his credstick around, you lend him an ear.

This is an easy one, he tells you. A simple extraction on a mid-grade manager who has some useful information. She's not even in a secure site. Mr. Johnson just wants some muscle to pick her up safely, possibly to brush off a few corporate followers who may be shadowing the target. He's paying ¥5,000 per runner, plus medical expenses, if needed.

If the shadowrunners take the job, read on:

The target is a Ms. Shirley Marquis, a small cog in Natural Vat Foods. She lives in a medium-security NatVat condo complex in the Auburn District of Seattle. The area contains heavily wooded parkland, perfect for a quiet extraction. Mr. Johnson gives you a map of the pickup zone: Grantleigh Park, where Marquis takes a walk every evening, about sunset. She has been told that someone will approach her with the identifying phrase, "We're from the Easter Bunny." You go, you pick her up, you take her to a drop-off spot. Easy money.

That's about it. He gives you a dossier chip on Shirley Marquis, with recent holos, her personnel profile from NatVat, some personal background, and so on. Mr. Johnson claims not to know the motive for the extraction. He has no "need to know."

Read to players when they reach the park:

Quiet evening in salary-land. Street lights just coming on as the last rays of the sun fade, turning the trees into shadow shapes. You walk up the hedge-bordered path to the quiet plaza. A few people stroll through the mild evening. There, by the center bridge. Check the picture…yep, that's Marquis.

She looks at you. Calm. Smiling. You get closer. Still the calm smile. No change of expression. This dame's a little too cool. You say quietly, "We're from the Easter Bunny." (Where do they get this I-spy drek, anyway?) Nothing. The light overhead catches her eyes at just the right angle to let you see her pupils. Huge. Shirley Marquis is drugged to the eyebrows. She's bait. You're hosed.

Read to the players when Ariel shows:

Oh cripes, one of those fraggin' patrol cars is barreling straight at you, with AKs blasting away from both front firing ports. You grab cover and listen to the music of the ricochets. Ziiing! Piiing! Ka-BOOOOM!

Kaboom? You look up to see the flaming wreckage of the Patrol-1 sailing every whichaway. What the heck did that? The answer appears out of the night in the form of a lean, fast-looking van. Small-arms fire from the NatVat heat bounces off its sleekly armored sides as the van hops the curb and slews around on the grass so its rear is facing you and your team. The back doors pop open and a woman's voice sings out, "So, are you guys going my way or would you rather stick around and wait for your new friends to catch up with us?"

Read to the players when they get in the van:

The dark-haired knockout at the wheel says her name is Ariel Nasir. She could stand a few driving lessons, but since she got your butts out of that little mess, maybe you'll forgive her a few bumps along the way. She pulls the van onto a side road. You glance out the windows. Nowhere. Boonies cubed.

She turns and lights up the place with a smile you'd like to admire for awhile, if only…if…eyelids getting heavy…hey, where'd she go, she's ah, whassappen'nng…GAS!

BEHIND THE SCENES

This is an absolutely legitimate deal. Mr. Johnson does have a minor extraction to arrange and has chosen the shadowrunners for valid reasons: either they are favorites of his and he wants to send some easy nuyen their way, or else he doesn't know their style yet and wants to see how they handle themselves on this kind of run. If there is a Mr. Johnson that the shadowrunners trust, at least a little, or perhaps a company with which they have had profitable dealings in the past, let the job offer come from one of those sources. Any legwork the team does will bear out what Mr. Johnson has told them.

Ariel has been maintaining tight surveillance on the runners from Astral Space, using clairvoyance as well as the best street snoops money can buy. She decides to use this run to trap them.

She establishes contact with NatVat security, using Ehran's extensive network of influence. She produces "evidence" for NatVat of a major raid being set up, one that starts when Marquis turns over the passcodes for the company computer network to a bunch of shadowrunners. The security director buys the story completely and plans a massive stopper on the Marquis extraction. The shadowrunners' "walk in the park" will turn into a deadly trap.

If the runners turn down the job, Ariel will back away. Any time the runners are on the losing end of a fight in the future, she can bail them out as described here. She will bide her time until then.

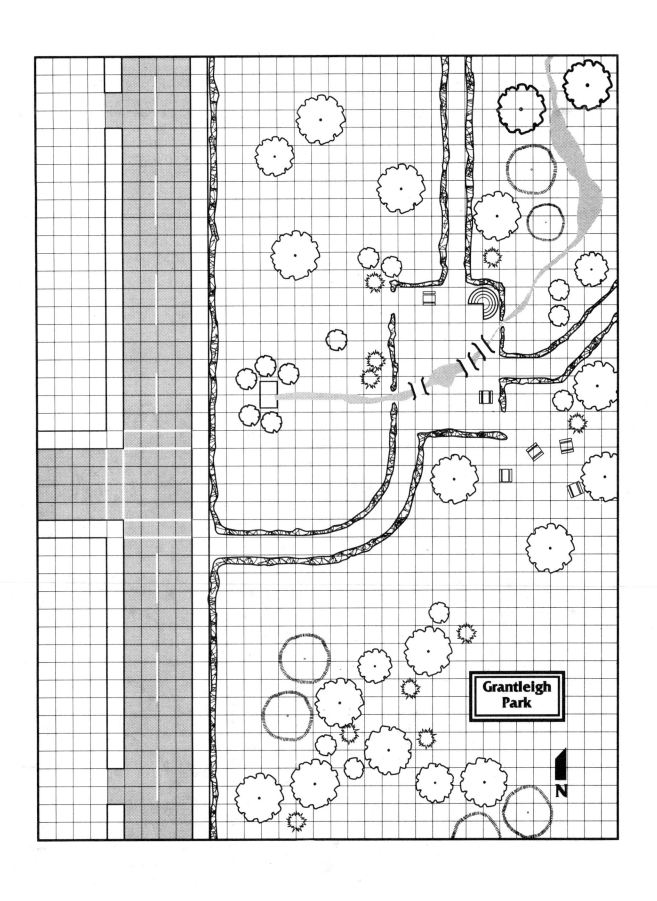

Grantleigh
Park

N

AT THE PARK

A ridiculous amount of security is scattered around the scene. As soon as the team discovers that Marquis has been drugged, or if they get suspicious before that and try to run for it, all hell will break loose. Even if they try some clever recon, it is too late. As soon as some of the shadowrunners are on the map, they're in the trap. Any attempt to leave the scene triggers the opposition.

For purposes of the story, most of the fire directed at the runners should miss. This fracas is not the reason for the adventure. However, as soon as the heavy artillery shows up in the skies, a couple of lucky shots will wipe out their vehicle(s).

NATVAT CORPORATE POLICE

Officers use the **Former Company Man**, p. 37, **SR**. Grunts use the **Corporate Security Guard** (p. 165, **SR**).

Unless specified otherwise, NatVat Corporate Police on this mission wear Partial Heavy Armor (Ballistic 6, Impact 4) and carry AK-97 Assault Rifles (5M3). Officers' weapons are Smart. Grunts' weapons are equipped with Laser Sights.

Plainclothes

Four plainclothes grunts, wearing street clothes (corp-tailored Armor Clothing, Ballistic 3) and carrying Browning Max-Powers (4M2, Concealability 6) are in the plaza. Two men sit at a table, playing chess. A couple necks passionately in the shadows by the bandstand. No one else is in the park. The plainclothes' job is to keep the runners occupied until the heavy infantry hits the scene.

Heavy Infantry

There are two squads on foot, concealed in the park. Each squad consists of an officer and six grunts.

One grunt in each squad is carrying an Ingram Valiant LMG on a gyro-mount harness, equipped with Laser Sight (5S3).

Squad A is concealed in the woods, northeast of the plaza. It will take them a combat turn to reach the plaza.

Squad B is concealed in the clearing. They will move to cut off the path from the plaza to the street. It will take them two turns to reach the path.

Patrol Vehicles

Three Chrysler-Nissan Patrol-1 vehicles (**Shadowrun**, p. 141) appear on the streets leading to the park, cutting off escape. Each contains a driver and two other passengers. All are grunts, but the driver has Driving 6 Skill. The passengers fire their AK-97s from the firing ports.

Each Patrol-1 is concealed in a garage in various buildings along the street. The driveways are shown on the map. At a signal from the heavy infantry that things are happening, each vehicle pulls out of its hiding place and blocks the streets leading to the park, firing on any shadowrunner vehicles.

A Patrol-1 will pursue any vehicle that escapes from the park area.

Helicopters

One PRC-44b Yellowjacket (**Street Samurai Catalog**, p. 74) is on alert a few blocks away from the park. When the trap is sprung, the Yellowjacket will lift off and head for the scene, arriving five turns after the action starts. The copter is armed with an autocannon mounted in an under-chin hardpoint. The pilot is a grunt, but with Piloting and Heavy Weapon Skill, both at 6.

The Yellowjacket will concentrate its fire on shadowrunner vehicles. If the runners' vehicles have managed to break away from the park area within five turns, then it will pursue and try to cripple them.

ARIEL ARRIVES

The driver of the van is Ariel. With her is one of Bonecrack's gangers who goes by the handle of Chuckles. Chuckles is the one who put the AVM into the Patrol-1. While Ariel urges the shadowrunners into the van, Chuckles is busy laying down covering fire with an LMG. He can keep the cops' heads down for the moment—but only for the moment, as he will profanely point out if the runners hesitate about gettin' into the fraggin' van!

Ariel will wait no more than a few turns for passengers, then will slam the doors, jump behind the wheel, and peel out. If the NatVat police are pressing too closely on the group, she will use spells (probably Sleep) to help keep them back. Once the runners are aboard, the van will get away from NatVat, though the gamemaster may wish to stage a hairy chase scene first.

Any shadowrunners who don't get into the van will have to get out of the mess on their own. The corp cops' attention will be focused on the van for a turn or two. If the runners move away from the action without drawing attention to themselves, they get away clean. Otherwise, they must fight it out or surrender.

If captured by NatVat, dying runners will be stabilized. Others can suffer untreated, as far as NatVat is concerned.

Prisoners are stripped of armor and weapons, then tossed into the slammer for several hours. They are then gassed into unconsciousness. When they come to, they find themselves in a different prison cell. They have been delivered to Ariel by her contacts in NatVat security, who think she represents UCAS intelligence. Pick up with **By the Beautiful Sea**.

It is entirely possible that some of the shadowrunners will get away. See **Spoor of a Spirit**, p. 85, for what escaped runners can do to help their buddies.

If all the runners refuse Ariel's help and get away from NatVat, they have beaten the counterstroke. This section of **Harlequin** is over, unless the gamemaster wants Ariel to try again in a later adventure.

THE TRAP

Ariel drives a few kilometers clear of the ambush site. She tells the runners she is working for their Mr. Johnson. To corroborate this story, she can provide any details they may want. Remember, she knows their affairs almost better than they do.

Ariel parks the van on a side road...and vanishes! She has dropped her Manifest form and left the van via Astral Space. The van is about to become an airtight container. If she stays inside, she will be disrupted: banished from the physical world for weeks.

When Ariel disappears, Chuckles presses a button. The van's doors and windows seal tight. The vehicle is flooded with knock-out gas. Chuckles follows directions and takes a deep breath as soon as he releases the gas. He's in dreamland. By the way, if a runner murders Chuckles for having trapped them, it will be recorded (the van is, of course, bugged for video and audio) and Bonecrack will kill the offender when he sees the tapes.

The gas is rated 6D3 Stun, and works by inhalation or on skin contact. Its Speed is instantaneous. Anyone still in the van at the end of a turn must resist the gas all over again on his first action.

The van is armored, so small-arms fire won't puncture the windows or walls. The doors and locks are reinforced. A Strength Test to jimmy one open has a Target Number 12 for a jimmy or crowbar, 14 for improvised tools, or 16 for using brute strength to try and spring the latch. If someone has an anti-vehicle weapon or explosive, and wants to try to blast his way out, remind him that he's inside a van. Everyone inside must resist the damage of an explosion, though with −1 to the power and staging if it is a shaped charge. That is, a blob of plastic explosive doing 6D3 to the wall of the van would expose everyone inside to the same damage, or to 5D2 if it was a properly laid demolitions charge or a missile. For grenades and such, refer to the overpressure rules on p. 66, **Street Samurai Catalog**.

Ariel hovers outside the van, in her Human form again, though the sight of a pretty girl floating three meters off the ground might clue in an onlooker that all is not as it seems. She clairvoyantly watches things inside the van. If anyone manages to get out, she will attack them magically, trying to make it look like she is just another magician. She will fight to kill only in self-defense. Otherwise, she will use non-lethal attacks. Ariel will also use her powers to subdue anyone the gas does not affect.

A magician might send his astral body out of the van, but his body is still breathing, so the gas will knock it out. Stun damage to the physical body affects the astral body, so the effects of the gas will cause the astral body to be sucked back into the physical. If a magician attacks Ariel astrally, she will defend against his onslaught until this happens. Remember, though, that she will counterattack if he is wounding her, and will fight to kill.

If everything goes according to plan, Ariel soon has a load of unconscious shadowrunners in the van. She will inject them with additional drugs to keep them out cold for several hours. Any magicians will be gagged and blindfolded as well. If one or two runners have escaped, Ariel will not pursue as long as she has at least three prisoners. If there are fewer than that in the van, she will try to recapture as many runaways as possible. If Ariel has even one prisoner, however, she will continue the counterstroke.

Ariel drives her prisoners to a transfer point. There, she abandons the van and uses a second car to take the captives to her hideout.

If everyone gets away from this trap, the counterstroke is foiled.

BY THE BEAUTIFUL SEA

TELL IT TO THEM STRAIGHT

Read this only to players whose characters have been captured by Ariel. Send any others out for pizza or something:

You open your eyes. Bad mistake. The light stabs into your throbbing skull like red-hot needles. Your mouth tastes like toxic waste. It's true you've felt this way before, but in the past it was always because of something that seemed like fun at the time.

After a few centuries, you get enough strength to sit up. When the world stops spinning, you see that you are in a small, bare room. Concrete floor, with a few threadbare futons tossed here and there. Walls and ceilings coated with plaster, painted a light green. Ventilator grills up near the ceiling. A wash basin and commode in one corner. Barred door in one wall. Most of your team is also sitting up and taking notice. They're stripped. You look down. So are you.

The magician is curled into a fetal ball in one corner. You nudge his shoulder. No response. You prod harder. He grunts and rolls over. Taking his thumb out of his mouth, he murmurs, "Aw, Ma, I don't wanna go to school today." You peel back an eyelid. His gaze is hazy with drugs.

Great.

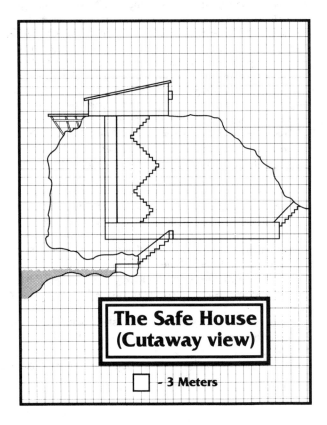

The Safe House (Cutaway view)

☐ - 3 Meters

Read this section only to players whose characters have been captured by Ariel sometime after the above paragraph:

The barred door opens. You are staring into the snouts of a pair of shotguns. You can hear the rest of the team start to shift position. The shotguns swing to bear. The men holding them look tough. Combat badges on their sleeves say they are corp war veterans. Mercenaries. Behind them is a man with a harness-mount machine gun held low and ready. "O.K.," he says, "nobody do anything stupid and you may live through this."

He gestures at you. "Outside." You hesitate. He puts a burst into the ceiling. It rains plaster and rock chips for a few seconds. "Next one will be lower. Outside."

You go outside. The three men fall back, maintaining distance, covering you and the doorway in a neat crossfire. One of the shotgun carriers slots a magnetic keycard into a wall unit, and the cell door slides shut.

There's a wheelchair in the corridor. "Sit." Under those guns, you don't have much choice. You sit. Snik-snap! Padded manacles clamp your chest, arms, and legs. One of your guards slings his shotgun and guides the chair down the corridor. The samurai with the LMG follows, maintaining distance and cover. The third guy stays on guard outside the cell. These guys are good. Too good.

Your escort wheels you around a few corners and into a softly lit room. Assorted equipment lines the walls, and several gizmos stand in the center of the floor. Some of it looks vaguely familiar, but you can't quite remember where you've seen stuff like this before.

The wheelchair stops. The merc fiddles with some attachments. The chair ratchets into something resembling a dentist's chair. The position triggers memories and you realize where you've seen this setup before. In a clinic.

BEHIND THE SCENES

Ariel has set up shop in a safe house in the Seattle area. It was originally in use by a UCAS security agency for covert ops in the Seattle area, but was dropped from active duty for a while after a particularly nasty mission last year.

The site consists of a small bungalow set on a cliff overlooking the sea, and screened from the road by woodland. It is built over an underground installation. A tunnel leads to a small cave at sea level, useful for clandestine arrivals by boat—or for the secret disposal of certain items.

The runners have been stripped to the skin and deprived of any removable equipment. They were then dumped in a cell to recover from their Stun damage normally after being given the antidote to the knock-out drugs. All are wearing Taser anti-augmentation restraints.

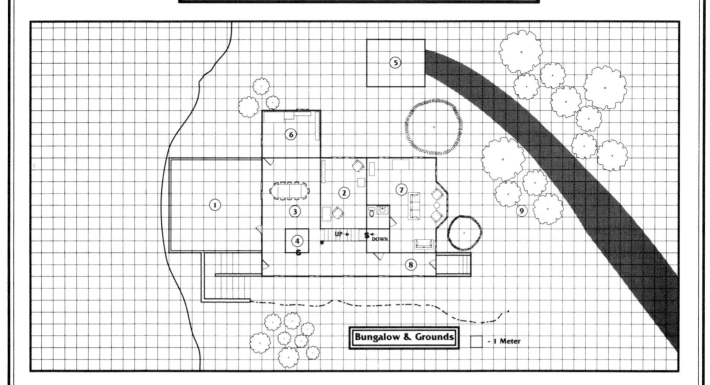

Bungalow & Grounds | | - 1 Meter

Any magicians on the team are given a "prison drug" that makes it almost impossible for them to concentrate: +10 to all mental and magical tests until given the antidote! Even the act of astral projection takes five to ten minutes to attempt, and requires an Unopposed Willpower Test with a Target Number 10. The stuff wears off in 24 hours.

An obvious monitor camera watches the characters from one corner of the room. An armed guard stands in the corridor, about five meters from the cell door. He ignores all attempts to speak to him.

THE LONG WALK

This is the drill whenever a shadowrunner is taken from the cell for interrogation. The mercenaries are loading Stun rounds, but Bonecrack's LMG is loading standard ammo. You should inform the players that this counts as being held at gunpoint. Regardless of Reaction times, if the shadowrunners start trouble, the three gunmen will all get an action to fire even before Initiative is checked. With armor, they might still have a chance, but buck naked?

All the prisoners (except the drugged magicians) get to make an Etiquette (Street) Test (6). Any who succeed will recognize Bonecrack. If they let him know it, he will murmur, "Nothing personal, chummers. Biz." He does not respond to any other questions or conversation.

If the prisoner being taken out defies Bonecrack, even after the warning shot, the mercs will put him down with Stun rounds. Two will provide cover while the third drags the unconscious body out of the cell and dumps it into the wheelchair.

The wheelchair is equipped with restraints that snap into place when the chair's sensors detect a passenger. Locking the prisoner down are a restraint on each arm- and leg-rest and a chest strap. The chair can also be locked in place to prevent it from rolling and can switch from an upright to a reclining position. All the chair controls for the restraints, wheel locks, and position change are mounted in back, away from the passenger's easy reach.

To break out of the chair requires Success Tests for Strength, Quickness, or an appropriate "escape-artist" skill. The Target Number is 20 minus the attribute or skill. Each success releases the prisoner from a single restraint. The chest strap remains till last. Each attempt at escape takes one minute. If a prisoner is discovered trying to get out of the chair, he will be beaten unconscious. When he comes to, he'll be in the clinic, and matters proceed as described in the next section.

THE BUNGALOW

First Floor and Grounds

Deck (1): Formed plastiwood deck.

Den (2: A terminal plugged into the major newsnets. Racks of datareader chips. Bound volume technical manuals.

Dining Room (3): An intercom to the underground complex is in the sideboard.

Elevator (4): Elevator to the underground complex. The panel leading into the shaft is built into the wall, and requires a successful Perception Test (15) to spot.

Garage (5): Room for two vehicles.

Kitchen (6): No supplies. The kitchen has not been used in a long time.

Living Room (7): The trid unit against the north wall can tap into the vidscreens displayed in the Security Booth (see p. 78).

Parlor (8): A secret panel in the walk-in hall closet opens to the staircase down to the underground complex.

Woods (9): The woods extend from the map edge to the bottom of the hill, as shown on the Safehouse Map.

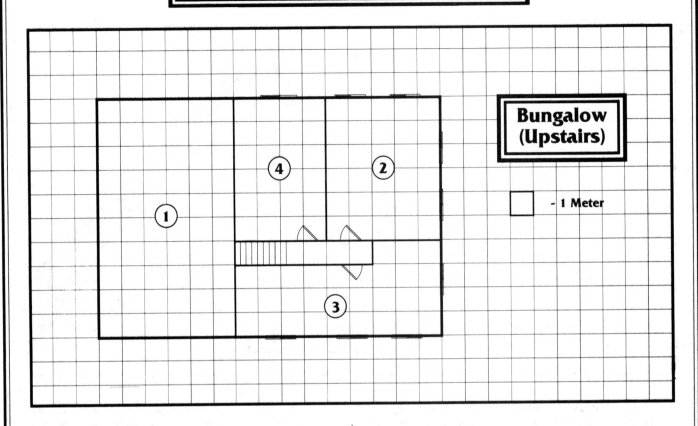

Bungalow (Upstairs)

□ - 1 Meter

Second Floor

Attic (1): Empty.

Bedroom (2): Ariel is using this as her "quarters." She does not sleep or have other physical requirements (clothes, bathing, and so on), so there are no signs of someone living here, just some equipment on the dresser:

·A coded wristphone: It only connects to a number in Tir Tairngire (one of Ehran's, of course). The commcode is 3503 (395-6985). Dialing any other number causes the phone to self-destruct. Digging the code out of the phone requires an Electronics B/R Test (8). The test also takes a microtronics toolkit. If the test fails, the phone destructs. Tracing the number requires a Matrix run into the Tir Tairngire RTG. Ehran will have the number erased 24 hours after the adventure ends.

·A certified credstick for 60,000 dollars. (That's UCAS dollars, chummer. See the **Neo-Anarchist's Guide To North America** for a conversion, or assume ten dollars to every nuyen.)

·A small holodisplay. It projects holos of several paintings. Close examination by an art historian will verify that they seem to be authentic period pieces, or at least painted in the proper style. One shows a delicate-featured nobleman in French court garb of the 17th century (Ehran). One is a stylized portrait of a lady in Spanish dress, who is recognizably Ariel. It dates from the early 15th century. Though it will be obvious that the latter portrait is of Ariel, recognizing Ehran is another matter. That will require a Perception Test, or at the gamemaster's option, an appropriate Etiquette or Special Skill, against a Target Number 10. If the character making the attempt has somehow actually met Ehran, he makes the test against a Target Number of only 6. Consult the Success Table below:

Successes	Result
0	Well, you know, all these Elves look alike, am I right?
1 – 2	Kinda looks familiar. Maybe you've seen the painting before?
3 – 4	Say he kinda looks like...looks like...gosh, what's his name again?
5+	HEY! That sure looks a hell of a lot like that Ehran the Scribe guy...

Bedrooms (3 and 4): Empty.

THE UNDERGROUND COMPLEX

Elevator (1)

This elevator leads up to the bungalow, taking two turns to make the trip. A ladder also runs up the side of the shaft, which is 20 meters long. Elevator power can be cut from Rooms 3 (Security Booth) and 18 (Power Substation).

Stairs (2)

Stairs leading to the Parlor in the bungalow. Climbing these covers a distance of 35 meters.

Security Booth (3)

An armor-glass window looks out at the elevator and stairwell door. A rack in the southeast corner holds an FN HAR assault rifle and an Uzi III, both loaded and equipped with laser sights.

The booth is not manned unless the prisoners have attempted (and failed) to escape already.

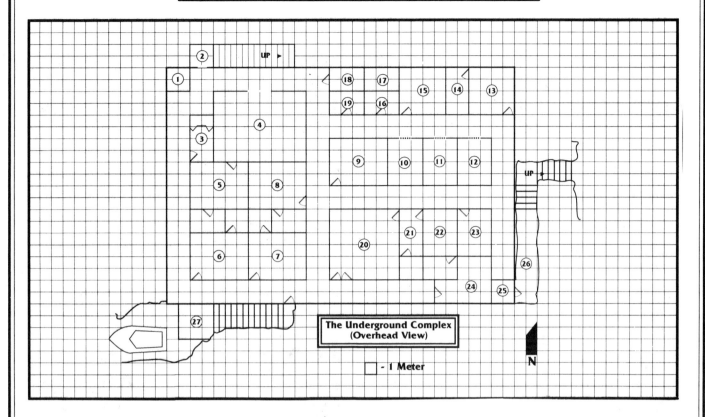

The Underground Complex (Overhead View)

☐ - 1 Meter

N

A console with the following controls occupies the north half of the room:

Air Seal: Can seal the facility air supply, switching to recycled air. This would make the underground complex a sealed environment, and harmful to Ariel.

Alarm: Triggers flashing light and klaxon alarms in the underground complex. Also triggers discreet flashing light alarms in the bungalow.

Armory: Can lock or unlock the door to the Armory (Room 23).

Cells: Can lock or unlock cell doors (Rooms 10 – 12).

Elevator: Turns elevator power on and off.

Fire Extinguishers: Can activate chemical extinguishers in any room or combination of rooms in the underground complex. The chemical foam creates treacherous footing and visual cover (+2). It really messes up thermographic vision (+4 visual cover vs. Thermographic Vision).

IR: Turns IR illumination on or off in any set of rooms in the underground complex.

Lights: Turns lights on or off in any set of rooms in the underground complex.

Vidscreens: Three screens with controls allowing a view of any room in the bungalow or the underground complex.

Common Room (4)

This room has tables and chairs, Entertainment/datareader workstations in the northeast corner, and vending machines. A large trid against the south wall plays recordings only (no broadcast pickup facilities).

Kitchen (5)

Nothing more unusual than some stuffers scattered about.

Living Quarters (6 – 7)

These rooms have been converted to temporary barracks for the mercenaries. Unless the facility is on alert due to an escape, an Ork Mercenary will be sacked out here. If overcome, his weapons and armor will be available as loot. In addition, a search will turn up various goodies. Make a Perception Test with a Target Number 6. Each test has a base time of ten turns. Divide the base time by the successes rolled to determine the real time it takes. A successful test finds one of the following things. Cross each item off the list of possible finds as it is uncovered:

- A Browning Max-Power, loaded with standard ammo.
- A certified credstik for ¥5,000 nuyen
- A survival knife
- A packet of three shuriken
- A Lined Coat

In addition, escaped prisoners can pull on clothes and shoes if they want to take the time. In a fracas, most folks feel more secure with a pair of pants on.

Living Quarters (8)

Bonecrack and Iggy bunk here. If the facility is not on alert, Iggy is present.

Magic Lab (9)

Lancelot has moved a bed into this nicely equipped lab. There are four units of ritual materials for summoning Fire Elementals here. Any magical gear taken from the prisoners will be stored here, too. If there is no torture session going on and the facility is not on alert, Lancelot will be meditating here.

Cells (10 – 12)

Each has a light fixture over the sink and a camera in the southwest corner, about two meters off the ground. The shadowrunners are held in Cell 11. A maglock slot for the door to each cell is located about 60 centimeters to the left of the cell door. Doors are barred rather than solid.

Storage Room (13)

Various technical gear is stored here. A microtronics kit (government-issue) is neatly packed in one corner.

Monitor Room (14)

A one-way mirror looks into Room 15. Items such as voice-stress monitors and recording equipment are set up in here.

Debriefing and Interrogation Room (15)

Sections of the floors and walls show signs of having been scrubbed clean.

Small Office (16)

A desk console is set into the north wall, next to a massive vault door.

Vault (17)

The UCAS agents removed everything of value from the vault when they cleared out of the safe house last year. Ariel and her team haven't bothered trying to get in. Nothing here.

Power Substation (18)

This station can cut power to the entire underground facility. All lights go out and darkness is total. Thermographic vision is effective, but Low-Light is not. From here, it is also possible to cut power to any equipment in the facility, but tracing the circuits for such surgical blackouts requires an Electronics B/R (6) Test. The base time for such a task is ten turns.

Utility Room (19)

In this room is a control panel that can seal the air conditioning system, making the underground facility an enclosed area, which is dangerous to Ariel.

The Infirmary (20)

During a torture session, Doctor What, Lancelot, and two mercenaries (as well as the victim) will be here. In the event of an alert, the guards and Lancelot will leave, but Doctor What will continue working on his victim.

The Infirmary contains two medkits (Rating 3), a deluxe Stabilization Unit, drug lockers with a complete assortment of antidotes, slap patches, and other medicines, with ratings ranging up to 5, and assorted medical equipment.

Sickroom (21)

Doctor What is using this one-bed sickroom as his quarters and will be here if no torture session is occurring. If an alert is in effect, he will be hurriedly packing his belongings.

Sickbay (22)

A two-bed sickbay.

Armory (23)

The door to this room is locked (Maglock Rating 6). It can be unlocked from Room 3. The correct card to open it locally is not in the safe house, and so the intruders have left it strictly alone. Forcing it will trigger an alarm (Disarm Rating 8). The alarm goes off in the downtown offices of the CIA, in the UCAS Federal Building. If the alarm goes off, the place will be lousy with agents (Use **Former Company Man**, p. 37, **Shadowrun**, wearing Partial Armor and carrying Uzi IIIs) in 20 minutes.

The room contains:

• Six Uzi IIIs with Laser Sights. 3 clips per weapon loading standard ammo.

• Three FN HAR Assault Rifles. 2 clips per weapon loading standard ammo.

• One Ranger Arms SM-3 Sniper Rifle.

• Three Ares Predator IIs. 2 clips per weapon loading Firepower ammo.

• One case of 12 Defensive Grenades.

• An ammo locker containing 200 rounds of ammo and spare clips for each weapon.

• Three sets of Armor Clothing (one-size-fits-all jumpsuits). Ballistic 3.

Storage Area (24)

Janitorial supplies, bedding, and so on. Also stashed here is any gear taken from the shadowrunners after their capture.

Secret Room (25)

Secret room leading to the escape tunnel. To spot the secret doors opening into Room 24 and into the corridor to the north requires a Perception Test (15).

Escape Tunnel (26)

This passage leads to the woods around the bungalow.

The Cave (27)

The cave opens to the sea. At high tide, the mouth of the cave is submerged. It is otherwise navigable until an hour before high tide and starting again an hour after high tide. A Samuvani-Criscraft Otter is moored to the small pier (**SR**, p. 141).

THE DOCTOR IS IN

TELL IT TO THEM STRAIGHT

Read this to the guy in the chair. Other prisoners can listen. Any players whose characters were not captured by Ariel should not hear this:

All smiles, a chubby little guy bustles in, looking like a beardless Santa Claus. "Hello! What is my name." It's a statement, not a question, and he laughs with innocent delight at your double-take. He ties on a vinyl lab apron and wheels some gear up next to your chair. "How are we feeling today, hmmm?" He starts hooking you up to some cable leads. "You know, the funniest thing happened on the way here…" He rambles along with a pointless little monologue for a few minutes, all the while clipping electrodes to various points on your body.

"I think we're ready now," he beams. He flips a switch, turns some dials. Pain!

"Oh, that looks like it tingled. How about this one?" More dial-turning. A lancet of white-hot agony pierces your left eye, then settles as a burning throb in your jaw.

"Most people hate toothache worse than anything," your tormentor confides with a giggle. "I find that when you hit just the right nerves, they really don't like it." He picks up a slender gizmo from the table and connects it to a wire.

You force the words out through clenched jaws. "Whatever you want to know, chummer, forget it."

The twinkling blue eyes widen in mock surprise. "Oh, mercy me, right now, I don't want to know anything. Maybe later we'll find a few things to talk about." He finishes his adjustments to the device he's holding and leans close, whispering like someone sharing an amusing secret. "Now here's something I know you'll find interesting." His hand moves and something buzzes, but the sound is drowned out by your screams.

Back in the cell, the rest of the team sees the lights flickering. After a time, they, too, will find out what that means.

BEHIND THE SCENES

Once an hour, Bonecrack and the guards show up, pick a new shadowrunner at random, clamp him in the chair, and wheel him into the Infirmary, where Doctor What does his little act. After about 15 to 30 minutes, the victim is returned to the cell, unconscious, having taken a full dose of Mental damage (all 10 boxes filled in on the Mental Condition Monitor).

Besides Doctor What, all sessions are attended by Lancelot Windtree and two mercenaries. Bonecrack is only present when transferring the prisoner between the Infirmary and the cell.

Lancelot assesses the subjects, informing Doctor What of how truthful their answers seem to be and how they are resisting the pain. When magicians are in the chair, he makes sure they don't go astral undetected.

Lancelot enjoys his duties. The victims will hear his coolly elegant voice sneering at their agony. The strong ones he mocks for resisting pointlessly. Those who break he mocks for their weakness. Non-Elves are informed that their obvious racial inferiority explains their behavior, while Elves are castigated for making such a poor showing in adversity.

After going through the mill, each prisoner is left in the cell for six hours. Then the torture starts again, but now Doctor What wants information. He's been ordered not to kill the victims, which limits the use of his beloved knives, but he is content with nerve stimulators, electrical probes, and other such devices.

Doctor What asks about earlier runs made as part of **Harlequin**. He wants information about the Mr. Johnson(s), any information the characters discovered about their employer, amounts paid, and so on. He also wants to know what actually took place on each run. While the actual progress of the interrogation is handled via dice rolls (see below), the players should be familiar with the subjects about which their characters are being questioned. They learn that this run is linked to those previous jobs, and that those jobs are, apparently, linked to one another.

In each session, make the Doctor's Interrogation Tests. His target number is the shadowrunner's Willpower or Body, whichever is higher. Keep track of his successes. When Doctor What has totaled up ten successes against a shadowrunner, he is satisfied that he knows everything of interest that the character can tell him. Each time Doctor What makes one of these tests, the victim in the chair must resist 6D3 Stun damage. Obviously, he cannot dodge or defend against this damage. If he is still conscious, the Doctor can make another test. And so it goes, until the Doctor gets his ten successes or until the victim passes out. Each test takes ten minutes.

When a prisoner passes out, he is returned to the cell, and another victim is chosen. Prisoners who have provided their ten successes worth of info do not undergo more sessions. After all the prisoners have gone through a round of interrogation, there is a two- to three-hour break, and the cycle starts again.

Magicians are firmly strapped down for their interrogations, given an antidote to the prison drug, and then blindfolded. They are given a fresh injection of the prison drug when the session ends. The magician will see that the antidote is in an injector color-coded blue, and the drug is in one coded green.

If a magician uses astral projection to escape the pain, Lancelot attacks him astrally. If the magician tries to flee the area, Lancelot warns him to return to his body or they will kill it. If the magician ignores the warning, Lancelot returns to his own body. Instead of killing the magician, however, Doctor What will render him unconscious (which snaps the astral body back into the physical body). The magician is injected with the prison drug again and returned to the cell. Future interrogations will be done without neutralizing the drug.

FIGHT TO FREEDOM

TELL IT TO THEM STRAIGHT

At some point during the first round of interrogations, the characters in the cell will have the following encounter:

You hear a faint sound like a siren. It gets closer, but not much louder. Then a model of a Lone Star Patrol 1, lights flashing, siren wailing, whizzes in through the bars and thuds into your foot. What the frag?

A deep, hoarse voice with a slight lisp comes from the door. "C'n I have my polithe car back, pleathe?" A tough-looking Troll is looking down at you through the bars. His mouth hangs open in a slack-jawed smile as he points to the toy. "My big brother gave it to me on my latht birthday." This one's got a big brother? Oh, brother!

The Troll glances shyly at your face. "Thay, are you crookth? Are you in jail, huh?"

The guard comes up behind the Troll. It's one of the normals. "Beat it, feeb. You ain't supposed to be here." The Troll looks around at him. "But they got my car. Marty gave it to me an'…"

"So they got your fraggin' car! Nobody's supposed to be talkin' to 'em, trog, so buzz!" The Troll backs away, looking dazed. He stammers, and a tear rolls down one warty cheek. Then he breaks into a toothy smile and says, "Marty!"

An arm wraps around the guard's neck, as his weapon is plucked away. You hear a crunching thud as Bonecrack slams the struggling merc into the wall and presses a forearm against his windpipe. The merc gasps for air as the samurai increases the pressure. "You don't talk to my brother that way, chummer," says Bonecrack with icy calm. "Ever."

His hands blur, there is a flurry of meaty impacts, and the guard sinks to his knees, drooling, onto the floor. Bonecrack's voice is still calm. "Pick up your piece and get back on the job. Frag up again and I'll kill you."

He turns away from the guard. The mercenary glares at Bonecrack's back with hatred. He picks up his shotgun, grips it convulsively for a moment, then stomps down the corridor, pointedly ignoring his boss.

Bonecrack walks slowly up to the bars and studies you for a moment. "How about the kid's car?"

BEHIND THE SCENES

This encounter lets the runners meet Iggy and gain some insight into the relationship between him and Bonecrack.

If the prisoners are nasty to Iggy, the Troll will become very upset. Bonecrack will lead him away, and the encounter ends. Bonecrack will not refer to the incident again, nor will it change his treatment of the runners. They have behaved like typical denizens of the world as he knows it. No surprise.

If the prisoners simply return the toy car, Iggy will be happy. And very curious. "Why are they in jail, Marty? They aren't crookth, are they?" Bonecrack diverts these questions and tells Iggy to go back to his room, but the Troll will still be craning his neck back to look curiously at the shadowrunners.

If a runner is nice to Iggy, showing an interest in him, the Troll will be as ecstatic as a friendly puppy who's been petted. If the runner is a woman, this reaction will be even more intense. Iggy will decide that this runner is a new friend. If more than one of the prisoners is nice to Iggy, pick one at random that the Troll will find especially interesting. Again, if one of the candidates is a woman, he will focus on her. His mind is a child's, but his body and feelings are adult.

Iggy will be even more uncertain about why his new friend is in jail. Bonecrack will have to speak sharply to him before he leaves. This makes Iggy sad, but the samurai cheers him up with what is obviously an old game between them: "Hey, look over there! Who's that famous guy? Is it…yes it is, it's the great Kid Ignatius." Iggy perks up, and answers with the punch line: "And the crowd goeth wild!" Bonecrack actually smiles as he thumps Iggy on the shoulder, and the Troll goes skipping away.

But Iggy will not forget the incident. The next time his friend is taken in for interrogation, Iggy sneaks up outside the Infirmary and watches. When he sees the torture, he becomes frantic and tries to intervene. The runner will see Lancelot snarl an Elvish oath and start a spell, only to be backhanded against the wall by Bonecrack. The samurai intercepts Iggy as he tries to get into the Infirmary, and forces him out of the room. Doctor What watches it all with a bright smile on his face. If the runner tries to call out to Iggy for help, the doc paralyzes his vocal chords with the touch of a switch.

Ariel appears in the doorway as Lancelot scrambles up with murder in his eyes. Power flickers around his hands, but after a sharp command from Ariel, he subsides. She speaks in apparent Elvish, and if the runner understands that language, he will hear her say, "The master forbids fighting among us."

The torture session continues normally from there, but some information has been gained.

BREAKOUT

All right, we've mapped out the way the prisoners will be treated if they don't do anything. When Doctor What has 10 points of information out of each prisoner, Ariel and her team will simply leave the safe house. A timed command will be entered into the security console (in Room 3), and a day later, the cell door will simply open. The prisoners can walk out.

Of course, being rough, tough shadowrunners, it is unlikely the characters will sit around getting tortured and waiting for their captors to turn them loose. There are several factors that can help them escape.

Juice Out

As mentioned in **The Doctor Is In**, every time Doctor What's equipment comes into play, the power drain causes the lights in the complex to flicker. The circuitry hasn't been maintained in a while. Each time this occurs, make a Perception Test for the prisoners in the cell. Use the highest Intelligence Attribute among them for the test. The Target Number is 12. Keep track of successes accumulated.

Two successes lets someone hear a faint buzzing when the lights flicker.

Four successes lets the prisoners determine that the buzzing is coming from the door.

At this point, the gamemaster can hint to anyone with a skill related to security systems, electronics, maglocks, or the like, that the power drain of the torture setup is affecting the door lock. But testing the bars proves they are as solid as ever. Maybe an additional strain on the power system would overload the lock?

There are two powered items in the cell: the light over the sink and the camera. If the prisoners short out one or both of these during a torture session, and at the same time someone with a Strength of 6 or more slams against the door, it will spring the lock. Smashing either the camera or the light requires a Strength Test with a Target Number of 4. The person who does this will suffer 6S2 Stun when the current shorts into him. Of course, the prisoners may do something clever, like dashing water into the equipment.

The action has to be coordinated: a combination of force against the faulty lock and electrical surge on the already overtaxed circuitry.

The guard in the corridor will be taken by surprise. The character who opens the cell door has one action in which to try to take the guard out before Initiative is checked.

Iggy Helps

Unless the runners have been completely nasty to Iggy, the Troll will do something he saw on the trid last week if the runners aren't figuring out their own escape by now. Marty may get mad, but Iggy thinks it's wrong to hurt the "crookth" so bad, especially if he likes one of them.

He will sneak over to visit the prisoners while Bonecrack is occupied elsewhere. Put the same merc on guard duty that was there earlier. That chummer won't so much as look sideways at Iggy now.

Iggy will bring "a prethent" to make them feel better. It will be the toy police car. Iggy will insist that they keep it, 'cause they need cheering up. He gets very nervous all of a sudden, and runs away. The guard stares sourly after the retreating Troll, but doesn't actually spit until Iggy rounds the corner out of sight.

If anyone examines the car, they will see a small ceramic tube stuffed into the passenger compartment. Opening it reveals a monofilament utility saw: a meter of monofilament connecting two cerametal grips. It'll cut through a bar in one action. It really isn't well-suited for use as a weapon and the only reason it works on these bars is because they're old.

HELL BROKEN LOOSE

Once out of the cell, the prisoners are still naked, and if armed, only with the weapons from the corridor guard and their own cyber-implants. Against the heavily armed and armored opposition, they'll last about twelve seconds.

If a torture session is going on, the other prisoners have the best chance of moving undetected through the complex, but even then, they don't have time to waste. Once Bonecrack and his mercenaries get after them, not to mention Ariel and Lancelot, they've had it.

The team has to search through the complex, locating weapons and other resources, until they make a getaway to the surface or take their captors on in combat.

The safe house map key gives the locations of the opposition if no alarm has been given. Once an alarm is raised, all remaining mercenaries will join up and start searching through the complex. They will move at once toward the sound of weapons fire or other disturbance. Bonecrack will lead them and they will be joined by Lancelot.

Bonecrack and the mercenaries consider the prisoners lethally dangerous. Any shadowrunner with a visible weapon will be shot. Any that surrender will be clubbed senseless and tossed into a cell.

Iggy will run around the complex, in danger from both sides, intensely excited by all the fuss. If he is in the line of fire,

Bonecrack will not let his men shoot. Lancelot may not let this stop him, and Iggy's presence may cause an open rift between the samurai and the mage.

If either brother goes down, it will effectively take the other one out of play. If Bonecrack dies, Iggy will go berserk. If Iggy dies, Bonecrack will use every trick he knows to exact revenge, and will run away to fight another day without a qualm if that is what it takes. If the runners can save the dying brother, they will make allies of both Bonecrack and Iggy.

Ariel will patrol the complex astrally and then manifest to cut the prisoners off from escape. Ideally, this will occur at the elevator or stairway leading up to the bungalow. Ariel will drop her astral mask; the winds rise at her command. Any magician will know that she is some kind of Air Elemental, and if savvy enough, that she is possibly a Free Spirit. If the runners have observed the controls for the air system in Rooms 3 or 19, they can retreat there and disrupt Ariel via her vulnerability to enclosed space by sealing the complex.

Of course, they may do this under less dramatic circumstances, too. In such case, Ariel cannot get into the complex, and can only follow the fighting over the intercom.

The possible scenes and permutations of the fight are too numerous to mention. With so much material for dramatic moments, the gamemaster will want to take every opportunity to use it.

SPOOR OF A SPIRIT

If some of the shadowrunners avoided capture by Ariel, they will soon discover that their teammates are nowhere to be found. One hopes they will be loyal enough to try to locate the prisoners, and competent enough to try a rescue when and if they find them.

If they saw the missing shadowrunners escaping in the van, they may expect their friends to show up on their own. After 24 hours with no word, however, the free runners may start to worry. At that point, you can give them the information that an abandoned vehicle has Lone Star fretting. It is a heavily armored van, scarred by combat, wanted in connection with the fracas at Grantleigh Park. The van turned up in a field in the northern part of the Sprawl. Use of a Fixer, a police Contact, or a Mr. Johnson will gain the further information that the van showed traces of a potent knock-out gas inside (plus any damage the shadowrunners did to it while trying to escape).

No further information about the van is available. The case has a UCAS security rating on it! The Feds have clamped down because the van is CIA-issue, stolen from the safe house.

If the prisoners were actually captured by NatVat, then their friends learn from Mr. Johnson that NatVat broke off discussions after initial negotiations to release the runners. A source in the security office tips Mr. Johnson that the prisoners were turned over to federal jurisdiction.

Both sets of clues suggest (wrongly) that UCAS intelligence has the prisoners. Of course, the Feds are as much innocent bystanders in this as anything else.

Have the characters do legwork, maybe even create a minor system to invade if they have a decker. It doesn't much matter what they do, for their buddies are not, in fact, in federal custody. However, after about 24 hours, their efforts will draw the attention of the government spooks.

An agent will contact the runners. He will explain that unauthorized scoundrels may be misusing government property and reveal the location of the safe house. "Of course, this is all hypothetical. The facility was used for various research projects before funding was cut. However, there are indications that it may be in unsanctioned hands at this point in time. Though we really have no jurisdiction, I have been authorized to release certain declassified data to you, in the event that you wish to pursue inquiries as private citizens. Naturally, should there be any complications, the government would have to disavow any knowledge of your actions."

After this helpful hint from the government, the runners are on their own. The nice man from the agency may also drop a few remarks about the applicable penalties for illegal access to federal data networks on his way out the door. Darn touchy, these spooks.

The shadowrunners must now scope out the safe house and hit it as best they can if they want to try and rescue their teammates.

Additionally, if the runners are on the ball, and assuming the presence of another magician in their party or their acquaintance with one they can trust, they could trace their missing friends using Ritual Sorcery.

PICKING UP THE PIECES

Well, one way or another, this part of **Harlequin** is over. Apart from assorted lumps, what have the shadowrunners got to show for it?

INFORMATION

Those who were prisoners know that the earlier jobs in the adventure were related to one another. They can also surmise that these runs were aimed at a single, powerful target.

If they find the holos in Ariel's quarters (Bungalow, Bedroom 1), they have a mystifying clue that implies this stuff has been going on for a loooong time. If they unravel the clues in the wrist phone, they may also learn that Tir Tairngire is involved.

Lancelot's presence suggests that the Young Elven Technologists are still involved in their lives. If they take him alive, Lancelot may give them an "ear"-ful, though his loyalty to Ehran will require that they use forceful interrogation.

FRIENDS AND ENEMIES

If the opposition gets away, the shadowrunners may want to track down a few people for further discussion. We suspect they will particularly want a few heartfelt hours of conversation with Doctor What. This will be an adventure in itself, because the Doctor buys his personal protection from a powerful Yakuza gang. Getting to him will not be easy.

Lancelot will disappear back into Tir Tairngire if he survives the run. Going after him is impossible.

The most accessible figures in the whole mess are Bonecrack and Iggy, and they know the least. A lot depends on the situation at the end of the adventure.

If Bonecrack is dead, Iggy probably is, too, because he will have tried to kill whoever hurt Bonecrack.

If Iggy is dead, then Bonecrack better be dead because he will hunt down whoever did it and taken them out. If Iggy was killed by a shadowrunner, a future showdown with the deadly samurai is a must for an adventure. If Iggy was killed by Lancelot, which is not impossible, the shadowrunners will have a potential ally if they go after the puppet-masters who are pulling their strings. Of course, having a revenge-crazed killer like Bonecrack on your side can be like having a tactical nuke with an unstable fuse for a sidearm. Impressive, but hard to live with.

If, in the final combat, either of the Hallorans goes down and a shadowrunner manages to save his life by stabilizing the wounds, both brothers will be loyal allies in future.

KARMA

The group karma for this run is worth 3 to 5 points.

• All survivors get 1 Karma Point for coming out of another run alive.
• If the prisoners escape from the cell, that is worth 1 point.
• If the prisoners defeat their captors in combat, that is worth another point.
• The opposition is worth 2 Karma Points.

Besides the usual things, individual karma might be awarded for particularly good roleplaying under torture or for handling Iggy well. If medical attention is given to either a dying Iggy or Bonecrack, compassion is worth a point.

CAST OF CHARACTERS

LANCELOT WINDTREE

A typical, uptight Tir Tairngire Elf, Windtree is convinced of the superiority of Elves to everything else on the planet. A member of the Young Elven Technologists, he thinks that when Ehran sneezes, diamonds come out of his nose. When the patron saint of the YET told him to assist "my trusted associate Ariel Nasir" on a matter of "the greatest importance to the sacred goals of our people," Lancelot was thrilled to receive the orders directly.

Even as Elves go, Lancelot is gorgeous: handsome, elegant, thin features, silver hair, the whole nine meters. Unfortunately, he knows it. Elf wannabees would leave their best parts under the knife for a cosmeti-cut that made them look half as good as Lancelot.

Lancelot's manner is stinking rotten. Only Elves who use magic may be his equals. Other Elves are barely acceptable. Non-Elves are inferior, Orks and Trolls most of all. Only Ariel's stern intervention kept Bonecrack from putting the Elf in the morgue when he started in on Iggy one evening. An uneasy truce exists between them at the moment.

There is a dark side to Lancelot's racist arrogance. Sadism, insecurity, who knows? Whatever the source, it accounts for his behavior during the torture of the shadowrunners (**The Doctor Is In**).

Attributes/Skills: Use the **Elf Mage**, p. 100, **Sprawl Sites**. If the book isn't available, use the **Street Mage** stats, p. 45, **Shadowrun**. Along with the other gear for these archetypes, Lancelot has a Magic Sword Focus +3.

MARTIN HALLORAN, "BONECRACK"

Bonecrack is a cold-blooded mercenary, even for a samurai. His rep says it all: pay the fee, he does the job. Whether it's save a kidnapped child or kill a little old lady, it makes no difference to Bonecrack.

Bonecrack is a tall Human, 27 years old, scarred, bulky with muscle, both real and implant. His skin is very pale, his hair black, his eyes icy gray. Street word says looking into Bonecrack's eyes shows you the color of death.

Bonecrack rarely shows emotion. As for killing, he neither likes nor dislikes it. It is often the simplest solution to some problem. A dead opponent is a safe opponent, s'all.

Bonecrack never assumes an opponent is not a threat. He treats even an enemy on the point of death with the same cold-blooded caution and tactical concern as he would a fresh, fully armed street fighter.

Bonecrack's first loyalty is to himself and to his brother, Ignatius. Though everyone else uses the handle "Iggy," Bonecrack always calls him Ignatius or "kid".

Bonecrack gives Ignatius as much affection as his nature permits. This is the only crack in the samurai's emotional armor. If the shadowrunners kill Iggy during this adventure, they had better finish off Bonecrack, too. Otherwise, they have acquired a downright lethal enemy who will not rest until they are dead.

Bonecrack gives his employers the professional loyalty they pay for, but will not fight to the death to save a hosed-up job if it is past saving.

He gives his gangers the loyalty they expect: protecting their interests in the contract and taking care of medical or legal expenses.

Attributes/Skills: Use the **Street Samurai**, p. 46, **Shadowrun**. Add +2 to all combat skills and to Etiquette (Street).
Gear: 1 clip of Gel Rounds (32 rounds, 4L1 Stun), 2 clips of explosive ammo (32 rounds each, 5M5), 100-round belt explosive ammo (LMG, 5S5), 100-round belt normal ammo (LMG, 5S3). Ares MP-LMG with deluxe gyro-mount and Smartgun Link, Armor Jacket (Ballistic 5, Impact 3), Ingram Smartgun with integral Smartgun Link and Gas Vent-2 recoil suppression, Monfilament Sword (8M3, Reach +1), Shock Glove (5L3 Stun, touch attack)

ARIEL (AKA "ARIEL NASIR")

Ariel is a Free Air Elemental, as described in **The Grimoire: 2050**, the **Shadowrun** magic sourcebook. All the information needed to run the character is provided here, however.

"Ariel" is not the spirit's real name, but simply a handle. Her "true name," a magical formula that is the key to her existence and power, is known only to her and, at present, to Ehran. It is because Ehran knows her true name that Ariel must serve him.

On this run, she goes by the alias "Ariel Nasir," pretending to be a freelance mage.

Ariel can manifest physically in Human form or withdraw completely into Astral Space. Of course, when she is not manifesting on the physical plane, she cannot be attacked or even detected except by other beings in Astral Space.

Ariel can assume any Human or Metahuman form she wishes, be it old, young, male, female. Her attributes are always the same, whatever her form (see below). If she wishes to manifest her true nature physically, she becomes wrapped in clouds, her hair whipped by spectral winds. Her eyes turn to pools of glowing, pearly light.

In her favorite Human form, Ariel appears as a statuesque, beautiful woman with classic Mediterranean looks: olive skin, dark chestnut hair, flashing eyes so brown they look almost black. Her aquiline features are imperious, yet a glint of humor lurks at the corners of the mouth and in the depths of the eyes. Think of the young Sophia Loren.

Ariel can make her aura match her physical form. Only if she chooses does her aura reveal her true nature. Unless assensed by an initiate (also described in **The Grimoire: 2050**), her aura is completely disguised. An uninitiated magician has no chance of penetrating the deception.

Ariel is generally soft-spoken and courteous, but not servile. Her typical manner echoes the elaborate courtesy of Moorish culture at its height. If angered, she can be…er…stormy. She is decisive, and if opposed, she may silence opposition with a display of power.

By the terms of her oath to Ehran, Ariel is loyal. But servitude chafes a Free Spirit, and her first loyalty is to herself. Having tasted the gift of free will, she will do anything possible to regain it.

Ariel

Note that Ariel's ratings are for a Free Elemental, and much more powerful than those of a bound spirit.

B	Q	S	C	I	W	R	Armor	Force	Spirit Energy
6	11 x 4*	5	5	8	8	8	9	None	5	3

*As an Air Elemental, Ariel is capable of movement through the air at the same speed as on the ground.

Dice Pools: Defense (Armed) 1, Defense (Unarmed) 1, Dodge 1, Magic 11

Skills: Driving 5, Sorcery 8, Unarmed Combat 11

Powers: Aura Masking, Engulf, Human Form, Manifestation, Movement, Noxious Breath, Psychokinesis, Sorcery

Weaknesses: Allergy (Extreme, Confinement by Airtight Seal). Suffers disruption if confined. That is, she is driven off the physical plane for about a month. Vulnerability (Earth).

Gear: Ariel can seem to be wearing or carrying anything she wants. It is all illusion, however, for Ariel uses neither physical armor nor weapons.

Spells: Maximum Force for any spell is 5. Spellcasting does not cause Drain. Ariel cannot use ritual sorcery, focuses, or fetishes.

Chaotic World: 5	Mind Probe: 5
Clairvoyance: 3	Powerball: 5
Heal Deadly Wounds: 5	Stun Blast: 5

Notes: To hit Ariel in combat with normal weapons, attackers use Willpower instead of a combat skill. It does not matter whether the characters know this or not. Simply have the players roll Willpower dice instead of skill dice. Don't tell them why. Normal skills can be used to attack with magic weapons or in astral combat.

Because none of the attackers knows her true name, "killing" the Spirit in either form of combat will only "disrupt" her, driving her off the physical plane for about a month.

IGNATIUS HALLORAN, "IGGY"

Iggy goblinized at the age of 11 and is now 15. In the early stages of the change, his desperate parents rushed him to a doctor who advertised that his treatments could arrest or even reverse the transformation. The "treatment," of course, did no such thing, but did cause severe brain damage. A week later, the quack was found dead in his clinic. Rumor has it that Bonecrack killed him.

Iggy is a typical-looking Troll, but his expression is usually rather dreamy and unfocused. He speaks with a childish lisp, though his voice is the gravelly basso profundo of *homo sapiens ingentis*.

Iggy has a level of intelligence equal to that of a normal Human child of about seven. He knows many people seem to be afraid of him or say mean things about him. This bothers him, but his basic nature is cheerful and he quickly bounces back from distress.

Iggy is physically mature. He doesn't really understand the feelings in his body lately, but is pathetically nice to women of whatever race he meets these days, and very responsive to kindness from them.

Iggy calls himself "Iggy" rather than Ignatius. He does not like it if anyone but Bonecrack uses his real name. He always calls his brother "Marty."

Bonecrack has had Iggy heavily cyber-modified. In his value system, only such lethal power gives Iggy a chance of survival. Despite his warlike abilities, Iggy only fights under two conditions. He will fight when threatened or hurt. If the threat ceases, Iggy stops fighting. If his brother Marty tells him someone is a bad person, Iggy will try to kill the bad person.

Iggy loves his big brother very much. If Iggy sees Bonecrack attacked, he will try to kill the bad people who did it. If Bonecrack goes down from his wounds, however, Iggy will go to pieces and crouch protectively over his brother. He will not fight unless someone tries to hurt him or Marty further.

Iggy likes people who are nice to him, and does not like people who aren't. He remembers how people behaved, and can hold a long grudge. He is reluctant to hurt people he likes, even if Marty tells him to.

Attributes/Skills: Use the **Troll Street Samurai**, p. 108, **Street Samurai Catalog**. Skills are Armed Combat (General) 5, Armed Combat (Axe) 7, Stealth 5, Unarmed Combat 6.
Gear: Armor Jacket (Ballistic 5, Impact 3), Bandai-US Chrysler-Nissan Patrol-1 model, with action siren and real flashing lights, Club (11M2 Stun), Mr. Storeez (talking clown doll; expert system with over 100 hours of stories, riddles, and jokes), Wallacher Combat Axe (10S2, Thrusting Point: 5L3)

DOCTOR WHAT

Doctor What is a street doc with a rep known only to an elite clientele. Using drugs, biofeedback probes, and mostly good, old fashioned pain, Doctor What can extract information from anyone. His rates are reasonable, too. After all, the Doc loves his work.

This giggling little sadist looks completely harmless. With his clear, pink skin, cherubic face surrounded by a fluffy halo of white hair, and sparkling blue eyes, heck, he should be bouncing grandchildren on his knee.

Doctor What is as soft-spoken and pleasant as some friendly family doctor in a bad movie. When he is about his work, he gets even nicer. As his victims scream under his needles, probes, and blades, his cheerful voice just hums along, asking questions, describing what he is doing to the victim's body, asking questions, telling jokes, asking questions *questions QUESTIONS.*

Doctor What is a physical coward, and will whimper and beg for mercy if threatened, but if he gets half a chance at a shot from behind, he will kill in a moment, using his bio-injector.

Attributes/Skills: Use the **Street Doc**, p. 171, **Shadowrun**. Change Biological Sciences Skill to Unarmed Combat (Specialization: Bio-injector) 8. Change Negotiation to Interrogation (Specialization: Torture) 6.

Gear: Bio-injector: A wrist-mounted device that inserts a laminated monofilament injector spike with a sensor-guided tip into a target in melee (Reach 0). Does 4L1 Stun damage. If Dodge dice and armor do not prevent damage, the target is also injected with a dose of drug (Doctor What's choice). Use Impact Armor at half-value, because the injector spike is so smart, strong, flexible, and thin. The injector magazine holds four doses of drugs. Cost: ¥15,000.

Drug Loads: Narcoject (See **Shadowrun**, p. 147.) Doctor What carries one dose of this. Fugu-5: Ditto. Agonadine-delta: Damage: 4D2 Speed: 1 combat turn. As soon as the dose is injected, the drug causes nerve pain, adding +4 to the victim's target numbers. At the end of the turn when the poison was injected, the target must attempt to resist the poison. If it inflicts a Deadly result, the pain increases to extreme levels. The victim falls, screaming uncontrollably, and dies in a few minutes if not treated successfully. If the poison does less than Deadly damage, the pain diminishes to dull irritation. This is Doctor What's favorite poison and his injector is loaded with two doses.

Secure Clothing (Ballistic 3)

MERCENARIES

Bonecrack employs a number of mercenaries, equal to the number of player characters in this adventure, with a minimum of four. Half are normals, half are Orks. These are tough men and women, blooded combat veterans. They will not fight against odds if they don't see a chance to win.

Attributes/Skills

Ork Mercenaries: Use **Ork Mercenary**, p. 41, **Shadowrun**. Add Wired Reflexes (1) to one of each pair of Orks in the gang.

Normal Mercenaries: Use **Mercenary**, p. 40, **Shadowrun**. Add Wired Reflexes (1) to one of each pair of normals in the gang.

Gear: 2 clips Firepower ammo (15 rounds each, 6M2), 6 Stun Rounds (4M4 Stun) if prisoners not armored, Ares Predator II, Armor Vest w/Plates (Ballistic 4 and Impact 3), AZ-150 Super Stun Baton (5L3 Stun damage and 5 rounds disorientation), Mossberg CMDT Shotgun, Standard Shells (5M3) if prisoners have escaped and gotten armed.

SPIRITUAL

Journal Entry: Another Day

I have sent them against him once more, this time to a place from which I do not expect them to return. Amazonia. A surprising destination for such people as this. Is this their work? Their desire? Or does one of us inflict ourselves upon them?

Is it my dear once-brother? His influence in that area is certain, but the concerns are not his. Unless he's changed…

Has he changed? The words he writes reveal the same arrogance, as do his actions with the youth-minds he oversees. His voice in that obscene nation-state is heard clearly, yet it is tempered by age.

And he has learned to love flowers since last we met.

INTRODUCTION

This time out, Harlequin has hired the runners through Anson Helms, with a mission to travel to the depths of the Amazon. He knows Helms' reputation will help convince the runners to take the job. And they're going to need a lot of convincing—and nuyen—before they'll take on this one.

He also wants to find out how Ariel's treatment has affected them. He's tempted to reveal the Ehran connection in all its glory, but is afraid they'll seek their own primitive form of *chal'han*. If the runners survive and achieve the goal Harlequin has set for them, he'll be even more tempted to take them into his confidence.

Fonte do Sul is Ehran's retreat from the world. Far from his usual concerns, he spends hours tending his flowers, which are his pride and joy. By striking at Ehran in his Amazonian sanctuary, Harlequin hopes to show that no part of him, not even his most reclusive, introspective aspect, is safe.

HAVE GUN, WILL TRAVEL

TELL IT TO THEM STRAIGHT

Read the following to the player character who typically serves as the party's negotiator or leader:

Things have been uncharacteristically quiet for several days now, but you've been enjoying the fruits of earlier labors. When you roll out of bed this afternoon, you immediately notice the flashing icon on your computer that indicates a message waits for you on one of the local, private bulletin-board systems. A few quick keystrokes and a password or two later, you download it. The text reads:

"I am most anxious to meet you and your partners. I need the services of a team willing to perform the…unusual, and I assure you that the price is right. If interested, please bring your partners to Gate 12 at the Seattle-Tacoma International Airport tomorrow morning at ten and ask for Anson Helm."

Anson Helm, you recall, is one of the most well-connected Fixers in Seattle. If he says the price is right, it's likely to be a quite a mountain of nuyen. On the other hand, if he says the job is "unusual," you'll likely earn every cent.

When the player characters arrive at the airport, read this:

The Seattle-Tacoma International Airport (commonly called Sea-Tac) handles a drekload of traffic, for Seattle is the Hong Kong of the 21st century. The airport is chockful of people of every type, from suits and their bodyguards to street trash escaping the rain. As you pass through the weapon detectors under the scrutiny of a trio of rent-a-cops, you can't help but feel a bit naked without your normal hardware. But that can't be helped. No one carries heat into the airport without a license and an awfully good reason. You just hope that any licenses in this crowd are legit.

Security at the gates is even tighter. When you reach Gate 12 and ask for Helm, a gray suit who wears a mirrored visor frisks each of you, then ushers you to a stairwell leading to the tarmac. A brisk wind whips across the field, carrying the whine of aircraft engines. The suit leads you to a powered cart, then drives you 30 meters to the door of a Lear Platinum Custom. Two minutes later, you're sitting in a plush red chair, holding a cold, refreshing drink and wondering where your host is.

The intercom chimes, and a cultured voice announces, "If you'll buckle in, my friends, we'll be taking off shortly. Once we're airborne, I'll be back to speak with you."

The whine of engines cuts off abruptly as the outer door is sealed. This baby is insulated well. Cool, antiseptic air flows gently through the cabin. The jet begins taxiing to a runway. As the engines power up, you can't quite hear them, but can feel the rising vibration and the tension of the brakes. Then acceleration presses a gentle hand against you, and the plane is off. It lifts smoothly into the sky, then suddenly banks into a powerful turn, before leveling off once more.

An immaculately groomed man in his late forties enters the cabin. "Hello. I'm Anson Helm." He smiles and shakes hands all around. You feel a power in his grasp that is usually lacking in his type.

"I hope you don't mind meeting me here. I just bought the plane and wanted to try it out. And it's so private up here, it seemed the perfect place to conduct our business. We'll return to Sea-Tac when we've concluded."

Fixing himself a drink, Helm continues, "I indicated that the job offer I have for you is 'unusual.' Not many people would be able to carry it off, but I've heard good things about you.

"I need a team to travel to a plantation near the source of the Amazon—yes, that's the Amazon River—to acquire and bring back a rare orchid cultivated there. The mission will require stealth. You'll have to get in and then out quietly, without stirring up the plantation's occupants. There's a bonus for causing no casualties.

"The plantation belongs to the Aquilars, an important family of Portuguese descent. Over the years, the Aquilars have become renowned for their horticultural prowess.

"Our employer would like you to leave a small datachip in place of the flower you've cut. It may seem odd, but my instructions about this were very specific.

"Now comes the really unusual part of the mission. Obviously, you can't approach the plantation by air because of the need for stealth. You'll have to make your way by unconventional means through the rain forest. And I hear tell some pretty spooky native tribes inhabit the area, even, reputedly, some headhunters.

"Once you've got the orchid, you'll get away by commandeering one of the many aircraft right there at the plantation. Go to Lima, Peru, where you'll find airline tickets waiting to get you back to Seattle. Once home, you'll deliver the orchid and receive the balance of your pay.

"Now you can see why I need people who can think on their feet, not just someone with glitter and steel. You come highly recommended, and if you've heard anything about me, you know I pay well and give my operatives every possible edge. I've got a map of the plantation and some linguasofts of Tupí, the region's main language. I've even got a couple of pilot chips if you want them.

"What do you say? Do we talk business?"

BEHIND THE SCENES

Anson Helm is exactly what he seems, an honest fixer. Other fixers vary with street temperature, making promises when it's cool and disappearing when it's hot. But when Helm makes a deal, he delivers, a reputation that has earned him wealth beyond most Fixers' dreams. (How many other Fixers could afford a Lear Platinum?)

Of course, Helm seldom goes out on a limb, either. He'll be perfectly forthright with the player characters and give them every edge he can. Once they begin the mission, however, they're on their own, and he's never heard of them.

To play the part of Helm, the gamemaster can use the **Fixer Contact** (p. 167, **Shadowrun**), but treat the character as a mobile Mr. Johnson. That is, at Helm's level of operations, he does not put shadowrunners in touch with employers, he *is* the employer. Helm contracts with organizations to take their special jobs, then pays his operatives out of pocket. He maintains a small staff of agents for really short-term tasks. For the longer-term, tougher stuff, he likes to hire shadowrunners because they're replaceable.

Because of the difficulties involved in penetrating Fonte do Sul, Ehran the Scribe's plantation, Harlequin has hired Helm to get the job done and fronted him a lot of nuyen. Helm is willing to pass some of that prosperity along, but only to the right people. His first offer to the player characters is ¥150,000 nuyen apiece if they take the job, 10 percent now, as earnest money, and the balance upon delivery of the orchid. Use the standard Negotiation rules to adjust this figure. The group can earn a 10 percent bonus if they complete the mission without causing any casualties at the plantation. (Fat chance of that). The team may choose to take payment either as certified credsticks or credited to their accounts.

Helm will not speak of his employer at all. If the runners insist on questioning him or attempt some unfortunate action to learn more, consult **Running Harlequin**, p. 146.

The datachip is not specially encoded or sealed. If examined, it turns out to be a conventional optical chip, ten megapulses in size, containing a single line of programming code. The line itself is unexceptional, but if any runner with Computer or relevant skill examines and compares it to the program copied from the Young Elven Technologists (see **Love**), have him make a Success Test with a Target Number 9. The base time for the test is one day. If the test succeeds, the character matches the lone line of code with the back-door program subroutine taken from YET. Like the subroutine, the line of code is useless alone.

Helm will also offer the player characters four linguasoft chip copies of the Tupí-Guaraní language (Skill Level 3), the region's main Indian language, and two skillsoft copies of Winged 4. Anyone with a datajack can use the Linguasoft; a skillwire rig of at least Level 4 is required for the Winged skillsoft. Helm will also foot the bill for any other equipment the team needs, with the single requirement that they actually take the stuff with them on the mission. (The gamemaster needs to keep in mind that the runners will have to travel by raft or boat for 140 kilometers and on foot the last 16. It might be a good idea to limit the runners' purchases to a total of half allowed by the normal encumbrance rules, the reduction representing the difficulty of toting the stuff through the rain forest.)

Helm will also arrange for a covert insertion near Macapá, Amazonia; boat transport upriver to Fonte Boa, at the mouth of the Juruá; travel by seaplane from there to a point 650 kilometers up the Jutaí; and air tickets from Lima, Peru back to Seattle. Finally, Helm has a map of the plantation, pinpointing the location of the greenhouse where the rare orchid is cultivated.

Once Helm completes his deal with the runners, he returns to the cockpit for the landing, and the plane heads back for Sea-Tac. After landing, the team is ushered back to the airport terminal. Their flight out is scheduled for a morning two days hence.

When the runners attempt to gain access to the gate area of Sea-Tac, consult **Getting There by Air**, p. 144, which provides a general overview of airport security practices and hardware.

THE ROAD TO FONTE DO SUL

TELL IT TO THEM STRAIGHT

Read the following to the players when their characters show up at Sea-Tac for their flight to Amazonia:

As instructed, you proceed to one of the private gates, where you are escorted around security and led to Helm's Lear jet. The wait on the runway is brief, and within moments, the jet is airborne. You've been told that the flight plan will take you over several Native American Nations, but the pilot assures you that he has filed all the proper papers. You hope so: some of the Nations have been known to routinely shoot down any unidentified aircraft on the assumption that they are smugglers. Definitely an ignominious way to go.

The jet touches down briefly at Kansas City, where you fully expect to encounter some kind of security check, but none comes. The Lear touches ground only long enough to take on another full tankload of avgas and then roars skyward again.

Helms has been cagey about exactly how he'll be getting you into Amazonia, claiming that an explanation of the details would require a discussion of assets he does not wish to reveal just yet. He has confirmed that your entry into the country will be plenty covert. Ever since Awakened forces toppled the government of Brazil 17 years ago, the country has hardly welcomed tourists with open arms. You've all read the reports about the powerful magics the Amazonian government employs to promote accelerated regrowth of the devastated rain forests, magicks on the scale of those once wielded by the American Indian Ghost Dancers. The former Brazilian cities are said to be pits of urbanization and decay overseen by rulers with little concern for the inhabitants. Emigration is encouraged, but rarely achieved because of the cost.

You expect the jet to land in Atlanta, but it continues on out over the Atlantic instead. When the plane finally does land, it is on a grassy strip on some island barely large enough to hold the plane, let alone a landing strip. A tall, dark-skinned man dressed in fashionable white and tan island garb greets you as you disembark and retrieve your gear from cargo. Speaking with a decidedly out-of-place Boston accent, he introduces himself as Mercer, an associate of Helms. He leads you to a nearby pickup truck, loads you and your gear into it, and drives off.

He takes you to a small lagoon, where a seaplane sits waiting. Again you and yours load on board, and the plane launches into the sky with Mercer at the controls. He is affable during the flight, talking freely about local politics and sights, but he will not divulge any information about Helm's plan. If pressed, he will say only that it is "one of the prettiest things I have ever seen."

Meanwhile, the seaplane is taking you out of sight of land, toward the southeast and into the night.

A few hours later, Mercer begins his descent, apparently relying on the aircraft's inertial and satellite-assisted navigation gear. The landing on the water is so smooth that you don't notice the dark bulk of the freighter until the plane is right up against it.

The crew throws ropes down, then hauls you and your gear onto the deck. After securing the seaplane, Mercer joins you. Aboard the freighter (an oil tanker that you take to be of Portuguese origin, based on the language the crewmen are speaking) you find little hospitality. The sailors seem fearful and either ignore you or rebuff any attempts at conversation. Mercer speaks briefly with one and then leads you into the bowels of the vessel.

The lower corridors of the ship are tight and dark, until you suddenly step into the blazing light of a half-dozen arc lamps. Sitting there in an area undoubtedly designed to hold at least one large oil tank is a black, aerodynamic shape. It takes only a moment to recognize it as an old Soviet IL-290 VTOL stealth transport jet. Its pilot, a rigger with cold silver eyes, waits near its nose. He nods at Mercer, who directs you into the main cabin, which has only enough seats for you and your team. As you buckle up, Mercer speaks.

"The jet will drop you off west of Macapá, Amazonia. From there, it's a short trek overland until you reach the river. Here's a tracking device that'll lead you to your contact point. A man with a boat will meet you there to take you upriver. You'll recognize him by the pink bandanna tied to his left arm.

"Once the VTOL grounds, you'll have only a couple of seconds to get out and clear. Those Amazonians are real touchy about their border security, and they don't rely exclusively on radar.

"Good luck."

Mercer passes the tracking device to one of the runners, then with a quick nod, he leaves. The door closes and seals behind him.

A moment later, the dull throb of the jet's engines becomes a powerful roar. The cabin lights wink out and the VTOL leaps skyward.

Read the following when the runners reach the Amazon river:

The wet jungle peels away before you and you catch the low rumble of voices and the clank of metal on metal. Peering through a break in the flora, you spot perhaps the ugliest, most battered boat you've ever seen. It looks like an ancient tug, apparently with a retrofit electric engine. A tall Latino with a slim cigar in his mouth is leaning against the cabin, overseeing a handful of laborers who are moving crates from the dock to the vessel's deck. Occasionally, he straightens up sharply to bark out an order in Portuguese, then leans back against the cabin once more. On his left arm, the man sports a stained, pink bandanna.

Apparently spotting you, he nods, and you see two small

boats, still inflating, being dropped quickly over the side of the tug and then they head your way. Within moments, you've climbed aboard and reached the larger boat.

Once you are aboard, two crewmen escort you into the presence of the man with the bandanna. As you approach, he straightens up, smiles engagingly, and welcomes you with a broad sweep of his hand. "Friends," he says in very good English, "I am Captain Colón, and this is my ship, the *Esperança*. Welcome aboard. Come, we have quite a trip before us."

Read the following when the runners reach Fonte Boa:

Only a few hours of daylight remain when the *Esperança* pulls into Fonte Boa. An elderly man with a thin white moustache stands waiting for you on the dock. He wipes the sweat from his face with a soiled pink bandanna as you approach.

"Are you Helm's people?" he asks in a clipped British accent. Upon receiving your confirmation, he identifies himself as Graeme Greene, the owner and pilot of the *Marsh Rose*, the amphibious plane Helm hired. Greene calls to a group of dock workers and instructs them to take your equipment to his plane.

"They'll handle things just fine now," he assures you. "What do you say we go into town for a bite to eat?"

BEHIND THE SCENES

GETTING THERE

Getting to Amazonia isn't much more than a ride for the runners, so let them enjoy it. It's important that the gamemaster use the trip as the chance to impress the runners with Helm's wealth and influence, for that, too, was one of Harlequin's instructions to the Fixer.

The key word for the trip is professionalism. Someone has gone to great expense and effort on this mission. It may give the player characters something to think about.

THE DROP

Perhaps an hour after the VTOL goes airborne, it banks suddenly and a cold, emotionless voice advises the runners to stand by to disembark. They have reached Amazonia.

The gamemaster may handle the insertion as he wishes. It can be either textbook-perfect or seat-of-the-pants. If all goes well, the jet touches down in a clearing, the runners hop out with their gear, and the VTOL rushes skyward again.

If all does not go well, there may be evidence of pursuit or investigation by helicopters, light aircraft, or some form of flying creatures. (Could that shape have been a dracoform?)

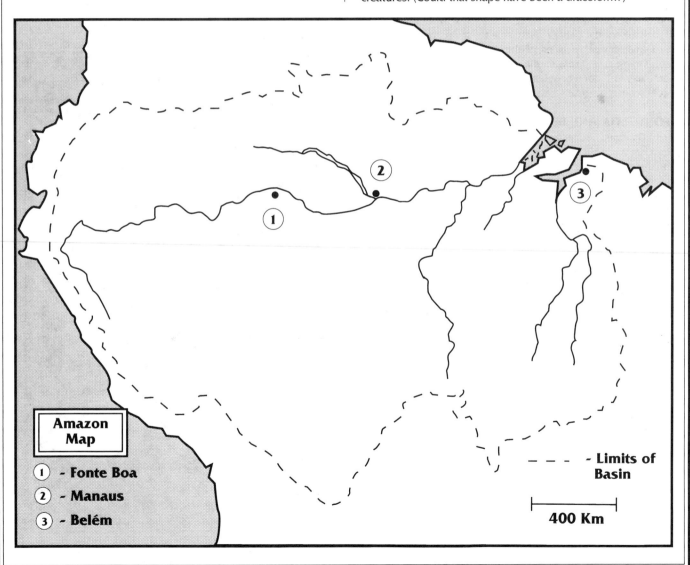

Amazon Map

① - Fonte Boa
② - Manaus
③ - Belém

- - - - Limits of Basin

400 Km

The tone of the actual landing should be reflected in the short trip to the river. The tracking device will work perfectly, but that doesn't mean the trip will be easy. The gamemaster may want to begin preying on the runners' worst fears of the jungle, but save the real scares for later.

ABOARD THE ESPERANÇA

The player characters can stow their gear in the cabin, where they find a number of hammocks strung for them and the Captain. The *Esperança* carries two other crewmembers, but with passengers aboard, these crewmembers sleep on deck. The vessel's two concessions to electronic technology are a high-frequency sound generator to keep insects away and a short-wave radio for listening entertainment and emergency calls.

In all, the boat trip takes ten long, uneventful days. The only breaks in the monotony are the refueling stops approximately every other day at small cities along the river and a 24-hour period near the end of the trip during which Colón transacts business in Manaus. Manaus is a city with a population of slightly less than five million people. Finally, the *Esperança* pulls into its destination, Fonte Boa (approximate population 70,000), and the shadowrunners and their equipment are offloaded.

There really isn't much for the runners to do during this portion of their travels, but they'll probably think of something.

If asked, the Captain will gladly tell the runners about the pro-environment policies of the Amazonian government. If something is a threat to the ecology of the rain forest, it is probably forbidden or at least greatly restricted. The long-term goal is an ecologically balanced nation and society.

FONTE BOA AND BEYOND

Graeme Greene, owner and pilot of the amphibious plane that Helm has hired for the mission, takes the runners into town on the night they arrive in Fonte Boa. He invites them to a good meal (which he charges to Helm) and gets them settled in a boarding house. During the course of the evening, Greene will ply the runners with questions, many of them suspiciously pointed. Accustomed to the dog-eat-dog world of the Seattle sprawl, the player characters are likely to become uneasy under Greene's scrutiny. They may begin to suspect that he is actually working for someone else. That possibility should make them very uncomfortable, considering that in the morning Greene is going to fly them out into the boondocks, more than 600 kilometers from the nearest city, and drop them off. If Greene isn't on their side, he might just drop the team far from their objective, leaving them to make their way back to civilization through hundreds of kilometers of uncharted rain forest.

Greene is not a counteragent, however. He is simply a lonely old European, living out his last years in a backwater region of what he still calls Brazil. He misses the excitement of brighter lights and bigger cities, and is simply trying to recapture some of that excitement by talking with the runners. If his questions seem especially pointed, it is because of the sharpness of his mind.

In playing Greene, the gamemaster should try to make the shadowrunners uneasy, but not so suspicious that they decide to cancel their trip with him. If that happens, Greene can suddenly realize that he must have seemed too nosy. He apologizes, explaining his loneliness. If the apology is abject

enough, the runners will probably take pity on the fellow, especially if he is extremely careful not to question them anymore.

The runners will be in Fonte Boa long enough to notice something significant about the town: it is slowly but steadily losing its battle against the encroaching jungle. If asked, Greene can tell them that the new, Awakened government has instituted regular, powerful rituals to induce re-growth of the rain forests to repair the damage done by years of industrialization. In many areas, restraining the jungle has become a real battle. Many areas in Fonte Boa show clear evidence of flame damage and heavy cutting where the jungle threatens to intrude. Every morning the town's inhabitants have to cut their vehicles free of the flora that began to engulf it during the night.

Greene will eventually take them out to where the plane is hidden. It will take almost an hour to reach the spot, but he dared not park it any closer because the craft uses an illegal gas-burning engine. Pollution, you know.

When the runners board the *Marsh Rose* the morning after their arrival in Fonte Boa, they are beginning an air journey that will cross 650 kilometers of river in a period of five hours. That trip will use up half the plane's fuel; Greene will need the rest to return to Fonte Boa. From here, the runners have roughly another 160 kilometers of river to traverse by raft. The next section covers events during that time.

BACK TO NATURE

TELL IT TO THEM STRAIGHT

When the runners begin their raft trip, read them the following:

"Well, this is it, people," Greene says as he banks the *Marsh Rose* into a descent toward the river. The plane drops smoothly, touches down with a jolt, then skids upriver, throwing plumes of sparkling water from the pontoons. It finally coasts to a stop on a sandbar near the right bank.

You set about assembling your raft and then sliding it out onto the edge of the sandbank. Greene shakes hands all around, wishing you well.

"If you're ever in the neighborhood again, drop by and see me." He grins sardonically at the joke, then mounts a pontoon and poles his plane off the sandbar. You watch as he clambers into the cockpit, starts up the engines, points the plane downstream toward civilization, and lifts off into the clear air. As the *Marsh Rose* disappears into the distance, you reflect on the fact that with it goes your last real chance to scrap the mission and return home. Now the only way out is forward to your mission goal, where a plane sits waiting to be commandeered for your flight to Lima. You hope.

Not for the first time, you wonder what possessed you to accept this job. You're city people, used to the flash and flair of the streets, not to the slow ebb and flow of nature's rhythms. And here you are, facing five days of sunburn and hard rowing, with mosquitos for sleeping companions. Well, the sooner we start, the sooner we finish, you think as you push off in the raft, find a seat, and slip a paddle into the water. As you settle into a rhythm, the green walls of jungle lining the river banks slip steadily by. You're on your way.

Read the following to the runners when they meet the Amahuaca Indians:

The equatorial sun hammers down on the river as you row. Wavelets sparkle around you like shattered glass. For relief, your eyes turn to the cool green stretches of jungle along the banks. Several hundred meters upstream, an unusual movement catches your attention. A trio of canoes launches outward from the shore in a course that will intersect your own, each canoe containing two to four natives. They row powerfully, while your own arms are almost trembling with fatigue.

Certain that you cannot outrace them, you decide to give your muscles a rest for the possible confrontation to come. The native canoes sweep toward you, then slow at about three meters' distance to begin coasting downstream with you. The occupants wear very little clothing, but the fellow in the prow of the lead canoe wears scores of shell necklaces around his swarthy neck. Another man in the rear of the same canoe wears paint and feathers in some elaborate scheme that makes you believe him to be a shaman.

The one with the shell necklaces flashes a smile and speaks to you in his native dialect. When you fail to respond, he tries another. On the third try, he uses a form of Tupí-Guaraní.

"You come rest on shore, come eat with us?" he asks. "Much food, good hunt."

If the runners agree to accompany the natives, read the following:

Thinking that you probably have little choice short of opening fire on these natives (who knows how many more that might bring down on your heads?), you agree.

Grounding your canoe on the bank, you follow the Indians uphill to a clearing, where an iron pot bubbles over a fire. Inside it is a white, pasty substance, apparently a tuber stew. Lying to the side on platter-sized leaves are strips of roasted meat that taste like pork. One husky fellow opens a damp leather bag and pulls out a meter and a half-long worm, runs his pinched fingers down its length to squirt out the dirt inside, and offers it to your group. When you politely decline, he tilts his head back and slurps the thing down like a strand of spaghetti.

After the meal, the chief pulls out a gourd containing some yeasty-smelling liquid and passes it around. It proves to be a tart and fiery brew. With the gourd making its way around the circle in a comradely manner, the chief begins conversation once again.

"Why you come this far from cities?" he asks. Seeing that he doesn't intend to beat around the bush, you turn to your companions and begin discussing how to answer.

If the runners resist going with the Indians, read the following:

The shaman in the back of the lead canoe smiles broadly. "The Laughing One say you maybe come. He say you maybe be drekheads." The last word is mangled and butchered, but is quite obviously an insult not indigenous to the area.

With that, the lead canoe turns and heads back toward shore.

When the runners meet the Jívaro Indians, read the following if they are travelling by raft:

Deciding that it is time for a break to stretch your legs and answer other of nature's calls, you guide the raft to shore, stowing it among the roots of what looks like a giant cypress. Walking uphill, away from the water's edge, you find the area dim and still under the rain forest's canopy, but showing surprisingly little undergrowth. Not much light gets down this far to support smaller plants. High overhead in the branches of the trees, colorful birds and small animals sport and screech, but the distance makes the sounds seem small and insignificant. The leaves underfoot absorb the sound of your footfalls, and there is not a breath of wind.

Suddenly, the quiet seems to deepen. Even the insect noises are hushed. You stop and peer around warily. From behind the bole of one of the giant trees ahead steps a grinning Indian, clutching an ancient shotgun to his chest. More step from behind trees to either side of you, some holding shotguns, others with bows, arrows nocked. Finally, an elderly Indian appears, muddy bits of bone, feather, and fur stuck or tied to his hair and his limbs. Shrunken heads dangle from his loincloth strap. His eyes roam wildly over your group.

"You are invaders." His raspy voice makes the Tupí-Guaraní words difficult to understand. "You are not wanted here."

If the runners are walking overland when they encounter the Jívaros, read the following:

It is dim and still under the rain forest's canopy, and not much undergrowth because so little light penetrates this far to support smaller plants. High overhead, colorful birds and small animals sport and screech among the tree branches and tangled vines, but the distance muffles the sound. The leaves underfoot absorb the sound of your steps, and not a breath of wind stirs. Hitching your packs another few centimeters up on your backs, you set off at a rapid pace over the level ground.

Some time later, the quiet deepens further. Even the insect sounds are hushed. You stop and peer around warily.

From behind the bole of one of the giant trees ahead steps a grinning Indian, clutching an ancient shotgun to his chest. Others step out from behind trees to either side of you, some with shotguns, others with bows, arrows nocked. Finally, another Indian appears, older than the others, with muddy bits of bone, feather, and fur stuck and tied to his hair and limbs. Shrunken heads dangle from his loincloth strap. His eyes roam wildly over your group.

"You are invaders." His raspy voice makes the Tupí-Guaraní words difficult to understand. "You are not wanted here."

BEHIND THE SCENES

TRAVEL ON THE JUTAÍ RIVER

If the runners push it, they can make 32 kilometers a day upriver by canoe. They can use the river for four and a half days, a total of 144 kilometers, but they must travel the last 16 kilometers to the plantation on land. Because the terrain is less rough at this point and because their packs are lighter (most of their supplies have been eaten by now), it will take approximately half a day to travel the last 16 kilometers on foot.

Every time the characters cover 16 kilometers, the gamemaster rolls 1D6 to determine if they have been spotted by the Amahuaca Indians. In effect, there is one chance at noon and another near nightfall. On a result of 1, the runners have encountered Amahuacas; see **Friendly Indians** below. The Amahuaca encounter occurs only once, so the gamemaster need make no more rolls for the Amahuacas once the runners meet them.

When the runners reach a point 96 kilometers from the horticultural plantation, there is also a chance of encountering Jívaro Indians. Again, every 16 kilometers the gamemaster should roll 1D6. At 96 kilometers out, the characters meet Jívaros on a "6"; at 80 kilometers out, on a roll of "5" or "6"; at 64 kilometers out, on a roll of "4," "5," or "6"; and so on. Once they are within 16 kilometers, they must abandon the river and

travel overland to reach the plantation. Their chances of encountering Jívaros becomes automatic at 16 kilometers. See **Headhunters**, below, for details of this encounter. As with the Amahuacas, the runners will only have the Jívaro encounter once.

Note that it is entirely possible for the player characters to encounter the Jívaros before the meeting the Amahuacas.

FRIENDLY INDIANS

If the shadowrunners meet the Amahuacas before covering the first 144 kilometers of their journey, the encounter will most likely occur on the river. If, for some reason, the runners are hoofing it at the time, the gamemaster can simply adapt the description under **Tell It To Them Straight** to match the conditions. In either case, the team encounters 2D6 Amahuacas.

The Amahuacas are a wide-ranging, relatively peaceful group of hunter/gatherer tribes that have dwelt in the Amazon basin for thousands of years. Harlequin sought out the acquaintance of these Indians sometime ago after discovering Ehran's plantation and his ties with the Jívaros. Just before hiring Anson Helm to put together the plantation run, Harlequin contacted the Amahuacas and instructed them to watch the river for the arrival of the team and to aid its members in any way possible, short of participating in the run on the plantation. As the runners are obviously neither missionaries nor anthropologists, the Amahuacas are fairly certain that this is the group Harlequin had in mind.

The Amahuacas will give food, advice, and medical aid to the player characters if need be. Advice might include describing the savagery of the Jívaros, for example, or such basic tricks of survival as which plants to eat and which to avoid. The Indians will also follow the runners at a distance and keep an ear open for conflict with the Jívaros, as described in **Headhunters**, below.

For the Amahuaca chieftain, use the **Tribal Chief**, p. 172, **Shadowrun**. For the shaman, use the **Shaman** (Snake Totem and Healer spell package), p. 44 of that book. For the other members of the band, use the **Tribesman**, p. 48 of those rules, but limit their gear to knife, bow, and 20 arrows.

The shaman has had the most recent contact with Harlequin, though the Amahuacas tell stories of previous visits by the Laughing One. The shaman will say nothing about "the Laughing One," and in fact, eventually denies even mentioning those words.

If asked about Fonte do Sol, the Amahuacas will say only that a great demon-spirit lives there.

HEADHUNTERS

The Jívaros are savages who have resisted with violence the incursions of other peoples. They have a nasty reputation among the Amahuacas, and even some outlying farms and plantations in the vicinity of the city of Eirunepé have suffered their attacks.

The Jívaros honor great killers, men with "livers of stone." The trouble with being a great killer, however, is that the Jívaros believe that the souls of victims will arise to destroy their killers unless those souls can be contained somehow. That somehow is by sewing up the eyes, ears, nostrils, and lips of a victim's head within a few hours after death, before the spirit breaks its ties with the body. After these orifices are sealed, the skull is

crushed, and the head is tanned, during which process it shrinks to the size of a fist.

Being violent by nature, the Jívaros hold shotguns as their most cherished possessions, trading or stealing them from civilized areas. Jívaros are also great bluffers, often allowing victims to believe that all has been resolved through an amiable understanding, then murdering them when they are off-guard.

In actuality, the Jívaros are native to an area much further west, near the Ecuadorian-Peruvian border, which is where most of their people remain. Sometime ago, Ehran was walking in the Jívaro region when some of the Indians encountered him. After feeding and entertaining Ehran, the Jívaros arose and attacked, expecting to take him by surprise. But Ehran had heard of their deceitfulness, and he was prepared. In the battle that followed, he killed eight of their bravest men before the rest of the tribe could retreat.

Unaware of the Jívaros' beliefs concerning vengeance taken by a victim's spirit, Ehran let the bodies of the slain lie for two days while he waited for the tribe to return and claim them. Finally, to end the stench of decomposition, he dug graves and tumbled the bodies into them.

The Jívaros, watching from the forest, interpreted Ehran's actions as a calculated unconcern for the vengeance of the dead. When he failed to sicken and die, they returned and worshiped him as the avatar of some warrior god.

Ehran then sought out half a dozen tribes and commanded them to move east to the rain forest around the plantation. He charged them not to set foot on the plantation, nor to let outsiders enter, unless they came by air. Thus can visitors come and go from the plantation by aircraft, but traveling overland will surely bring down the wrath of the Jívaros upon intruders' heads.

With this knowledge, the gamemaster should be able to play the part of the Jívaro party well. To determine how many Indians are present, roll 3D6. Half of them (round up) carry old shotguns given them long ago by Ehran; the others are armed with bows and arrows. All carry knives. Use the **Tribesman**, p. 48, **Shadowrun**, for these warriors, but limit their gear to that

listed for the Amahuacas, above. Accompanying these warriors is the group's equivalent of a Raven shaman; use the **Shaman**, p. 44, **SR**, and give him the Deceiver spell package.

The shaman will not stick around for the fight, particularly if his side is doing poorly. At the gamemaster's discretion, the shaman might cast spells from a safe distance. If he can keep the the shaman alive, the character can return at the conclusion of this part of the adventure.

If things are going poorly for the runners in this battle, a band of Amahuacas (2D6 warriors) will come to their aid. The Amahuacas have been following the shadowrunners at a distance, watching for just such an occurrence. If the runners have not as yet encountered the Amahuacas, run the encounter given under **Friendly Indians** after this battle is over.

Once the encounter with the Jívaros is done, the shadowrunners can proceed to the plantation.

RUNNING THROUGH THE JUNGLE

It is likely that the runners will have strong fears about traveling through the Amazon jungle. Remember, the Awakening touched everything on the planet, fauna and flora alike, and the Amazon jungle is no exception. There are things down here to make even the most jaded paranaturalist salivate.

Various forms of paranatural lizards and snakes are abundant, most with Awakening-induced cosmetic changes, but some with real power and abilities. Birds of all types abound, most of them with minor, insignificant changes. Don't forget the insects. They're everywhere.

Don't forget plants, either. The Awakening didn't. The obvious ones to use are carnivorous flora such as the Venus Flytrap, but sticky, articulate, heat-sensitive vines can also be fun.

The gamemaster may consult **Paranormal Animals of North America** for ideas on paranatural critters. If he designs his own, the player characters will have no idea what they are up against. It may even be possible to inspire the tiniest bit of real fear in their hearts.

FINAL APPROACH

TELL IT TO THEM STRAIGHT

As the shadowrunners approach Fonte do Sul, read the following:

As you work your way south through the rain forest, you begin to catch glimpses of a lighter area up ahead. Almost without warning, you come to the edge of a clearing approximately a hundred meters square, surrounded by a five-meter-tall chain-link fence.

You're near the northeast corner of the place, looking across an airstrip at what appears to be a hangar building. Parked out front is a Cessna C750. Far to your right stands a veritable mansion, with a greenhouse built onto one end. Farther back on the property you can see a large shed, a barn or stable, and some fenced-off stretches of land.

It's quite a nice setup, if someone doesn't mind spending his days a million kilometers from nowhere.

BEHIND THE SCENES

SCOUTING

If the shadowrunners circle the Fonte do Sul complex to scout it out (and they would be extremely foolish not to), the gamemaster should use the map included in this chapter to describe to the players what they see. Each lettered item on that map is described below.

FONTE DO SOL MAP KEY

Fence (A)

This chain-link fence is five meters tall and carries enough voltage to keep natives from climbing into the complex. If the runners have gloves to insulate their hands, they can climb the fence safely by making an Athletics (2) Test. If a character makes at least one success, he makes it over the fence without mishap. If no successes are rolled, or if bare skin touches the fence, the character takes 5L2 Stun and is disoriented (+4 Target Modifier) for five turns (divided by the number of successes on a Body Resistance Test).

The other way over the fence is to first disrupt its electrical charge, which requires an Electronics (4) Test. The shadowrunners get one complete turn of action for every success scored. After that time, someone comes to investigate the loss of power.

Airstrip (B)

This smooth, grassy stretch of land offers absolutely no concealment to the shadowrunners, should they traverse it. At night, the strip is kept well-lit, not so much in case of incoming aircraft but to hold the darkness of the surrounding rain forest at bay.

Mansion (C)

A huge, three-story building with two wings, the Fonte do Sul mansion houses all the staff of the complex. The entire third floor of the house is kept in waiting for Ehran's occasional visits (about one per month). He is known to the staff as Señor Aquilar, the last member of the Aquilar family. When he does visit, he maintains a Mask spell on himself to shift his features to those of an individual of slightly more Portuguese descent.

If the shadowrunners end up in the mansion for some reason, the gamemaster will have to invent details of the interior floor plan and furnishings. Day or night, there will be scores of servants to run screaming from the player characters and out onto the grounds, which will bring the guards from the hangar rushing to the rescue.

Of special interest in the house is a painting of Ehran that hangs in an upper-floor study. It is the original of the hologram that Ariel has in her room in the **Counterstroke** segment.

Greenhouse (D)

Attached to the mansion's west wing is a rather large greenhouse, used to keep humidity and temperature just right for the Fonte do Sul orchid. The shadowrunners must sneak into this part of the complex to steal a bloom and plant the evidence implicating the Young Elven Technologists.

If the shadowrunners gain access to the greenhouse during daylight hours, there is a fifty-fifty chance that a single gardener will be working inside. Use the **Squatter**, p. 170, **Shadowrun**, for the NPC. The gardener will offer no resistance.

There is, however, something else to consider in the greenhouse: a Barghest (p. 190, **Shadowrun**). To spot the creature sleeping among the larger foliage of the landscaped greenhouse, the observer must make a Perception (Intelligence) Test, with a Target Number 8. One success will allow the viewer to notice something in the flora, two successes will reveal that it is dog-shaped, and three or more successes will identify it, assuming the observer would recognize it.

At that point, the Barghest has a chance of noticing an intruder as well. If it does, or as soon as it is able after being attacked, it will howl. That sound will alert the guards.

Hangar (E)

This hangar was built to keep the plantation's lone plane in service. (Yes, there's only one, the Cessna, which should thrill the runners no end.) The hangar is roomy enough to hold the plane, but the craft is usually left outside on the airstrip in case of emergency.

The hangar has a radar dish built on top to monitor the approach of aircraft and a shortwave radio inside to report any aerial intruders to contacts in Eirunepé, the nearest city.

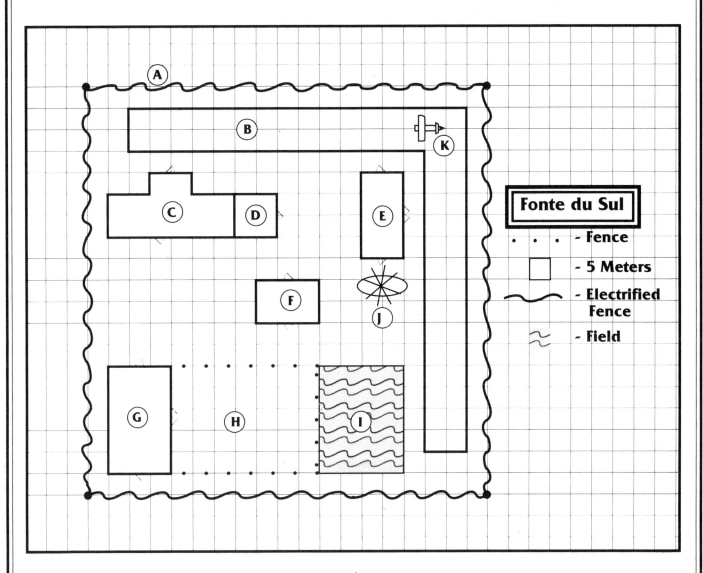

Fonte du Sul

· · · · - Fence

□ - 5 Meters

～～ - Electrified Fence

≈ - Field

When the shadowrunners arrive at the plantation, they will discover that an armed helicopter has landed behind the hangar. A band of six mercs rode the chopper in and have taken up residence back there. (Use the **Merc**, p. 40, **Shadowrun**, but arm each with AK-98 Assault Rifles instead of LMGs.) There is also a rigger for the chopper (Use the **Rigger**, p. 42, **Shadowrun**, but change the skills from Bike 4 and Car 6 to Car 4 and Rotorcraft 6). Like the mercs, the rigger bunks in the hangar.

Work Shed (F)

This building is divided into four rooms, each equipped with tools for a different type of repair or construction work: electrical, mechanical, carpentry, and optical-electronic. During daylight hours, there is a 3 in 6 chance of one person working in the building, with a 1 in 6 chance of a second person as well. At night, the building is usually empty.

Barn/Stable (G)

Kept in this building are a pair of riding horses, two milk cows, 15 hens, and enough food to last all of them for six months. During daylight hours, there is almost always—5 chances in 6—someone working in the barn. At night the chance is reduced to 1 in 6.

Pasture (H)

This is a grassy paddock where the horses and cows are let out for exercise.

Vegetable Field (I)

Year-round sun, modern farming practices, and a little bit of fertilizer keep a wide range of vegetables continually ready for harvest in this field. There is a 2 in 6 chance of one person working in the field at any time during daylight hours.

Hughes WK-2 Stallion (J)

With the number of attacks that have been made on his holdings, Ehran has stepped up security everywhere. To bolster the defenses of Fonte do Sul, he sent a Hughes WK-2 Stallion (p. 141, **Shadowrun**) with six mercs to the plantation. (The mercs and the rigger who flies the craft have set up shop in the hangar.) The chopper is a fully militarized version, with two heavy MGs mounted on its hardpoints and a pair of AK 97s on the firmpoints.

If the shadowrunners have any sense, they will change plans and steal the Stallion instead of the Cessna to make their exit.

Cessna 750 (K)

This aircraft is normally used once a week to fly to Eirunepé for mail and perishable supplies. The runners could make their escape with this craft were it not for the unexpected complication of a helicopter gunship on the plantation to give pursuit.

MAKING THE RUN

After the shadowrunners have scouted out the plantation, they must decide from which side to enter. By day, the most active portions of the complex are the mansion, the greenhouse, the hangar, and the barn. Some sporadic activity occurs around the workshed, and occasionally someone might be seen in the pasture or the field. By night, the airfield and mansion are the most well-lit areas of the complex. Day or night, an eastern infiltration is easiest, as it offers both low visibility and quick access to the greenhouse.

Note that there are no locks on any doors of the plantation's buildings. Other than getting over the fence and the possibility of encountering a staff member, the runners should have no problem getting into the greenhouse, planting their false evidence, snatching an orchid, and getting back out.

This part of the mission, then, should be a snap for the characters. It is the next part that proves unexpectedly difficult.

MAKING THE ESCAPE

As mentioned earlier, when the runners prepare to leave, the Stallion is a better choice than the Cessna because it would prevent the mercs from using the chopper to cut their trip very short. If necessary, the gamemaster can remind the players that even if their Rotorcraft skills are low, the Stallion has an auto-

pilot. It is, of course, theoretically possible for the runners to destroy the chopper and then take the Cessna, but this may mean fighting their way to the Cessna and/or taking fire from the mercs as they try to get the plane into the air.

If the shadowrunners take the Stallion, the mercs will attempt to follow in the Cessna, hoping that the runners cannot manage the chopper's weapons. As soon as the runners open fire, however, the mercs will abandon the chase and return to the airstrip.

OUT OF THE FRYING PAN

At this point, the referee should let the players believe that they are home free. As they begin congratulating themselves, he can spring the next surprise upon them.

While the shadowrunners have been busy invading the plantation, the Jívaro shaman has been busy conjuring a Force 3 Storm Spirit. While the runners are making their escape, the shaman sends the Storm Spirit to intercept their aircraft and prevent their escape.

The first indication that the runners have of the Spirit's presence is when the sky around their aircraft turns unnaturally dark. Immediately thereafter, the craft begins to rock and buck in turbulent winds, and it is a struggle for the autopilot to keep the ship aloft. When the player characters check the windows, they discover that thick clouds obscure vision beyond a few meters, even blocking any view of the ground.

Then there is a blinding flash of lightning—a manifestation of the Spirit's Electrical Projection power—followed by a deafening clap of thunder. Inside the craft, the runners are insulated

from electrical shock, but to their horror, all the instruments go dead, including the autopilot.

This leaves the characters in serious trouble. With the autopilot dead, someone will have to take the controls. Yet, the instruments are out so they will be flying blind in every sense of the word. This is a manifestation of the Spirit's Confusion power.

A magician will recognize the nature of the Storm Spirit immediately. He can attempt to banish the Spirit, but during that battle, the aircraft remains engulfed in clouds and the instruments remain inoperative.

Unless the Storm Spirit is busy resisting a magician's banishing attempt, it next begins to turn its power of projecting Fear onto its victims. The gamemaster secretly makes an Opposed Willpower Test against the Spirit's Force Rating for each player character. The net number of successes for the Spirit should set the amount of fear imposed. If the pilot has not succumbed to Fear, the referee should make a secret roll versus that character's Piloting Skill, but regardless of the result, the gamemaster should just shake his head and wince.

Weapons can be used against the Spirit, but they should follow the rules for such combat given on p. 75, **The Grimoire: 2050**, the sourcebook of magic in the **Shadowrun** game system. Remember also that the chopper is a manufactured, technological item and so has a Resistance Rating of 7, as per the table and rules on p. 81, **Shadowrun**.

It will be tough, but the runners should be able to defeat the Spirit, especially if a magician is present. When they do, the autopilot can "miraculously" begin working again if the characters are really in hot water when it comes to controlling the aircraft. Or, perhaps, someone can make an Electronics B/R Test.

If the craft crashes, the runners are down in the jungle, possibly hurt, and with a Storm Spirit who can now do little more than rain on them once they are out of his Domain and into the jungle. At this point, the possibilities are endless and the gamemaster is encouraged to go wild.

WE GOTTA GET OUTTA THIS PLACE

Depending on the gamemaster's mood, the flight from the plantation to Lima, Peru, could be either smooth as silk or a hell ride. Are the runners cautious? Do they fly low to avoid detection, or are they typically foolish as they try to buzz the locals? Ehran has, shall we say, special dispensations for his internal combustion vehicles, but stupidity is stupidty.

Helms has already arranged the team's travel from Lima to Seattle, but that does not mean the runners can't sweat a little.

Then, when they finally do return to Seattle, Helms tells them to hold onto the flower and to stand by for further contact from another Mr. Johnson.

KARMA

GROUP KARMA

For surviving the adventure	1 pt
For achieving the mission goals	3 pts
For causing no casualties on the plantation	1 pt

INDIVIDUAL KARMA

Per the normal **Shadowrun** rules.

FUTURE

*"The future's uncertain, but
the end is always near."*
—Jim Morrison

INTRODUCTION

In this section, the shadowrunners are hired to travel to Columbia, Missouri and kidnap a certain Jane Foster. Jane, unbeknownst to the runners, is the subject of the deleted bio-medical/genealogy record at Sylvan Information in the **Physical** segment. She is Ehran's daughter.

Jane does not know who her parents were, much less that she is Ehran's daughter. She's barely even heard of Ehran. What she does know is that someone tried to kidnap her.

It wasn't the runners, for they haven't even arrived in Columbia yet. Who then? Well, Ehran, fearing Harlequin's *chal'han* had gone too far, dispatched a team of his employees (read "thugs") to grab Jane and hide her away safely. Unfortunately, the thugs blew it and Jane's gone into hiding.

Her protection is a wizzer gang known as the Pretenders. Should be a hot time in the old town tonight.

MISSOURI BOUND

TELL IT TO THEM STRAIGHT

You are blissfully sleeping away the effects of last night's encounter with one too many Green Neon Fizzes, when the phone starts chirping in your ear. Like a persistent cricket, it begins to bore a hole in your brain until answering it is the only way to save your sanity. Without a word of greeting, the man on the other end plunges right in. "You have the flower? That is very good. Mr. Johnson would like to meet with you for one more run. Be at the Tacoma Style tonight, eight sharp. I know I don't have to remind you to leave the heavy toys at home. By the way, there's a strict dress code. Don't make me come to you. The results would be most unpleasant. And bring the flower. You will be needing it."

You stare at the ceiling as the line goes dead. It looks like you're in this one whether you want to be or not.

Fourteen hours later, you ease over to the curb and park your vehicles in front of the Style, one of Tacoma's trendiest restaurants. You check your watch and discover you still have ten minutes to the meet. Heading for the door, you straighten your jacket and run a hand through your hair. Once through the reinforced door, you see Betty, the Style's head doorman, or doorwoman, or doortroll, whatever you want to call her. She never stops grinning as she pats you down for hidden weapons. This is obviously her idea of a good time.

Once cleared, the interior door opens to let you in to the Style. You walk down a clean white hallway to the maitre d' stand at the other end. A tuxedo-clad Elf smiles politely. "You are with Mr. Johnson? Come this way. "

Without looking back, he leads you though the elegant dining room to a table near the window. He pulls back the chairs and assists you in sitting. "Mr. Johnson will arrive shortly. He has taken the liberty of ordering for you. Appetizers will be served shortly." He smiles, perhaps sympathetically, and turns to leave.

You are halfway through the salad when Mr. Johnson arrives. He slides quickly into his chair, opening his napkin with a snap. "Gentlemen, forgive the delay. Please continue with the fine repast while I outline your run." One thing about Mr. Johnson, he takes a lot for granted.

"You will be going to a small town called Columbia, in the state of Missouri. It is in the western section of the UCAS. While you are there, you will retrieve Ms. Jane Foster, a wayward corporate secretary who works for a small software firm called CommTech. You are to leave the flower you now possess at Ms. Foster's apartment. That is critical, but I understand that you have some experience in dealing with such unusual circumstances. Ms. Foster will accompany you back to Seattle. You will take public transportation to Columbia and return by private jet. Call this number when you are ready to return with the goods. The transport will be ready at Columbia's airport within 30 minutes."

Mr. Johnson slides a sheet of paper across the table. On it is Jane Foster's address in Columbia. "I will pay ¥70,000 nuyen upon Ms. Foster's safe return to Seattle. Is everything understood? I trust so. Now, if you will excuse me? I'm afraid I must be off. Here is a small advance. You will find ¥10,000 nuyen on each of these certified credsticks. You are booked on the twelve-oh-five Delta flight to Kansas City, where you will catch a small commuter to the Columbia Airport. The travel voucher is on the credstick. Enjoy the meal, with my compliments."

Mr. Johnson stands up abruptly and heads for the door. You suddenly realize he didn't give you a chance to utter a single peep.

Read to players upon arrival:

You step out of the Cessna, cramped and sore from the 90-minute flight. You stretch your limbs as you gaze across the lighted tarmac to the terminal. To the east, you can just see the beginnings of the dawn. Several members of the maintenance crew mill about the plane and its attendant service truck. Your baggage is dropped next to you as you wait by the plane. No baggage check for this flight. Gear in hand, you head for the terminal. Once inside, you scan the nearly deserted terminal. There are three rental car companies represented along the far wall. Choosing one at random, you approach a dozing attendant. You rap the counter and startle her from her sleep. Blushing, she asks if she can be of assistance. It's not much surprise to learn that the selection is not that good. Cars and bikes come in all the basic shapes and sizes, but none of them would announce your presence with real authority. You finally select your vehicle and slot your credstick. The clerk directs you to a small parking lot to the side of the terminal building, where your transport awaits, fully gassed and ready to go. Pulling out of the parking lot, you head for Highway 63, which runs north to Columbia and south to Jefferson City. North you go, as sun crests the wooded hills on your right. You begin to make plans for getting your hands on this corporate secretary Mr. Johnson wants so bad.

BEHIND THE SCENES

By now the team should realize they are in this run for the long haul. Swept up in events beyond their control (at least for the moment), they should see that the safest path is the one of least resistance, namely going to Columbia. The team doesn't have a lot of free will in this matter, but they will get the chance to do more later. The Tacoma Style is a fashionable restaurant and bar that does not permit patrons to enter with any type of weapons. Light handguns are, of course, allowed for personal protection.

The Style also has a strict dress code. Team members will discover that Betty, the bouncer, will not allow anyone to enter if they are dirty, too casually dressed, or too outrageously dressed. Making a fashion statement is one thing, but this is a somewhat conservative, corporate hangout. The team will automatically know this if they have worked in Tacoma before. Those that do not make the grade can wait outside. The team should know better than to start a fight, but if they attack Mr. Johnson or Betty, they will be rushed by the waiters of the Style. The maitre d' will hit the PANICBUTTON and half a dozen Lone Star officers will arrive soon after.

Mr. Johnson will suffer no interruptions during his speech. He will state the facts and attempt to leave as quickly as possible. He will not bargain with the team over any matters concerning the run. If the team resists or seems hesitant, he will remind them of any unfortunate situations stemming from previous runs. After the excellent dinner (last supper?), the team has just enough time to head back to their homes to pick up any gear they might be able to stow away on the plane. Hopefully, they will not try anything too stupid. Once at the airport, the team can proceed directly to the gate. (See **Getting There by Air,** p. 144.)

After a short wait, they will board and head for Kansas City, from there, transferring to a Cessna C750 commuter plane to Columbia.

For Betty the Bouncer, use the **Troll Bouncer,** p. 173, **Shadowrun**. Raise her Quickness to 5, Reaction to 3, and Armed Combat to 6. Add a sap, Armored Vest, and Trés Chic clothing.

For the maitre d', use the **Elven Hitman,** p. 166, **Shadowrun**. Lower his Firearms to 5. Add a Beretta 101T Smartgun with Silencer and Armored Tuxedo.

For the 12 waiters, use the **Bartender,** p. 163, **Shadowrun**. Give them Armored Tuxedos as well.

Lastly, Mr. Johnson uses, well, **Mr. Johnson,** p. 170, **Shadowrun.** Add an Armor Jacket and a Fichetti Security 500.

By now the team may be a little upset with their employer. If they are hesitant to take the job, conspire against them. The best way would be to force them out of town. If the team plans to miss the meeting in Tacoma, one of the runners gets an urgent message from a trusted contact. Somebody has put out a ¥150,000 nuyen bounty on each of the runners, and every street punk in the city is after their hides. "You'd best find a place to chill, chummer, or you'll be cold meat."

Make sure the team is hounded, no matter what they do or where they go. It's O.K. to herd them to the Style for the meeting with Mr. Johnson. If the team is still persistent, kidnap them. When they awake, they are in the Cessna, approaching Columbia Regional Airport. Harlequin certainly has the power to track them down and the muscle to overpower them. He wants to finish the ritual, however, so don't let the team get into a firefight with Harlequin's men. Just take them out and go to the adventure section entitled **Present**. Have another team bring Jane Foster in, and place the appropriate spin on Harlequin's attitude toward the runners.

During this segment, the runners may attract unwanted attention by involving themselves in certain situations. These situations are signaled in the text, and the gamemaster will keep track of the team's performance. If they do attract the wrong kind of notice, the gamemaster secretly assigns a "mark" against them. At some point, too many such marks will have consequences. More information occurs in the respective sections below.

WHEN THE RUNNERS ARRIVE

Allow the team to rent whatever type of vehicle they want. The cost will be 1 percent of the vehicle's purchase price per day of rental. That will include mileage, gas, and insurance on the car. A return date is mandatory, as is payment in advance. Failure to return the car by the specified date results in a warrant being issued for the runners' arrest on charges of grand theft. The car is completely insured, though the runners may not realize this. Even if they destroy the car, they are charged only the 1 percent per day.

Highway 63 leads north into the city of Columbia. At this early hour, traffic is sparse. From here, the team can head in several different directions. If they want to check out CommTech, go to **Techies,** p. 112. If they want to hit the streets looking for some information, head for **Columbia Boulevards,** p. 119. Finally, if the team wants to investigate Ms. Foster's apartment, go to **Downtown Flat,** the next section.

DOWNTOWN FLAT

TELL IT TO THEM STRAIGHT

The sign on the door says "Foster," so you must be in the right place. You are standing on Ninth Street, half a block from Broadway, in the heart of the Columbia downtown. Ancient brick buildings line both sides of the street. The tallest of these structures reaches only eight or nine stories, reminding you once again that Columbia is a truly small town. You open the heavy door and discover it leads to a set of stairs. The stairway light is burnt out, but you can still make your way up the single steep flight to the third floor of the building.

If your sense of direction is accurate, you are directly above an accountant's office, which is, in turn, above a dress shop. Both of these businesses, however, have their main doors on Broadway, the city's main east-west thoroughfare.

At the top of the stairs is a small landing and a short hallway leading to a pair of doors. The first door appears to open into a storage closet. It has a heavily reinforced door with an industrial maglock. A beaten and abused thumbprint scanner rests over the lock. The other door looks made of reinforced wood and also opens with a thumbprint scanner. A single peephole is set at eye level.

Though it is not obvious at first glance, the door is unlocked and slightly ajar. It appears as though the maglock was poorly bypassed, fusing the mechanism into so much slag. It looks like the calling card of an amateur thief. Cautiously pushing the door open, you step into what turns out to be a beautiful apartment. You enter the living room and close the door behind you. The room is tastefully furnished and contains several pieces of expensive Navaho pottery, and the walls are hung with fine paintings and etchings. The remains of one of the pots is scattered around the floor in front of the door, along with a good deal of blood. You fan out and begin to search the adjoining rooms.

BEHIND THE SCENES

When Ehran's team caught up with Jane, they almost had her out the door when she slipped from Sunny's grasp and clobbered Victor with her most expensive piece of pottery. She managed to get away, mostly through luck, and has not returned since.

If the team makes a careful search of the apartment, they will discover the following pieces of information. Each runner must make a successful Perception (4) Test when in the appropriate room to receive the listed information. Information listed at lower success levels should also be given for higher levels of success.

KITCHEN

0 Successes	Mostly stocked with soy, the kitchen has a few expensive items of real food. The cookware is functional, but nothing special. Jane must eat out a lot.
1+ Successes	A payroll stub from CommTech, Inc. lies on top of a blank note pad. The corp's address is listed on the check.

LIVING ROOM

0 Successes	The broken piece of pottery was used as a weapon of some sort. It must have been a truly beautiful piece of work.
1 Success	The amount of blood on the carpet indicates that the wound caused by the broken pot must have been painful, but was probably not fatal.
2+ Successes	Somebody got pushed into an unfinished oil painting near the front door. A small hand smeared the paint before pushing though the thin canvas. The painting is on the opposite side of the door from the bloodstains, leading you to believe Jane was facing two opponents.

BEDROOM

0 Successes	It looks like Jane was sleeping when her attackers came. The bed is unmade and a corporate suit lies on a valet next to the dresser.
1 Success	The attackers allowed Jane to dress quickly. Her nightgown is in the corner, and a drawer holding several heavy sweaters and pairs of jeans is open.
2+ Successes	Next to the dresser is a small disposable lighter with the words "B. K. Lounge" etched into the side. The lighter is almost full.

BATHROOM

1 Success	The room is small, but functional. It was obviously used in haste several nights ago. The room is messy, with several open cosmetic bottles and an unidentifiable jar lining the counter.
2 + Successes	The mirror is heavily smudged with finger prints that form a kind of pattern. (If the runner's steam the mirror, these words appear: "HELP GET PRETENDERS." Jane wrote this note when allowed to use the bathroom prior to leaving the apartment.)

Because Ehran's team does not think Jane will be stupid enough to return to her home, they have decided to forget about watching it. As Jane will, indeed, stay away until the heat dies down, the team will not pick up any additional points for unwanted attention in this chapter. Once the team is done looking through the apartment, they can continue the search by going to CommTech in **Techies**, p. 112, or they can wait until this evening to look for Jane at the B. K. Lounge in **You Call This A Party?**, p. 113. If the team wants to gather more information on the street, they can go to **Columbia Boulevards**, p. 119.

At this point, the possibility exists that the runners will use magic in their investigation. There are certainly enough of Jane's personal effects around to search her out using Ritual Sorcery. If any runner tries it, he will find that he cannot track Jane Foster. A successful Magical Theory (8) Test will reveal to the magician attempting the Ritual Sorcery that something has been done to conceal her, something powerful enough to obscure the path to her.

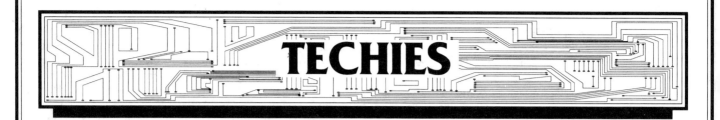

TECHIES

TELL IT TO THEM STRAIGHT

You wheel up to the circlular drive of CommTech, which is located on the outskirts of Columbia. The facility sits on a half-dozen wooded acres, well back from the road. Though you are initially surprised to discover no fence around the compound, you remember that this area of the country is safer than Seattle. You pull into a visitor's parking space, directly in front of the building's main doors, and stroll inside.

The interior atrium is spacious, but bare. Doors lead further into the building to your left and right, and an ugly concrete and steel stairway stands next to the elevator directly in front of you. To your immediate left is a receptionist area, with a single smiling blonde behind a massive wraparound counter. Though she has a clear view of the door, she seems dwarfed by the size of her work area. As you approach, her smile widens even more.

"Can I help you?" she says.

You almost believe that she means it. You ask to see Jane Foster, deciding on the spur of the moment to take the direct approach. The receptionist's smile never wavers. "I'm sorry, but she is not in today. Could someone else be of assistance?" She continues to smile up at you. You are beginning to believe she does want to help. "Her boss, Mr. Rehndig, is available." That sounds good to you.

She motions you over to a padded chair, then keys the phone system. Within moments, a tall man in jeans, boots, cowboy shirt, and a string tie comes bounding down the steps. "Howdy, gentlemen. Name's Josh." He stretches out a hand in turn to every member of the team. "I understand you were asking about Janey. Maybe we could talk for a moment."

Without waiting for a response, he ushers you through the right-hand door, down a short hallway, and into a small conference room. Josh asks you to sit down, then does the same. "Now, fellows, do you have any idea where my secretary is?"

BEHIND THE SCENES

Josh Rehndig has been the senior software vice president of CommTech for the past five years. He has been very successful, increasing the firm's profits and generally making a name for the small company in the UCAS market. His relaxed style of management has made him a hit with his peers and employees for his entire career, but make no mistake. Josh has never missed a deadline, and he has never failed to take appropriate action, no matter what the situation. His tenure at CommTech has been nothing short of remarkable.

Josh hired Jane (or Janey as he calls her) after his last secretary mysteriously vanished. The former employee was never heard from again. Though no one ever learned the cause of her disappearance, Josh blames himself for her seeming demise.

Now that Janey is missing, he is beside himself. He barely knows her, but dreads to think something terrible has happened to her, too.

There is actually no connection between the two disappearances. Josh's first secretary eloped to St. Louis with a member of that city's championship UrbanBrawl squad.

Josh is not very well-informed about Jane. If the team convinces him that they are here to find and assist Jane, he will help them in any way he can. To see if the team can fool him, have one of the team members make an Opposed Charisma Test against Josh's Intelligence. Josh will answer two questions per success. If the team does not score any successes, Josh clams up and offers only vague references to Janey. He will not provide any useful information to the team. If the team can get Josh to talk, he knows that Janey lives in the city and he can provide her address, though he is not sure where the address is located. He knows that Janey likes music and that she frequents one of the clubs in town, but he is not sure which. He also knows that she hangs with a pretty tough crowd. It is some type of bar gang, or biker gang, but again, he doesn't know the name of the gang.

Josh will assure the team that Janey is not working on anything that could get her in trouble. She doesn't even have headware memory, he points out. Though she occasionally handles some industry-specific information, most of it detailing market research or sales figures, it was never anything that would make it worth stealing his secretary.

If asked, Josh will blame the biker gang for Jane's disappearance. If the team is having trouble, the gamemaster can use Josh to keep the players on line and provide them with clues or additional information. Josh will ask the team to get in touch with him when they know something concrete about Janey. If the team calls again, Josh may be able to give them more clues. No matter what the results, going to CommTech gives the team one mark for unwanted attention. If it gives the team four marks, go to **Company Is Coming**, p. 115. If the team wants to look for information on the streets, go to **Columbia Boulevards**, p. 119. If the team knows where to find Janey, and they want to check out her apartment, go to **Downtown Flat**, p. 110.

For Josh Rehndig, use the **Company Man**, p. 164, **Shadowrun**. For his receptionist, use the **Corporate Secretary**, p. 165, **Shadowrun**.

YOU CALL THIS A PARTY?

TELL IT TO THEM STRAIGHT

After some diligent work on the streets, you finally come up with the name of the place Jane Foster is said to favor: B.K.'s Lounge and Danceateria." On the corner of Stadium and Broadway, the Lounge commands the city's best location. B.K., whoever he is, seems to have made the most of it. A glittering sign is clearly visible from a kilometer away, and the twin spotlights out front cut through the night with megawatts of halogen sunshine. To the right of the lounge is a small helipad, which sees near-constant use. You shake your head sadly. So this is what passes for nightlife out in the boondocks.

You pass between rows of milling patrons and head for the door. It isn't even midnight and the front of the place is packed. You open the heavy wooden door and a barrage of sound assaults you as you walk toward the bouncer's stand. Two Human bouncers ask for your credstick and point to the sign on the wall. "Twenty-nuyen cover charge." One of them slots your stick and you amble through the archway into B.K.'s. Early American tacky.

That's your first thought as you look around. The bar is a strange mixture of cheap dive and high-class tavern. Rough wooden floors and cheap tables line the walls under plexiglass-framed works of art. On the far wall is a row of black and white air brush canvases depicting famous trideo stars of the last century. You head for the bar, where a single man serves kamikazes to a score of waiting clients. You have to wait almost ten minutes before you can even get to the rail. You hand him your credstick as he begins to make you a 'kazee. Evidentally that is the only drink they serve around here. You ask about Frosty as he hands you several plastic cups. Shaking his head slowly, the bartender says, "Try the Pretenders by the back bar. I think they're friends. That's five nuyen apiece for the drinks." You stare doubtfully at the two fingers of pale liquid in the bottom of the cup as you hand over your credstick.

You head around the massive, speaker-lined dance floor. B.K. has obviously spared no expense on the sound. The system here, currently cranking out an ancient blues tune, is as good as any you've seen in your normal haunts. In the middle of the floor, three dozen mirror-shaded punks are lying on the floor, in the blues position. You have heard of the so-called dance, but this is the first time you have seen it performed. The object is to remain as still as possible while lying on the dance floor, assaulted by a wall of screaming sound. These dancers must have had a lot of practice.

You head for a group of similarly clad people in the corner. They all wear faded leather jackets bearing the logo, "The Pretenders." A tall, bearded man turns at your approach. The conversation stops as you draw near. When you explain that you are looking for Frosty, the bearded man smiles. "So, you're the ones. Hey, boys, these dudes are still looking for Frosty. What's

wrong? Didn't find what you were looking for when you busted into her place the first time? Well, the Pretenders take care of their own, and Frosty's with us." Without another word, the man lashes magical power out at the nearest runner, signaling the rest of his gang to attack.

BEHIND THE SCENES

The B.K. Lounge, as it is sometimes known, is the hottest spot in Columbia. Sooner or later, everybody that is anybody will show up. The booze is cheap, the sound is wiz, and the decor allows for a little rough and tumble. Columbia is a peaceful enough town that bar owners don't usually need Trolls to man the doors or to check for weapons. That being the case, the runners could easily get into the Lounge with some heavy gear. Allow the two doormen a Perception Test versus the Concealability of the weapons. If they spot the weapon, they may be slightly surprised and ask that it be checked. The runner will receive a token for the gear checked in. He can collect it later in the evening, provided he is still able.

When the runners enter the bar, they will be directed to the Pretenders, a small go-gang that runs the 46-kilometer stretch of Highway 63 between Columbia and Jefferson City. The Pretenders are the gang that initially helped Frosty escape from Ehran's recovery team. They are concerned about her safety, and will do what they think is necessary to discourage further pursuit. Because they did not get a good look at Ehran's team, they believe the runners are attempting to find Frosty through them. In the course of the brawl, the gamemaster should warn the team about pulling guns. Columbia has its share of crime, but the problem is not nearly as bad as in Seattle or other large cities. Fights are usually limited to hands and blades, though many people carry handguns for desperate situations. The Pretenders will not pull guns unless shot at first. If a runner pulls an automatic weapon, he will become the immediate target of all the Pretenders. Likewise, the staff of the Lounge will target that runner first. Once the fight starts, the runners will have five turns before bouncers arrive. These individuals will attack whoever is nearer. If the bouncers are at the same distance from both the runners and the gangers, they will go for the runners. The team is, after all, new to the area. The remainder of the patrons will remain clear of the fight, unless given no other choice. Fights are so common in this place that no one will call the police unless someone draws a gun. By the time the boys in blue get to the Lounge, however, the team should be long gone.

If the team is still standing when the smoke and dust clear, they can interrogate any of the Pretenders. Despite being beaten, the gangers still want to look after Frosty and they will not talk unless the runners can break them. Make a Resisted Interrogation Test versus the Pretender questioned. The team will have the opportunity to make two checks before the police arrive through the front door. Higher levels of success will reveal the information listed for fewer successes.

Successes	Result
1	"Yeah, we helped get her underground. After the break-in, it seemed like the best thing to do. I haven't seen her in two days."
2 – 3	"We stashed her at our place for a couple of nights, but somebody came sniffin' around. A couple of the boys moved her last night. As far as I know, they're still there lookin' after her. No, I don't know where."
4+	"All right, already. She's at the St. James Home for Wayward Women. It's on Ash Street. Now will you let go of my arm?"

Having a fight in the bar is enough to earn the team one mark for unwanted attention. If they get the information about the St. James' Home, they earn another mark. Once the team has the information they came for, head for **Sisters of Mercy**, p. 116. If the team has called enough attention to itself, however, by earning a total of four marks, first go to **Company Is Coming**, the next section.

THE PRETENDERS

The Pretenders enjoy some notoriety in the Columbia-Jeff City area. There are not, however, nearly as tough as their reputation. They spend a lot of time being seen in all the right places and they have the talk down pat, but a determined team could take them. The members at the bar represent only a portion of the gang's total strength, though probably the best the gang has to offer.

The Great Pretender is the leader of the gang, and his word is law to the other members. He has a secret crush on Frosty, and will do anything to help her out. Use the **Combat Mage** p. 98, from **Sprawl Sites,** removing all but his combat magic and reducing the Force of those spells by 50 percent. Also remove his spell locks and various foci. Instead of the SMG, he carries a Colt L36 in an ankle holster.

Rico is the Great Pretender's most trusted lieutenant. Having known him so long, she suspects his feelings for Frosty. When the team arrives with questions, she will be ready for her leader's response, striking at the same time he does. Use the **Street Mage**, p. 45, **Shadowrun**. Add an Armor Vest and a Walther Palm Pistol.

The other members of the gang are just here for a good time. They will follow their leader without question, jumping into the fight at the first opportunity. They are not really killers, however, so the team will have an edge on them in the fight. Use the **Wiz Kid Gang Member**, p. 121, **Sprawl Sites**. Remove all cyberware.

LOUNGE PERSONNEL

As to the Lounge bouncers and doormen, these boys are big-time in this area, but out of their league when it comes to a team from the big city. They will try to stop the fight and halt property damage as much as possible. Use the **Bartender**, p. 163, **Shadowrun**. Remove both Special Skills. Add Armor Clothing.

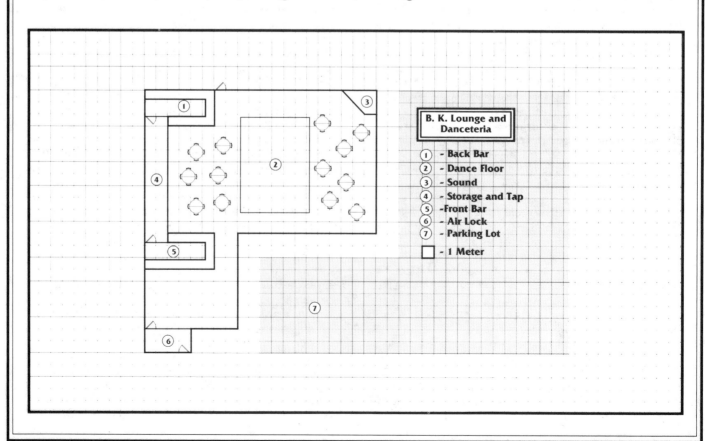

B. K. Lounge and Danceteria

① - Back Bar
② - Dance Floor
③ - Sound
④ - Storage and Tap
⑤ - Front Bar
⑥ - Air Lock
⑦ - Parking Lot
☐ - 1 Meter

COMPANY IS COMING

TELL IT TO THEM STRAIGHT

You pull over to the curb and check the streets. The coast is clear, so you begin your approach. Suddenly, a Westwind 2000 appears over a small rise in the road. The driver slams on the brakes and sends the car into a four-wheel drift in your direction. The 2000 slides to a stop, crunching your vehicles into the curb, then the car's far doors pop open. Out pile a group of toughs, weapons primed and ready. It looks like negotiation is not on their agenda.

BEHIND THE SCENES

Ehran's original team has finally caught up with the runners. This encounter occurs when the team has accumulated four marks for unwanted attention. Once they have called enough attention to themselves, the goons move in. The four members of Ehran's team attempted to grab Frosty three days ago. Not only did they fail to get her, but they forced her underground. They have been looking for her ever since. Ehran's group discovered the team was looking for Frosty and correctly deduced it was the same group Ehran had warned them about. Because of the runners' arrival, Ehran's people have had to split their time between the search for Frosty and the search for the runners. If they can't get to Frosty, they can at least halt the other team that is after her. When the car crests the hill, have each runner make a Quickness (6) Test. Each success allows the runner one action before the car stops and the doors open. That time can be used to seek cover, start a spell, or draw weapons. Team members can shoot at the car itself, but the occupants are protected until the actual start of combat.

At the time of the ambush, the street is deserted. The runners will be able to find some cover, but nothing heavier than a dumpster or brick wall. Because this encounter occurs at a random point in the adventure, the gamemaster should choose an appropriate place for the encounter, unless it occurs immediately prior to another section. Good times to run this encounter might be when the team exit's B.K.'s Lounge, for example, or when they approach the St. James Home.

Ehran's guns will come in firing. They are not concerned about the rented car and they are more than a little desperate. They will lead with their best weapons and follow up with whatever else they have. Most of all, they do not want to fail. If the team tries to get away, they will give chase, either in the car or on foot. Whatever the outcome, the guns will fight to the end. They will not try to get away, even if reduced to one member. Though motivated, they are not that experienced at shadowrunning.

Once the team has dealt with Ehran's hired muscle, they should continue on with their original plan. Go to the next section as appropriate.

There is, however, a short avenue of investigation that the runners might pursue with the hired muscle. Banger is the only one who knows the connection to Ehran the Scribe. The others work for Banger. All Banger knows is that Ehran instructed him to find Jane Foster, grab her, and take her to a safe location that Ehran would relay to him once she'd been found. That's all he knows.

Ehran's muscle is staying at a small Nights Inn on the edge of town. In their room is a small datachip containing a full, detailed file on Jane Foster. If a runner familiar with the medical/genealogy file found in the Sylvan Technologies system in the adventure entitled **Physical** examines the Foster file, there is a chance he will notice a connection. He makes one of the following tests: Biology (Genetics) (12), Perception (15), or an appropriate Special Skill (gamemaster sets the target) Test.

Success will link Jane Foster to the deleted entry in the biomedical data extract.

EHRAN'S GUNS

Ehran threw this team together at the last moment to retrieve his daughter. Though he wanted to send people with more experience, the chaos caused by Harlequin has made that impossible. The team takes their responsibility seriously enough, but they are in way over their heads.

Banger is the leader. He is intelligent, but this is his first command and he has made some serious tactical errors. Frustrated, he has decided to push the issue with the runners by using brute force. Use the **Former Company Man**, p. 37, **Shadowrun**.

Anastasia (Ana) has had just about enough of Banger and this whole mission. She considers him a moron and the whole UCAS a backward pit of drek. She will fight with real fury, seeing the runners' team as one more thing that has gone wrong. Use the **Street Mage**, p. 45, **Shadowrun**. For spells, use the Combat orientation, but add Detect Enemies 3 and Chaos 4. Also add an Armor Vest with Plates.

Victor Vee is content to let the other members of the team do the arguing and talking. All he wants to do is fight. The tougher the better. He considers the runners to be potentially worthy opponents. Use the **Ork Mercenary**, p. 41, **Shadowrun**. Replace his AK-97 with a T-250 Shotgun and a Ruger Super Warhawk. He has a Mild Allergy to Plastic.

This is Sunny's first shadowrun and it shows. A hot-shot driver, she is not good for much else. It was her mistake that let Frosty get away in the first place. Since then, she has been trying to get back in Banger's good graces, but without much success. Use the **Mechanic**, p. 168, **Shadowrun**, but replace all B/R skills with Car 6, Firearms 2, an Unarmed Combat 2. Add an Armor Jacket and Ares Slivergun.

SISTERS OF MERCY

TELL IT TO THEM STRAIGHT

You head up the walk to the porch of an old wooden home. Despite a fresh coat of paint, the building has obviously seen a lot of winters. You bound up the steps and knock on the front door. Through the side window, you see a small face peep under the shade, then hear the door bolt being thrown back. The door opens to reveal an older woman dressed in sweat pants, a Columbia College tee-shirt, and a faded pair of running shoes.

"Good day. I am Sister Ann. How can I help you?" She has the quiet strength of someone who has seen and done many things in her life.

You hesitate for a moment, then say, "Excuse us, sister. We're looking for Jane Foster." Suddenly, the nun screams, "Beat it, Janey, they're here!" You're not sure what you were expecting, but this was not it. Behind the nun, you can see several women running for the back of the house. Sister Ann glares up at you, daring you to do something.

BEHIND THE SCENES

Sister Ann is no sister. She is a hardened criminal who fronts for the Flames, an all-girl gang that works the downtown area of Columbia. She took over the St. James Home under false pretenses. Since then, she has used the aging house as a base of operation. Though the home does good works on the side, it is used primarily as a halfway house for women returning to life on the streets after a stint in the state correctional institute for women. Sister Ann selects prospects with appropriate skills and uses them to rob businesses and homes in the city. Because Jane is not part of her organization, and because Ann was sure nobody would come looking for her, the team's question surprises her. That and the fact that Jane is in the room right behind her make the woman panic. If the team tries to force its way inside, Ann will call for assistance from the other resident girls. If the team rounds the house, they can catch Jane jumping off the back porch. She is trailed by the two members of the Pretenders.

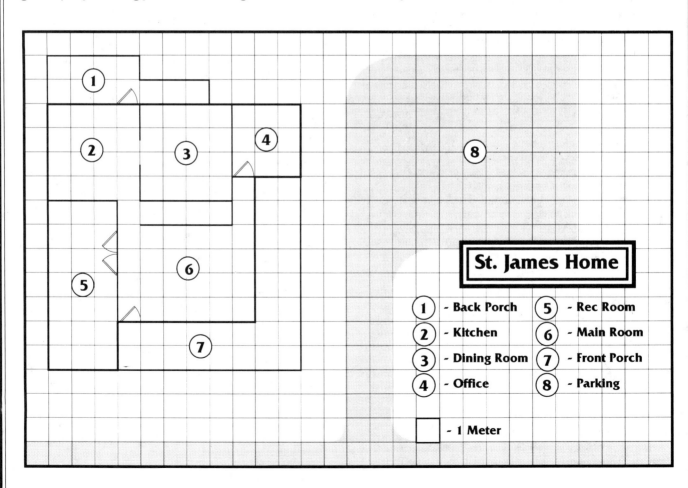

St. James Home

1 - Back Porch   5 - Rec Room
2 - Kitchen   6 - Main Room
3 - Dining Room   7 - Front Porch
4 - Office   8 - Parking

☐ - 1 Meter

As long as the team does not enter the building, Sister Ann will stay out of the fray. She feels sorry for Jane, but will not put her operation at risk. If the team enters the building, however, she has no choice.

Wherever the team catches Jane, the two Pretenders will fight the player characters while Jane attempts to escape. They will do their best, but they are under-armed. Their defense may buy a little time, but it is unlikely to be as much as Jane needs to get away. The Pretenders will lead with their best weapons and fight until they are subdued or suffer serious wounds.

If the team enters the St. James Home, the defenders will use whatever is available to attack the runners, while the other members gather weapons.

The Flames are currently going about their daily business. If the team enters late at night, some will be in bed asleep. At any time, some of the gang members will be out of the house on business. They will work as a team, supporting each other as much as possible.

If Ann is threatened or captured, they will surrender Jane and themselves if the runners will guarantee Ann's release. Once the team has captured Jane, go to the final section, **Later, Dude**, p. 118.

THE FLAMES

The Flames are beginning to make a name for themselves, but as yet, their most daring and successful robberies have not been connected. If they continue to be successful, however, they will have the money to become a force in the city.

Sister Ann is in her early forties, but the years have been kind to her. She can still turn a man's head, and often does. Despite the profits from her current operation, she is beginning to feel restless and a little nervous. Playing the part of a nun is definitely not in character. She knows it is only a matter of time before the church discovers her operation and reveals she is not really Sister Ann. Use the **Fixer**, p. 167, **Shadowrun**, but remove all cyberware. Add a Browning High-Power (hidden in the kitchen).

The nine Flames will move to protect their boss, but they will not put her in any danger. If the team manages to neutralize Ann, the rest will surrender. The Flames are thieves by nature, and though armed, they are not very good killers. Use the **Street Cop**, p. 171, **Shadowrun**, but remove Special Skill and add a Knife and an L36 Pistol.

The two Pretenders here, both women, are Jane's friends and they will attempt to protect her. Though initially surprised by the team's arrival, they recover quickly and do what they can to get her away. Use the **Corporate Security Guard**, p. 165, **Shadowrun**, but raise their Unarmed Combat to 5. Also add Ares Light-Fire Pistols and Armor Clothing.

If Frosty somehow manages to get away, the team should be able to catch up with her quickly. She will most likely be barefoot, and does not have the means to stay hidden. Most of her clothes and other possessions are in her room upstairs. If the team loses sight of her, or the fight with the Pretenders proves tougher than anticipated, the runners will more than likely sight Frosty again within one or two hours (depending on how long you want them to sweat). She will not be able to put up much resistance.

LATER, DUDE

TELL IT TO THEM STRAIGHT

You hustle Frosty back to your waiting vehicles. She seems tired and out of it, as though the last few days have been too much for her. She isn't used to this type of life, but then, who is? She will not talk to you or follow your spoken commands, but lets herself be led.

You make the call to your unnamed SIN en route to the Columbia airport. The male voice on the other end answers quickly. Once you identify yourself, he breaks in quickly and tells you to head for the private plane terminal to the left of the main terminal. He hangs up before you can say another word.

You head down 63 and within minutes are back at the terminal. This time, however, you pull over to the entrance marked for private flights. You usher Frosty onto the tarmac and toward a waiting Lear Platinum.

At the bottom of the Lear's steps waits a young woman with a portable computer. As you hustle Frosty on board, she asks for the keys to the rental car, seemingly oblivious to the proceedings around her. The engines on the plane begin to warm up as she retrieves the keys and hands the computer over for you to slot your credstick. With a smile and a quick thank-you, she retrieves her computer and is off. You watch as she climbs into the car and heads toward the main terminal.

Inside, the plane is as luxurious and comfortable as you remember. You ease back into the seat as the plane begins to roll forward. You smile at the thought of another job done. Seated ahead of you, Frosty looks out the window. Your smile vanishes as you wonder whether you are doing the right thing. It is obvious Frosty doesn't have a clue to what is going on. You settle back into the seat and try to console yourself with the thought of all of those nuyen.

BEHIND THE SCENES

The Nightsky limo full of muscle will meet the team at the Seattle airport. Mr. Johnson gets out of the car and motions the team over to the car after the Lear's ramp is finally lowered. He nods and informs you that there's been a slight change in plans. Apparently, the runners are about to meet their employer. Their *real* employer.

Go to the next adventure section, **Present**, p. 123, at this time.

COLUMBIA BOULEVARDS

Use this section when the runners are attempting to find information while in Columbia. Because the team is out of their element, however, every target number will be 2 higher, or 6. They will, of course, also have to locate the contacts from whom to obtain the information.

BUSINESSES

B.K.'S LOUNGE AND DANCEATERIA

B.K.'s Lounge is the hottest spot in Columbia. Sooner or later, everybody who is anybody shows up here. Below is a list of appropriate contacts and the number of successes needed to get information. Information for the lower levels of success should be given for the higher levels.

Appropriate Contacts

Anybody who has lived in Columbia for more than six months has at least heard of the Lounge.

Successes	Result
0	"The Lounge? It's, like, the place to be. Everybody knows that. Whatever your pleasure, you know? The Lounge has got the answers."
1	"The joint doesn't really start happening till around twelve. 'Course, you'll want to get there early if you want a place near the floor. Haven't heard of anybody coming to town this weekend, so the music will probably be piped. Not that it matters."
2	"Sometimes they'll let you get away with a little bit of the rough stuff, if you know what I mean. Nothing too heavy, but you can whack away at each other if that's your style."
3+	"I hear the Pretenders will be making their weekly appearance tonight. They're a tough bunch from the south side of town. They usually stake out some turf near the back of the bar."

ST. JAMES HOME FOR WAYWARD WOMEN

St. James Home has only been around for the past year and a half. Started by the local church to assist women returning to society after an extended prison stay, the home has managed to help these unfortunates, without offending the neighbors too much. As St. James is located on the edge of downtown, the women are often seen browsing in the shopping areas.

Appropriate Contacts

Any Street type, Bartender, Corporate, or Gang type.

Successes	Result
1	"Sure the women are a little rough around the edges. After a lock-up, wouldn't you be kinda anti-social? That's why the home is there. To help them readjust."
2	"Sister Ann, the nun that runs the place, is one tough broad. No offense intended. She started running the show a couple of months back."
3+	"I get the feeling more than readjustment is going on over there. Not that I've actually *seen* anything fishy, but if that place is on the level, I'm the pope."

COMMTECH INCORPORATED

CommTech started as a garage industry in the late 2020s and steadily grew into one of the best-known software companies in the area. The new facility, on the western edge of town, is one of the first sights people see when they hit the city limits along I-70.

Although still small, the company is going places.

Appropriate Contacts

Any Corporate, Decker, or Street type, any Technician

Successes	Result
1	"They make some kind of high-class IC program, most of which gets sold to corpers along the eastern seaboard."
2+	"I've heard that they're also dabbling in the shadow market. Seems like they've got some sort of hot-shot sleaze program in the cooler. They moved to the new facility for added security."

PEOPLE AND GROUPS

MS. FOSTER

Ms. Foster has worked as executive secretary for the president of CommTech, Inc. for the past three years. Though competent, she has shown no desire to move up in the company or to take on more responsibility.

Appropriate Contacts

Bartender, Club Owner, any Corporate or Company type, Troll Bouncer.

Successes	Result
1	"You're talkin' about Frosty. I haven't heard anyone call her Jane in years. Naw, I haven't seen her in a couple of days."
2	"I heard somebody tried to grab her outside her place a few days back. She managed to get away, but I don't know how. Some poor dude's probably singing soprano right now."
3	"You might check over at B.K.'s Lounge. She used to hang out there quite a bit. Most of the regulars know Frosty."
4+	"Slot this. She used to hang with some chummers named the Pretenders. Kind of a rock band gone bad, if you know what I mean. Anyway, these jokers payroll Highway 63 between here and Jeff. They might be able to help ya out."

THE PRETENDERS

The Pretenders were quite a bar band several years ago, but they never got their one big break. Frustrated and disheartened, they turned to their only other loves, booze and bikes. They have quite a rep in the surrounding area for creating mischief and mayhem.

Appropriate Contacts

Anybody who has lived in the Columbia/Jefferson City area for more than a year will know about the Pretenders.

Successes	Results
1	"Snot-nosed punks. That's all they are. 'Course, don't tell anybody I said that. They're a tough bunch, that's for sure. Some of 'em are mages, too."
2 – 3	"You can sometimes spot them over at B.K.'s. They always sport their colors, so they're kind of hard to miss. I hear they've been keeping a low profile for the last few days, though. Must be up to something."
4+	"I know you won't believe it, but I've even seen those goons over at the St. James Home. Can't tell if that makes them better than people give them credit for, or if it drags St. James' name through the muck."

FROSTY

Jane Foster grew up in several orphanages in and around the Columbia area. When she was old enough to get out on her own, she began to put herself through the University of Missouri and she has never looked back.

Jane has always wondered about her parents, especially her father, but has not devoted a single moment to looking for them. She is happy, for the most part, and has begun to make a name for herself at CommTech.

Jane likes what the city of Columbia has to offer, though she's barely ever been out of town. That's still O.K. with her. She enjoys riding with the Pretenders go-gang, but hasn't ever been with them when they're up to anything really illegal. Though Jane has many friends, the Pretenders are probably the closest thing she has to a family.

Unknown to Jane, she has a spell lock grafted to the bone of her right thigh. Ehran arranged for her to fall ill when she was a small child, and while she was in the hospital, he had an intricate pattern of special metals woven into that bone. At that time, Ehran cast a powerful but subtle spell that inhibited magicians of lesser power from tracking and finding her. When activated, the spell also allows Ehran to easily trace her. By the same token, it establishes an obvious connection between Ehran and Jane for those who know what to look for. Ehran has *not* activated the spell for fear of leading Harlequin to his daughter. What he doesn't know is that Harlequin already knows exactly where to look.

Jane is tall and thin, with a cascade of long, snow-white hair. She is equally at home in corporate suits or biker synth-leather. She dresses for effect and her clothes are of the finest quality, no matter what the outfit. She tends to look for one-of-a-kind items, and also wears simple, but elegant, jewelry. The most notable piece is a platinum ring in the shape of a coiled dragon. Though it is heavy and ostentatious, she never takes the piece off.

Jane is always in control. She does not like surprises and will go to great lengths to make sure she knows exactly what is going on in her world. She is constantly thinking about the future and what she wants or needs to get done. This tends to make her seem rather hard-edged at first contact, but the truth is she is a passionate person who makes friends easily if she so chooses.

Jane is loyal to her friends and herself, in that order. She does not want to see any of them get hurt on her account, either physically or mentally. She will do what she can to protect them at all times, often making somewhat unwise decisions in the process. Friends are Jane's only blind spot.

B	Q	S	C	I	W	E	M	R	Armor
3	5	1	6	5	6	6	—	5	None

Dice Pools: Defense (Armed) 1, Defense (Unarmed) 1, Dodge 5

Skills: Athletics 3, Bike 5, Car 4, Computer 3, Etiquette (Cor-

PRESENT

"Atque in perpetuum, frater, ave atque vale".
—Caius Valerius
Catullus, Roman Poet

INTRODUCTION

The Dance of Blood draws to a close, and the runners are circling in toward the center of the maelstrom. Elements of the master story are revealed in a clearer light, while others slide into darker obscurity.

Harlequin himself finally summons the runners: they are instructed to bring Jane Foster to the depths of the Puyallup Barrens. From there it's a whirlwind tour of the world of Harlequin and Ehran and their Hate.

Eventually, the story leads to Ehran's sanctum on the slopes of Mount Saint Helens, 150 kilometers south of Seattle. Althain, as Ehran calls it, is a place of splendor and mystery, offering glimpses of things rarely seen by any outside Ehran, Harlequin, and their ilk. Clues to some of the great mysteries of the world are here for the perceptive shadowrunner to discover and ponder.

Then the story of **Harlequin** draws to a close. For now.

WAITING FOR THE CALL

TELL IT TO THEM STRAIGHT

It's been 24 hours since your return to Seattle. With Jane Foster in tow, you've been sitting in this dark hole, waiting for the call. Waiting in the dark, ignoring Jane's sullen manner, and trying very hard not to jump at every sound.

Then, finally, the portable phone begins to flash. Someone grabs it.

"Yes?" you say.

"Ah," the voice on the other end replies, addressing you by name. "I'm very glad you answered. Pardon the cliché, but do you have the girl?"

"Of course."

"Bravo! My money well-spent. One more deed and your business with me is concluded. Bring the girl and your associates to the old Southwind complex in Tarislar at dawn tomorrow. Do not come before then or you risk provoking the wrath of the locals. They expect you, but with the sun. I look forward to our finally meeting."

With that, the line goes dead.

Read to the players when they reach Tarislar:

Tarislar. They say it means "remembrance" in Elvish, but remembrance of what? The dead? The power of nature? The living? No one can say. It's almost as though the place named itself.

The night is uncommonly clear for Seattle, but that changes fast as you head south. Puyallup always has a cloud over it, be it smog, ash, or despair. These early-morning hours are no exception. With every passing kilometer, the heaviness seems to grow. Soon it will be dawn, but you wonder if the light ever shines here.

Thirty-five years ago, this land was a suburb where many people lived happily enough. The day the Native American Ghost Dancers blew the volcanoes changed that forever. Ash, dirt, and rock fell over the area for days on end, burying homes, people, and dreams. Many say dreams will never return to Puyallup.

Though the road is well-marked, the dust and ash your vehicle kicks up remind you more of a barren desert than a place for people to live. The black and gray ash is everywhere, on the ground and in the air. Occasionally the high-beams of your car slice through and briefly illuminate a building or signs of life in some makeshift shelter.

Finally, you approach Tarislar. Ever since the Night of Rage, these abandoned buildings have provided a refuge for Metahumans, especially Elves, with nowhere else to go. These desolate structures sit a short distance from Seattle's border with the Salish-Shidhe Council, a cruel reminder of the sanctuary once promised Metahumans, but now denied by politics and prejudice.

Whether they heard you coming or were warned of your approach, figures now line the streets, the dark, shifting shapes barely visible in the pre-dawn haze. Their bodies are sheathed in dark clothing, with not much visible but the plastic sheen of filter masks on some faces. They are young, old, and in-between, but all remain silent as they stand and watch you pass.

To the east, the sun crests the hills and the light shifts, bringing a gray-green cast to this corner of the world. Ahead of you are the three buildings of the former Southwind office complex. Each is 40-odd stories high, a battered and broken spire of black metal and shattered glass.

You approach the buildings and begin to slow. The sharpest eyes among you spot him first, the shadow of a male figure standing in the forecourt of the buildings. Garbed in robes of white, he seems to be waiting.

For you?

BEHIND THE SCENES

Harlequin's call comes in the middle of the night. Let the runners sweat the time from their arrival at Sea-Tac until that contact. Mr. Johnson (from **Future**) will only tell them to lie low and await a call. He will provide them with a cellular phone in case their usual phones are bugged. Now that he has fulfilled his role, he has very little else to say.

The runners can stash themselves and Jane wherever they like. Nothing will happen before Harlequin's call, but the player characters need not know that. Let them wait. Let them fidget. Let them sweat.

If any of them pokes his head out for some reason, feed the group's paranoia. Is someone following them? Haven't they seen that car before? Didn't the bar seem to grow ominously quiet for a moment when they entered? Create some doubts and then let them fill in the blanks.

Regardless of what the characters believe, no one is actively looking for them. If any of Ehran's goons escaped during **Future**, he became immediately aware of his daughter's abduction. If not, the mere fact that he has not heard from his men is enough to tip him off. Ehran has traveled to his sanctum, Althain, on the slopes of Mount Saint Helens, to prepare his response to Harlequin's final *chal'han* gesture. There he waits.

Tarislar is a firmly Elven section of the Puyallup Barrens. Located along the southern edge of the Barrens, almost to the S-S Council border, the area still shows the devastation created by the eruptions of Mounts Rainier, Olympia, Adams, and Saint Helens 35 years ago. It is a place of darkness and despair.

SPLENDOR IN THE ASH

Gamemasters who need more information about the Tarislar area of Puyallup will find brief mentions on pp. 136–143 of the **Seattle Sourcebook**. They can also refer to the map on pages 174–5 of that book.

Devastated by the volcanic ash and lava accompanying the eruption of the area's volcanoes in 2017, the region has never recovered. Ash and debris from those terrible days still remain as a constant, grim reminder. Many Elves and other Metahumans live here in the various derelict and semi-abandoned buildings that survived the ashfall.

The gamemaster may treat the Tarislar people's solemn witnessing of the runners' passage as he chooses. Perhaps they were forewarned or perhaps they are on their way to the soup kitchens that open at dawn. Is this a bastion of power for Harlequin, or is he so aloof that his emotions are as far above the people as his current residence? Questions for the gamemaster to ponder, but not necessarily resolve.

The Southwind complex consists of three 40-story buildings that were once offices owned and licensed by a group of diversified insurance agencies. After being abandoned in the wake of the eruptions, the buildings became a haven for gangs and all types of dealers for years.

A year ago Harlequin arrived and took up residence on the upper floor of the center building. The gangs and the criminals soon left, afraid of the Laughing Man they couldn't bribe or threaten. That fear and nearly superstitious respect quickly spread to the locals, who were grateful for the peace the stranger's presence brought to the area. They nevertheless try to steer clear of the Southwind buildings.

The air here is so thick with dust and ash, especially at street level, that an air filter mask is almost a necessity. A basic filter mask costs about ¥20 nuyen and will last a couple of weeks before it needs cleaning. A cyberware air filter of any rating is also sufficient. Any character not wearing a mask must make a Body Resistance Test against a 3M2 Stun attack every 10 minutes he is exposed to the air. Upon leaving their vehicles for the first time, the runners must make the same test, assuming, of course, they have no adequate air filtration system.

As the runners approach Southwind, the first rays of dawn are beginning to light the sky, allowing them to see a male figure standing in the forecourt of the buildings. He is dressed in layers of white cloth and remains stock-still as the runners draw near. Closer up, they will be able to learn two things about the figure. First, the amount of dust covering him reveals that he must have been standing there for many hours. Second, when he lifts the cloth wrap that conceals his face, the milky whiteness of his eyes gives away his blindness.

When the shadowrunners come near, the Elf unwraps the cloth over his face and turns toward Jane Foster, nodding. (Yes, he is blind, but the gamemaster should play his manner and actions as though the man had full sight.) After a moment, he smiles and turns toward the other player characters. "He awaits you behind me, at the top. Join him with the woman." The Elf then wraps up his face again and says no more.

The building directly behind the figure in white is the middle Southwind building, the one where Harlequin waits at the top. When the runners enter the lobby, they find that the elevators have apparently long been out of service. The stairs are their only recourse.

At the 20-story and 40-story marks, the player characters must make a Body Resistance Test against a 4L2 Stun fatigue

STEEL GUITARS

TELL IT TO THEM STRAIGHT

Ten stories.

The stairs are dark and the climb tedious and grueling for some. Occasional shafts of morning light pierce the broken mortar and steel walls. You do not like what it reveals.

Twenty stories.

Jane Foster has said and done little since being abducted from Columbia, Missouri. Now, as she climbs, you see an odd light coming into her eyes. It is as though she senses a resolution coming, and welcomes it.

Thirty stories.

You see writing on the wall: *"One must know chaos within to give birth to a dancing star."* There is also a darkened smear of something leading to the ground. But nothing is there now. Ahead, from on high, comes the sound of music.

Forty stories.

The music becomes clearer now, the sound of one steel guitar. The stairs open onto a floor half-exposed to the sky. Much of the furniture and the false wall partitions are gone, having tumbled down into the street or fallen into ruin. You follow the music across the floor, through the offices, to the far edge of the building.

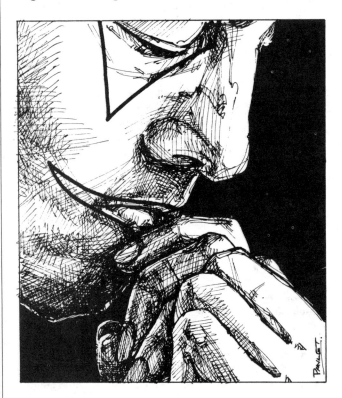

Standing there in a space that was once the sectionally sunken and raised office of the president of whatever giant corporation ruled from this tower is the figure of a man. His back is to you, and you see only the dark olive of his long coat, the gray-streaked black of his pony-tailed hair, and the thin, gleaming ebony and steel neck of his guitar.

You watch and listen as he plays, alternately slow and fast, but always powerfully. The music speaks of something grand and majestic, its melody at once alien yet somehow familiar and exhilarating.

The wind blows through the building and the sun touches the far mountains. The music becomes slower, softer, and comes finally to a stop with a single, long chord that echoes for several achingly long moments.

He turns, revealing a face painted in the harlequin-clown markings of old, then breaks into a wide grin.

"Gentleman!" he says, his voice distinctive and oddly accented. "Welcome to Mount Olympus. I've been expecting you."

BEHIND THE SCENES

Finally, this is Harlequin. The gamemaster can refer to the description of Harlequin at the end of this adventure for more information concerning his appearance and personality. The operative word, however, should be quicksilver. His attitude, demeanor, body language, vocal/speech patterns, and humor can and will change from one moment to the next. (If a player character has the appropriate special skill, he or she might notice that the guitar is at least 100 years old.) Harlequin then approaches them and introduces himself to each one individually, taking each runner's hands in a strong handshake. His manner should suggest that this is important to him. He introduces himself to each one as "Harlequin."

He saves Jane Foster for last. She reluctantly offers her hand, which he lifts gently to his lips. "Miss Foster," he says softly, "I've waited a lifetime to meet you."

Still holding her hand, he leads Foster to the center of the room. If the runners begin to ask questions ("O.K., chummer, what the frag is goin' on here!"), he will take the time to answer them. If they don't, Harlequin will begin **The Ritual**, as outlined below.

What he's willing to tell them follows. It has been written in Harlequin's voice to provide a launching point for the gamemaster. It need not be read completely or literally, but can serve as a reference for answering specific questions the players ask.

"Are you certain you wish to know?" Harlequin says. "There's truth to the idea that ignorance is bliss. But I will at least partially sate your curiosity.

"Let us just say that Ehran and I are old friends. Very old friends. Now, Ehran is very good at a certain game we used to play when we were younger. I, however, am even better. Only now has he become aware of it.

"Everything you have been asked to do has struck at some basic part of Ehran's existence. His Past, and Future, Loves and Hates, and Physical and Spiritual selves. By striking at each of these, I have proved his vulnerability to my power.

"You, however, need not be concerned. The ritual decrees that Ehran cannot strike at the agents of my challenge, so you are safe from any vengeance on his part."

Now, this may or may not pacify any runners who suffered through the encounter with Ariel and Dr. What (**Counterstroke**). If they continue to express concern, Harlequin dismisses it offhandedly. He says Ehran is a true parliamentarian. "Rules are everything to him."

If one or more runners look around, the gamemaster can let them learn one more thing at this point. A short distance from where Harlequin and Jane Foster are standing, the runner(s) notice a wall section on which has been written in black marker:

The RITUAL, to the best of my recollection, by —H—

From the focus of my heart, I call the words
Of anger spoken and desire revealed
By my Challenge of word and deed
By my blood consecrate thy bane invoked
Thy shape and form decreed never was

On thy Physical form, I call the words of rendering
On thy Hates, I invoke Justice, thy anger unappeased
On thy Past in shadows, I shine the light revealed
On thy Loves and joys, I gift separation
On thy Spirit, I speak abandonment
On thy Future, I bring fear and grief
On thee I Invoke all

The winds shall erase thy name
The sands the traces of thy path
The sun the coolness of thy shadow
And unto the waters I command thy essence
Thy shape and form decreed never was

If questioned about it, Harlequin smiles and laughs. "I wanted to see how it read in English," he says.

If there are no further questions, Harlequin will commence the Ritual.

THE RITUAL

Though it is not really a true Ritual, Harlequin will treat it as such. He gestures grandly (but needlessly), intones occasional words in a melodic, sing-song tongue none of the runners understand (a childhood rhyme about clouds), and moves about in what seems to be some kind of pattern.

He will also ask the runners to hum continuously while he does this. He works with them carefully to achieve the proper pitch. Eventually, he will accept what they can produce as the best he is likely to get. Mumbling something about "impurities," he returns to stand near Jane Foster.

As he begins his "ritual", Harlequin speaks to Jane like a doctor addressing a conscious patient during certain types of surgery. Again, the gamemaster may read the following verbatim to the players or else use it as a springboard, varying the content according to the runners' actions.

At this point, Jane Foster watches Harlequin intently. She says nothing, however, nor does she show any emotion in response to anything he says.

"Now, my dear Miss Foster, what you do not know is that you are the long-lost daughter of the illustrious Ehran the Scribe, as he currently bills himself. I should add that he did not lose *you*, but allowed *you* to lose *him*.

"He has, however, kept careful track of you, oh, these many years. How? Well, very simply. Before he so callously abandoned you as a child, or rather allowed you to be abandoned following your lovely mother's untimely demise, he placed a powerful spell lock on you.

"This was no ordinary spell lock, Jane, if you know anything about such matters. While you were still a child, he had special materials woven into the bone of your left thigh. These he enchanted to hold and maintain a spell of his own design, that would not only keep track of you, but help conceal you from prying eyes.

"Now, this spell is far beyond the ability of any current sorcerer, so he could reasonably assume that you were safe from prying eyes. What he forgot was that both he and I had undergone instruction from the same teacher. I understand the working of his link.

"It took me some time to unlock its secrets from a distance, but I managed it. And I am certain he does not suspect this.

"Ehran believes that I will use you to draw him out into the open where I can present the final challenge against his physical self. Instead, I'm going to strike at him directly through you. Through the link he has so thoughtfully provided."

With that, Harlequin turns to any of the magically active in the group (those that can participate in Ritual Sorcery) and asks them if they are ready. He intends them to participate in his Sending against Ehran.

If any of the magically active runners agree, he will ask for a volunteer to watch over the ritual, or at least to make a check now from Astral Space. Any character that tries this now, or at any other time, may notice the following:

•Harlequin shows the aura of a mundane. He is, of course, an Initiate who is Masking his Aura. There is *no* way that any runner will be of sufficient Initiation rank to see through his Masking, however.

•There are no astral beings present here, no Spirits or Elementals of any type.

•The magical background count (see **The Grimoire**) is above the norm, as though powerful magicks were regularly worked from this place.

•Harlequin and Jane Foster are standing in the middle of an area that seems surrounded by a hermetic Circle or Ward of some odd sort. It is dormant now, but an appropriate character making a successful Astral Perception (10) Test will notice it.

•Jane herself displays the aura of a mundane. A successful Astral Perception (18) Test against her at this point will reveal a faint power aura from the area of her left thigh. Note that nothing can be learned if this test is made *prior* to her entering the concealed magical circle. There is certainly no sign of a link between her and Ehran.

Any runners who choose to participate in the Sending with Harlequin need have no worry, though the gamemaster should not inform them of that. Harlequin will ask the non-magically active runners to take five steps back, but stress that they must keep humming the whole time. He then makes a broad gesture with his arms and gets down to business.

What Harlequin is doing is activating Ehran's spell lock. This is usually difficult, if not outright impossible. In this case, Ehran has been sloppy, believing no one would ever play with the spell; besides, Harlequin knows how the spell and lock are constructed. Harlequin intends to activate the spell lock and then, through the energy channel created by the lock, throw a physical spell that will explode the equivalent of magical fireworks around Ehran for a few minutes. The spell is showy, but neither dangerous or fatal.

Ehran does not know this. He expects Harlequin to discover the lock (if he doesn't know about it already), and has prepared himself. Using his own powerful magicks, Ehran has prepared a unique, volatile spell designed to channel through the lock to Harlequin via the energy Harlequin is expending to activate it. The spell is triggered to become active the moment Harlequin activates the spell lock, travel through the energy conduit from Ehran to the lock, and then go off, frying Harlequin big-time.

The Ritual Sorcery portion of all this will not have begun yet when Harlequin activates the lock, so none of the shadowrunners are in immediate danger. What they will witness, if they are assensing, is Harlequin performing some complex act of magic and activating the spell lock. The moment he does, there will be a sudden surge of magical power. Harlequin screams something and energy erupts from the lock (Jane's thigh), arcing directly into Harlequin.

The magical barrier surrounding Harlequin and Jane instantly activates, knocking any astrally projecting characters within the circle back into their bodies. As the circle activates, Harlequin casts some form of reflection spell, possibly by triggering a spell lock that he concealed or Masked somehow on his person. The energy flowing through the spell lock will arc to Harlequin and then suddenly flow backward as it is reflected back to Ehran.

As this happens, and the energy is bounced back to Ehran, the spell lock shatters, taking Jane Foster's thigh bone with it. Harlequin himself will spin and crash to the ground like a rag doll. The air in the area will rush outward for a moment as though a small concussion grenade had been detonated.

Any character assensing and looking south, past where Mount Rainier would be if visible, will notice a slight flicker of astral energy. Eight minutes later, all the runners will plainly hear the sharp crack and deep rumble of Mount Saint Helens' partial eruption. See the **Upslope** section, p. 130, for more information.

Harlequin will bounce to his feet like a puppet whose strings have been yanked. He gazes south for a few moments and then turns to look at the player characters, a distant, perhaps concerned look on his face. If none of the runners has moved to aid Jane Foster, Harlequin orders one of them to do so. Her left thigh is shattered. She is Seriously Wounded and Unconscious from full Fatigue damage.

If none of the shadowrunners present are able to assist her, Harlequin will angrily step in and cast Heal Serious Wounds on her. Assume that it is fully successful after the proper time has past.

During all this, Harlequin is ranting and raving in a harsh, almost guttural tongue none of the runners recognize. After Jane has been healed, or if his assistance was not needed, Harlequin begins to pace the area, cursing Ehran in that same tongue. Though they don't understand the words, Harlequin's tone is unmistakable and the runners are able to clearly make out the name Ehran.

Finally, he stops and turns toward the player characters, a dark and frightening look on his face. "Gentlemen, I ask one more thing of you. You must go to Ehran and see what has become of him. If he is injured, as I suspect, aid him if you can. The form of challenge I chose to invoke cannot result in harm to him. If it has, I have lost and my honor is forfeit. If Ehran yet lives, I am still forbidden by the rules of the challenge to be directly involved. Therefore, you must go."

As he speaks, the winds coming through the floor and moving around the building begin to pick up dramatically. Anyone assensing will notice the approach of a *very* powerful Air Elemental. Harlequin steps over to Jane, lifts her up, and begins to walk toward a hole in the wall.

"Ehran was in the northern slope of Mount Saint Helens when the spell struck. It seems to have partially erupted, implying that Ehran had some power woven through it. You must go there, find him, and await my word. If you do not do as I say, I will hunt you to the ends of the earth and you will suffer pain the likes of which this civilization has never dreamed."

Still holding Jane Foster, he turns, steps clear of the building, and drops from sight. If anyone is in a position to see, it will appear that Harlequin has been spirited away (so to speak) by a powerful Air Elemental. The winds will immediately die down.

The gamemaster should note that this entire section is actually a staged farce to get the runners to Mount Saint Helens and Ehran's sanctum. That is the ultimate goal; everything else is pure theatre. If the player characters deviate from the order of events in this section, the gamemaster should be prepared to direct them somehow to the **Upslope** section.

GOING TO THE MOUNTAIN

Read to the players when they arrive at Mt. St. Helens:

Mount Saint Helens is the site of three major eruptions in the last three-quarters of a century or so. The first occurred in the 1970s, the second in the 2010s, and the most recent a few hours ago.

The odd thing this time is the lack of a continuing ash plume or lava flow. It is as though the mountain simply blew its top and then went quiet again. Recently disgorged dirt, ash, and rock litter the slopes and ground surrounding the near-barren mountain. In a few places, steam or smoke rise from where some flaming piece of the mountain crashed into the ground.

Local S-S Council troopers are not having much success keeping spectators clear of the mountain, but most of the gawkers do heed the warning to hang back a few kilometers in case the volcano erupts again. The S-S Council troopers lack the resources to cordon off the whole area, so you should be able to find some holes by which to sneak through.

BEHIND THE SCENES

The runners are on their own in getting to Mount Saint Helens. Following are a few ideas if the gamemaster must provide the player characters with some travel options. Many groups may already have some "standard" means for crossing the border into Salish-Sidhe territory and will not need any prompting. Others, however…

MEANS OF TRAVEL

There are many ways by which the runners can make their way to Mount Saint Helens. If they lack ideas, the following suggestions may help.

Yes, We Are Tourists

The Salish-Sidhe Council regularly schedules tours from Seattle through the tribal lands, and runs daily tours to Mounts Rainier and Saint Helens. The gamemaster can fudge the timetables as necessary to make the tour convenient.

The trip, by bus, takes about three hours. (It is, after all, a sightseeing tour.) It costs the runners ¥50 nuyen apiece for seats, and they can only bring small carry-bags, which will be searched at the Seattle/S-S Council border. Unless the runners are extraordinarily clever, the border guards will discover any weapons greater than light pistol size.

The runners will also need to obtain a one-day travel visa from the S-S Council Lodge on Council Island (see p. 59, **Seattle Sourcebook**). Upon reaching Mount Saint Helens, the team will have to slip away from the tour group and strike out on their own. The tour takes four hours. If the runners can take care of business and return to the tour group before it leaves, they will have no problem returning to Seattle. If they are not able to rejoin the tour, explanations will be the least of their problems.

No News Is Bad Business

Mount Saint Helens has erupted again, at least partially. That is definitely newsworthy enough to assure that one or more local Seattle newsnets will dispatch news teams to the site. Odds are there will be a mad rush to get pictures, with the networks sending out choppers first.

All comers will be challenged at the S-S Council border, but with so many whirlybirds trying to cross at once, the runners may be able to bluff their way in, too. Another option, of course, is to hijack a real newsnet chopper and masquerade as the news team from that station. The problem with this is that the S-S Council border patrol will probably be alerted to their deception by the time the runners try to head back.

Redline!

There's always running the border. The gamemaster should balance it so that the runners face fairly equal opposition when they cross and then get chased about half the distance. The border patrol forces will not be too staggering because they are currently spread thin trying to deal with those wishing to cross the border to see the mountain.

BORDER CROSSING

Each border crossing point from Seattle is a cement and steel blockhouse manned by four border patrol officers, two working the road and two providing the back-up. Use the **Former Tribal Warrior**, p. 103, **Sprawl Sites**. The two guards working the road will be armed as indicated, while the two providing back-up will be armed with Colt M22a2 Assault Rifles.

If the runners crash the border, the S-S Council Border Patrol will quickly dispatch a pair of light helicopters after them, either two PRC-42b Wasp one-man choppers or two Hughes Stallions.

To evade them, the driver of the runners' vehicle should make an Opposed Test against the chopper pilots. Pit the driver's Car (or whatever) Skill against the signature of the vehicle he's driving. The pilots, relying on the electronic sensors of their vehicles, roll 4 dice against the signature of the vehicle (roll only once for both choppers). If the net successes favor the runners or in case of a tie, they have avoided detection. If the net successes favor the choppers, the runners have been tracked.

If the shadowrunners are able to travel relatively unmolested, they will reach the mountain in under two hours.

UPSLOPE

Ehran was using a magically controlled geothermal system to power and heat Althain, his sanctum at Mount Saint Helens. When his spell rebounded on him, he was knocked unconscious and the energy flash-over disrupted many of the spell structures he maintained around Althain. The small volcanic eruption was actually the venting of the geothermal systems to prevent a full-scale eruption. The only physical evidence of the venting is the debris littering the area and a change in the mountain's profile near the peak.

The gamemaster must remember that, from this point on, Ehran has set up a trap for Harlequin. He has gone to great lengths to let Harlequin believe that he, Ehran, was killed by the reflected spell. All evidence will indicate that no one is currently maintaining Althain, and that it is in extensive physical and magical disarray. The runners' journey to Althain should be full of trials and tribulations, but ultimately successful.

Althain is accessible through a series of fissures and caverns in the north slope of the mountain. It is a six-hour hike from the base of the mountain to the fissures, assuming the runners leg it. If not, their travel time is reduced accordingly.

While ascending the mountain, the runners risk being spotted by patrols. The S-S Council has moved a unit of guardsmen into the area to seal it off, for the safety of any foolish gawkers. The terrain surrounding the mountain is mostly barren, with the few areas of new-growth trees now battered.

Periodically, a survey or patrol helicopter will fly nearby. The chance of the runners being noticed on the slope depends on the team's method of travel. If they are carelessly moving out in the open, the chance of being spotted is high. If they are being cautious, stealthy, and using magic as a cover, the chances are good they will avoid detection.

There is also a chance that they will pass near a small group of soldiers and early-comer scientists who are surveying the area and searching for injured hikers or campers. Such a group will consist of two **Former Tribal Warriors** (p. 103, **Sprawl Sites**), and a **Corporate Scientist** (page 108, **Sprawl Sites**). Again the likelihood of detection depends on the runners' mode of travel.

An astrally perceiving player character can find the access fissure from the residual magical energy leaking from it. Ehran erected a series of powerful illusion and confusion spells in the often-visited caverns to prevent tourists from accidentally stumbling upon Althain. Those spells are currently disrupted, though some others that hide the sanctum from prying eyes are not.

The fissures and caverns leading to Althain were formed by escaping lava gases following the 2017 eruptions. They are visited during one of the tours of the mountain, but the current eruption will result in those tours temporarily halting far short of the mountain.

The artificial lighting installed by the Parks Department for the benefit of the tourists is out of order because of the eruption. The runners will have to stumble around in the darkness or provide their own illumination. The caverns are as extensive or simple as the gamemaster wishes, depending on what the runners expect. If they're anticipating trouble, make it simple (to a point). If they are ill-prepared, make the caverns something out of M.C. Ecsher's worst nightmare. If things get too difficult, they can always follow the residual energy to the actual entrance to Althain.

During the journey, however, the runners will encounter some of the most frightening terrain this side of Hades. The venting of the geothermal system has awakened some lava passages, which have again filled with molten earth. The player characters will pass numerous pools and small streams of blackened (partially cooling) or brilliant red, almost white-hot, streams of lava.

Toward the end, they are forced to cross a relatively narrow (1 meter across) stone "bridge" that is the only way over a river of molten stone flowing hundreds of meters below. The gamemaster should call for attribute and skill tests sufficient to make the crossing taxing but not fatal. While they are crossing, the rear of the group will be attacked by an Embracer. (See pp. 58–9 of **Paranormal Animals of North America** for more on this particular creature.)

The Embracer attacks the group ferociously, drawing character after character into its deadly embrace. If another character attempts to shoot the Embracer while it is hugging a character, the firing character receives a +2 Target Modifier. If he misses the creature because of that modifier, he will strike the character being hugged instead. Charged by Ehran with guardianship of the bridge, the Embracer will fight to the death. Use the following game statistics for the Embracer.

B	Q	S	C	I	W	E	R	Attacks
12	5 x 3	10	—	2/4	4	(6)*	6	9S2, +1 Reach

*The Embracer is a dual-natured creature.

On the far side of the bridge, the runners find a cleanly carved circular tunnel. Magical examination will reveal that this whole area, including the bridge, was once protected and concealed by powerful spells. Any magician can also tell that this particular tunnel was not naturally formed. The entrance is protected by a powerful Ward that no astral form can penetrate. No astral form the player characters can create or summon, that is.

From the tunnel onward, any player character attempting Astral Perception or Astral Projection will be buffeted by the background emanations of powerful magicks and emotions. Except for certain "clean" areas of Althain, it is not healthy for a magician of the runners' power level to involve himself with Astral Space. During the time such a magician perceives or projects, subject him to a 6M4 Stun attack per turn. Additionally, any Perception Tests are at +6.

Any Elementals already summoned and called while in Althain will operate at +4 Target Modifier penalty and be worth only half their Force for such functions as Aid Sorcery. See p. 63 of **The Grimoire** for more information on the background magic count of an area.

Additionally, any attempt at Clairvoyance or other similar scrying spell will fail if cast into an area that is not "clean."

WELCOME TO ALTHAIN

TELL IT TO THEM STRAIGHT

You run your hand carefully over the jewel-like surface of the tunnel wall, wondering at the power that created it. You take care, though, not wanting to risk getting cut on an unexpected sharp edge. As the tunnel begins to angle upward, you feel the faint stirrings of a breeze against your face.

Then light appears in the distance, growing steadily brighter as you approach. Even as you think the source is still a distance away, the light suddenly brightens. Without warning, you come upon a large room. High walls and a ceiling that looks carved from gold-veined white marble surround you. Ahead, a short stairway leads to a bronze and black metal door.

In front of the door stand four creatures that, except for their garb, fit the description of the monkey-like paranormal critter known as a munchkin. Each wears a knee-length, *justaucorps* coat, richly embroidered doublet over a fine lace shirt, and tight, tailored breeches ending in leather cavalier boots.

Two of them, flanking to either side, wear emerald green and ash, respectively, and hold trays of plump, fresh strawberries and tall, fluted glasses of champagne. Two others stand between, one slightly ahead of the other. The rear munchkin, garbed in deep turquoise, stands waiting expectantly but carries nothing. The foremost munchkin, wearing rich maroon and also empty-handed, smiles broadly as you approach.

"Prepared we have drinks of fine champagne and tastes of lush strawberries for our guests," he says in an odd, chirping accent. "Welcome to Althain. Come. My master awaits within."

BEHIND THE SCENES

For more information on munchkins, see p. 116–17 of **Paranormal Animals of North America**. Their game statistics are exactly as indicated in that book.

These four munchkins, referred to from now on as Emerald, Ash, Turquoise, and Maroon, have been specially trained by Ehran. They exhibit low to below-average Human-scale intelligence and would certainly provide ample firepower for the faction of parazoologists who argue that munchkins are sentient. These four, and a dozen others like them, perform the daily housekeeping and maintenance tasks around Althain. These four are the stewards of the sanctum. Each of the others is named for his or her function; "Cleaner," "First Cook," Chambermaid," "Librarian," and so on.

The champagne and strawberries are the finest. The munchkin named Turquoise offers to take the guests' coats and hats, but the runners may refuse. Turquoise will not ask them to check any weapons they are carrying.

The munchkins have been instructed to treat as honored guests any individuals who pass through the tunnel. As far as

Ehran is concerned, anyone who gets through the tunnel is either supposed to be there or has sufficient power to have passed through the safeguards. In the latter case, the presence of the munchkins might delay the unexpected visitor long enough for Ehran to take action.

In this instance, Ehran is aware of the runners' approach. To keep up the charade he has set up, he remains out of sight.

The munchkins are totally passive and will offer no resistance if attacked. Their deaths, however, will bring **Cleaner** and **Junior Cleaner** scurrying to, well, clean up.

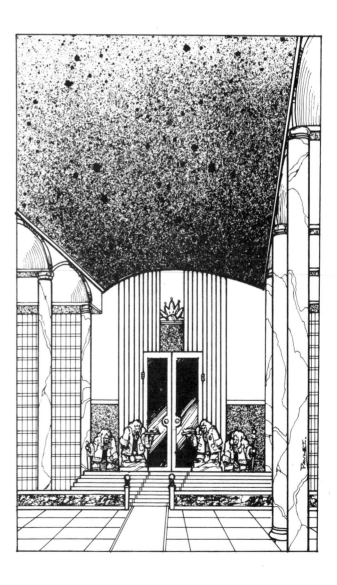

SANCTUM

TELL IT TO THEM STRAIGHT

Their greeting complete, the munchkins turn and lead you through the huge doors. Beyond lies a huge marble foyer, complete with a spiral staircase leading upward, a pair of white doors inlaid with gold, and skylights showing blue sky and clouds (which is odd, because you're supposed to be in the heart of the mountain). The room is decorated in late-eighteenth century European style, including many beautiful works of art. For those so attuned, the scent of magic fills the room.

The munchkin leads you through the far doors and into a short corridor. There are two sets of double doors on either side of the corridor, and another set at the far end. The lead munchkin opens the doors on the right and gestures you through.

"My master is busy at present, and he bids you wait here until he is not," says the munchkin, showing the creature's typical grin.

This room is also made from pale marble, but the contrasting black and white decorations are of modern style. The room is equipped with a snack bar and fully stocked liquor bar, as well as a full digital audio-visual system. It is the kind of splendor you have only seen in vids of lifestyles of elite corporate suits.

The lead munchkin closes the doors behind you, after letting the one dressed in ash color enter before he does.

"I am your servant." says Ash. "What is your wish?"

BEHIND THE SCENES

This room usually serves as a waiting room for visitors most at ease among the trappings of modern society. It is fully equipped for entertainment and social interaction, but has no phone. Any attempt to transmit a cellular phone or radio signal from within Althain will be unsuccessful.

Maroon leaves the runners here, and will return for them only when so instructed by Ehran—an order that will never come. The player characters can wait in that room until hell freezes over if they wish. Presumably, they will grow impatient and go exploring sometime before that happens.

Ash will remain with them, waiting on them and responding to their every need. If asked a question he cannot answer or faced with a problem he cannot solve (not too hard, considering his limited intelligence), he will leave to find Maroon to ask him. If Maroon can answer the question or solve the problem, he will. If not, the normal procedure would be to approach Ehran. At the moment, however, "The Master sleeps now in the Great Hall."

If one of the runners manages to follow Maroon, the munchkin will head directly to the **Great Hall (11)**. He approaches the still and twisted body of what appears to be Ehran (but is not), saying, "Master, they await you in the modern room." He then exits toward the munchkin living area.

ALTHAIN MAP KEY (Map on p. 151)

Tunnel (1)

As described above, this is a smooth passage cut from dark stone. The beginning of it, not shown on the map, marks the mystical border of Althain. It is protected by a powerful Ward impenetrable even to an Astral Form.

Entryway (2)

Also as described above, the room seems cut from white and other light-colored marbles, while the pillars to either side are cut from silver-veined black marble. The stairs leading to the door are also hewn from light marble. The doors are of bronze and black metal and have no locking mechanism.

As in most of Althain, the light in this area is provided by wall sconces that flicker with a magical light.

Foyer (3)

Again as described above, the foyer has white marble walls and ceilings and black marble pillars. The spiral staircase (ascending) is also cut from white marble, apparently a single piece. The side of the room opposite the staircase contains numerous pieces of artwork (flat and sculpted), some styles familiar to the runners, others completely alien in form.

The skylight appears to reveal sky and clouds above, but it is an illusion.

A pair of double doors, identical to those leading from the Entryway, exit this room.

Hallway (4)

A simple hallway, this time of gray marble. There are a set of double doors on both the right and left sides and at the far end.

Paintings and drawings in elaborately beautiful frames line the walls on either side of the hall. Some are recognizable as original masterpieces, others are equally original but unfamiliar.

Waiting Room (5)

This room is styled in modern black macroplast, chrome, and hammered steel. The audio-visual entertainment system includes a full selection of audio, video, and simsense chips. The room is also supplied with fully stocked liquor and snack bars.

Waiting Room (6)

This room is used for receiving certain types of special guests. Its style of architecture will not be familiar to any of the runners, though some with appropriate knowledge or special skills may note certain similarities to various European and Middle-Eastern styles of the pre-Christian era. The pillars and furnishings are cut from marble and quartz.

The reflecting pools are filled with chilled, natural water where strange varieties of ornamental fish swim. The water, by the way, is fresh, not salt-water. At this time, the waist-high tables scattered about the rooms are bare. A few round, cushioned seats are also scattered about.

Main Hall (7)

Though this room is used almost exclusively as a passage point to the various parts of Althain, it is decorated in the same splendor as the other rooms. The far wall is covered by a single, brilliant tapestry depicting a city of crystal and gold built into the top and face of a cliff. Closer inspection reveals the awe-inspiring amount of work that went into embroidering this magnificent piece, stitch by stitch.

Various other works of art, some familiar and some not, are hung or set in other parts of the room.

Munchkin Living Area (8)

The munchkins live here when not working. The area has been scaled down to better suit their size, making it uncomfortable for the runners moving through. The sleeping area consists of bunk beds, a communal bath, and an eating area. If the gamemaster wishes, a few munchkins may be present when and if the runners enter this area.

Guest Rooms (9)

The splendor and richness of these two rooms make them a wonder to behold, but little else of interest is here.

Kitchen Area (10)

All the cooking for Ehran, his occasional guests, and the munchkins is done here. Most of the cooking utensils and supplies are for normal, Human foods. One of the storage closets also contains a supply of Molybendum exclusively for the munchkins.

Great Hall (11)

This is Ehran's main room, with the exception of the library. He performs his magicks here, but the background count is unusually low, far below that of the other rooms.

The room is constructed of the same white marble as the rest of Althain, but the stone contains much richer veins of gold. Various alcoves contain large, visually powerful sculptures cut from black and gray marble. The subjects range from representations of individuals to stylized renderings of what could be mythological images. Only one of the subjects is familiar to any runner. It is a life-size rendering of a man whose face bears a distinct resemblance to Harlequin's, including his face paint. The garb of the man, a multi-layered robe-cloak, is completely unfamiliar to the runners.

The ceiling is vaulted, rising up a full three stories from the floor. Hanging at the five points of a hexagon and at its center are elaborate gold and crystal chandeliers, flickering with magical light. The ceiling is elaborately painted, depicting what looks like an astrological chart or diagram. None of the symbols or letterings are recognizable, however.

The floor is of smooth white marble inlaid with curved, arcing sections of darker stone. The center area is filled with an elaborate inlaid octagon of black and silver metals. Symbols and signs have also been engraved here. Any character with Magical Theory Skill will recognize some as symbols possessing ancient magical power, but the majority remain completely unfamiliar.

In the center of the octagon stands a bronze brazier full of flaming coals. The brazier has been knocked over, leaving the rapidly cooling coals spilled over the ground. Alongside the brazier lies the body of Ehran the Scribe, or so it appears. He is wearing a simple white tunic and breeches and black leather boots. The body is lying face-up, the eyes open but unseeing. No aura surrounds the body and no evidence of magical activity. If a player character examines the form astrally, he will find *no* emotional or magical residue, which should rouse his suspicions (see **The Grimoire**, pages 63–5). This body is not Ehran's, but that of a foolish member of the Young Elven Technologists who he decided was expendable (Windtree, perhaps?).

A marble balcony, one story above the floor, overlooks the room.

An examining character who succeeds at a Perception (10) Test or who uses an ultrasound vision system will notice a secret door in one wall section. The door is located in an alcove and is accessed by touching both sides of the alcove simultaneously, a feat the munchkins are unable to perform. Should the runners resort to force, treat the secret door as having the same characteristics as Thin Concrete.

On the far side of the door is a long, dark stairway that leads down and then curves off to the right. (See **Workroom** below.)

Balcony (12)

Accessible via the two curving staircases on either side of the **Great Hall (11)**, the balcony is simple in design, but the balcony wall facing the Great Hall is decorated elaborately with ornamental carvings. The wall is just a little more than knee-high.

Beyond the balcony is a short corridor that leads off to Ehran's private rooms.

Ehran's Suite (13)

All the runners can see of Ehran's rooms is what is visible from the door. An invisible physical and mana barrier protects the doorway, preventing passage. Because the walls, ceilings, and floors are made of natural marble, they too are impassable to an astral traveler. If the runners chance to pack enough firepower to attempt physical damage against this or any other wall in Althain, the effort will fail. The same holds true for physically damaging magicks.

By looking through the door, the runners will immediately see what looks like a small antechamber. Its simple furnishings are antiques from the mid- to late-1600s. A woman's portrait hangs on the far wall. None of the runners recognize her face.

Beyond the antechamber, through the open door, the runners can make out what appears to be a sitting room. All they can see is a fireplace, with plush chairs facing the roaring fire. On the mantel are many small items that sparkle slightly in the firelight. There is no other illumination in that room.

If the runners are able to add illumination or have some form of light-intensifying viewing system, they may notice an additional fact. Above the fireplace hangs a large portrait of a man in clothing typical of late-16th-century Spain. If the viewing runner succeeds at a Perception (6) Test, he may notice the resemblance between this figure and Ehran the Scribe. Three or

more successes will produce immediate recognition. With only one or two successes, however, the character will not recognize the resemblance until the *next time* he sees Ehran, even if it is the imitation Ehran sprawled on the floor of the Great Hall.

Other than this, nothing else is immediately visible in the room. Due to the magical background count problem, clairvoyance produces only mystical static.

Workroom (14)

Accessible only by the secret door from the Great Hall (see **Great Hall**, above), the workroom is where Ehran conducts some of his more time-intensive research.

The stairway to this area curves downward from the Great Hall in such a way that the rooms are actually situated *below* the Foyer, Waiting Rooms, and Great Hall. The exact position of this workroom is indicated by the dotted lines on the map.

The room uses the same magical sconces that light the rest of Althain, plus some additional coal braziers. It resembles a modern alchemical laboratory. Traditional research gear sits alongside modern molecular analyzers and scanning microscopes. The room is, in fact, a researching magician's dream-come-true, with some conditions.

The first is that much of the research conducted here is beyond the current understanding of magical researchers not at Ehran's level. The equipment and gear is fathomable, but their applications are not. At the gamemaster's discretion, any magician who wishes to devote time to examining the room can roll his Magical Theory plus his Intelligence dice against a Target of 20. **No Karma Points can be used to augment or affect this roll.** One success will tell the examining character that Ehran's research does not seem directed at determining an effect from a cause, but vice versa. He is attempting to understand *why* certain magical-related effects occur. His research also seems to be directed at predicting certain effects that are physically and magically impossible. It is at this stage of theorizing that the expanse of Ehran's research will completely overwhelm the shadowrunner.

The other condition concerning the room is its other contents. Two Dragons. To be precise, a young dracoform and a wyvern. Both are lying on the floor, meters from one another. The wyvern has been extensively dissected, as evidenced by the remains on examining tables around the room. Compared to the rest of Althain, this area is "clean," with a background count rating of 2 from the creature's emotional echoes. That means the wyvern can be examined astrally. A magician attempting such a task must make a successful Perception (6) Test to learn that the wyvern was not dissected. It was vivisected, magically.

The difference? Dissection is performed on a dead creature, vivisection on a live one.

The dracoform is still alive. A young Western Dragon, it is apparently constrained or immobilized by the effects of a magical spell. In the dim light, a faint red-orange glow shows around it. It appears to be breathing normally, but there is no other motion. The Dragon is, in fact, restrained by a powerful physical barrier that both restricts its movement and keeps the runners from harming it. A successful astrally targeted Perception (8) Test will reveal that the barrier is unraveling from within. Possibly the dracoform is using some magic of its own? It is impossible to tell how long it will take the spell to unravel, but the players may assume that it will occur at some inconvenient time.

The above description assumes that the gamemaster has allowed the runners to enter the Workroom prior to the arrival of the Elves from Tir Tairngire. If they enter after the Elves' arrival and the break-out of the Western Dragon, then only the wyvern is present in this area. See **Face To Face** for more information.

Arboretum (15)

This area is abundant with plant life, much of it familiar, but some not. Spread among the trees, flowers, and shrubs are small reflecting pools similar to the ones found in **Waiting Room (6)**. Many of the same style pillars and seats are also found here.

A small dining area is off to one side.

Light is provided by magical illumination from the ceiling. This area is only accessible via the spiral staircase.

Let the runners roam pretty much as they choose. Once they have been everywhere, or nearly so, continue on to **Face To Face**.

The gamemaster may also involve more munchkins in the story. Many are dispersed throughout Althain performing their tasks and chores. They could present an amusing diversion for the shadowrunners.

FACE TO FACE

TELL IT TO THEM STRAIGHT

Read the following to the shadowrunners only after they have sufficiently explored Althain:

Harlequin will enter through the tunnel and walk straight to the Great Hall.

Harlequin's mood is dark and his pace determined. Without so much as a glance, he passes you and stops less than a meter from Ehran's body. He stares down at it, then kneels slowly, reaching out his left hand and laying it on Ehran's head.

For a long while he says nothing.

"He is as you found him?" Harlequin says finally. You nod and again he remains silent for a long while.

Then he stands up slowly, clenching his fists till the knuckles go white. Lifting his face to the ceiling, Harlequin screams.

Once Harlequin has been in Althain long enough for the runners to talk to him or take any additional action they wish, read the following:

The door behind you opens and Maroon scurries in, approaches Ehran's body, and addresses it. "Master, men come from the Land of Promise to speak to you. They await you in the modern waiting room."

With barely an acknowledgement of Harlequin or you, Maroon leaves to order the kitchen to prepare foods for their new guests. Harlequin stares after the creature as it leaves, then smiles slightly. "Well, you must give him points for trying," he says.

Without warning, he spins to face you. "They're probably Ehran's goons. Go deal with them." He turns to contemplate the body.

Read the following to whichever of the player characters goes to meet the Elves:

You leave the Great Hall, letting the doors close behind you. Heading down the stairs, you are halfway to the main hall when you see a figure climbing to meet you. Garbed in dueling clothes of many centuries past, he carries two swept-hilt rapiers, one in each hand, blade up. He smiles as you draw near.

It is Ehran the Scribe.

"Ah," he says before you can act, "the threat to you now is not me, but those who've just entered. They really have no concern for what has been going on. They're quite pig-headed, you know, and they have their orders.

"If you excuse me, I have a challenge to counter."

Read the following to any shadowrunners who remain behind with Harlequin:

Harlequin stares down at the body, and after a moment, his eyes narrow. "I wonder…" he says quietly.

The doors leading into the Great Hall open suddenly, you turn, expecting to see either Elves or your teammates. Instead you see a single Elf. Ehran the Scribe.

He stands in the doorway, grinning, garbed in dueling clothes of centuries long past. In each hand, he holds a swept-hilt rapier, blade up. "*Te meravilhas, Har'lea'quinn?*" Ehran says, stepping into the the room. "*Que't destrui e't coton?*"

Harlequin laughs, a dark, cold sound that does not alter his malicious grin. "I wonder perhaps if your spirit is as dead as this simulacrum below me, *Eh'he'ran*. That damned tongue certainly is. Shall we find out?" With that, Harlequin reaches up and tears his left ear from his head. It falls to the ground with a dull clatter.

"So be it!" he cries as Ehran tosses him a sword.

They duel.

Read the following to the shadowrunners who enter the Main Hall on their way to meet the Elves from Tir Tairngire:

Allowing Ehran to pass, you leave the stairs behind and enter the main hall. As you do, the doors across from you swing open and four Elves enter the room. Wearing padded, studded white leather and ornate hooded cloaks of tan and gray cloth, they stop at the sight of you.

The three men and one woman tense as you approach, but take no immediate apparent action.

BEHIND THE SCENES

EHRAN AND HARLEQUIN

Harlequin has come to Althain after placing Jane Foster in a secure location. He has decided to learn the fate of Ehran the Scribe for himself. The status of the magicks in the lava caverns concerned him as he passed because they did not bode well for Ehran's survival. A small twinge of fear developed as he moved through the tunnel. He was well aware of the spells that guarded that passage, and seeing most of them inactive, leaving the entryway clear, is a bad sign.

Using his powers and abilities, he was able to enter Althain without the knowledge of the munchkins, who were not there to greet him as he arrived. Having been here once before, he knew in which room Ehran would most likely have attempted any magic: the Great Hall.

When he examines Ehran's body, he can find no indication that it is not Ehran, but does notice the lack of magic or aura residue. Now, this may be due to the time that passed, but…

The arrival of the Elves from Tir Tairngire will annoy Harlequin no end. He assumes they are followers of Ehran's, never even conceiving the thought that the Tir Tairngire High Prince would have the gall to interfere in the challenge between him and Ehran.

The "resurrection" of Ehran, however, changes everything. Harlequin is both pleased and angered to see the Elf. Pleased that Ehran did not die as a result of the rebounded spell—meaning that Harlequin may still yet win out over him—and angered that he's been played for a chump.

Ehran is carrying two rapiers of precision craftsmanship and great value. Following their exchange as described above, Harlequin and Ehran begin to duel. If one or more runners is present, Harlequin will say the following, as Ehran nods in approval.

"If this is to end it, it must be as it began. You!"—he gestures at a runner—"stand as Ehran's second." Ehran points to a place a meter or so to his rear.

If there is a second runner, Harlequin will instruct him to stand as his second. If there is no second runner, he will stand near the body of the false Ehran, indicating that a dead second is better than none at all.

At this point, Harlequin will raise his rapier in a salute to Ehran, who returns the gesture, but not before turning to the runner standing near him. "You should leave," he says. "Your involvement is at an end. Go help your friends."

As the two begin to close, Ehran swipes his blade twice through the air, saying, "I'll have the other one as well, you know." Harlequin laughs and executes a fine lunge.

Any runners who remain to watch will witness a duel of the most exquisite swordsmanship any has ever seen. Both men are athletic, which characterizes their fighting styles. So similar are their styles that an appropriately skilled observer would note that they probably had the same teacher.

The fight lasts a long time, the duration depending on the gamemaster and the needs of the story. At some point into the battle, a shimmering sphere of gold emerges from thin air, engulfing both Elves. A successful Astral Perception (8) Test will reveal that the glow is a manifestation of some subtle contest of magical prowess that is occurring between them, in addition to the physical battle.

Eventually, the battle will end. An ideal point would be just as the Tir Tairngire Elves and the rest of the shadowrunners return to the Great Hall. The battle, having ranged by now all over the room, will have taken the two Elves up the stairs and onto the **Balcony (9)**. There, finally, Harlequin besieges Ehran with a brilliant series of moves and countermoves. Then, with a quick flick of his blade, he removes Ehran's left ear.

Clutching his head, Ehran howls with rage and pain while Harlequin shouts joyously. Ehran points his blade at Harlequin and yells "You have not won! We are now merely even!" Harlequin turns toward his opponent, bows grandly once, blows him a kiss, throws his rapier to one of the player characters, and then takes a step backward. As he does, his image shifts prismatically and he disappears. Ehran howls again, takes a step forward, and disappears in the same manner.

If at any time during the battle the runners decide to interfere, the gamemaster may wish to have Ariel (see **Counterstroke**) appear in the room and warn them not to. This challenge is a matter of blood and the runners' interference would not be taken lightly by either party. Ariel's appearance may be mystifying to the runners, especially if they are unaware that she is a Free Air Elemental.

If the runners question her, she will divulge only the following: Harlequin's and Ehran's feud is long-standing, but the current friction comes from Ehran having cut off Harlequin's ear in a fairly recent duel (recent, at least, by certain standards), that she and Ehran and even Harlequin are much older than they appear, and that this place, Althain, reminds Ehran of the place he lived as a child. She will not name the place.

If she is present when Allaech and the other Tir Elves show in the Great Hall, she smiles at Allaech, who mutters a curse under his breath, then turns to look for Ehran. Ariel vanishes shortly thereafter.

TIR TAIRNGIRE ELVES

The High Prince of Tir Tairngire has sent these four Elves for two reasons. First, he has heard of some challenge involving the illustrious and influential Ehran the Scribe and some renegade Elven sorcerer named Harlequin. Taking his past history with Ehran into account, the High Prince decided to remain uninvolved, but dispatched spies to watch Ehran and to find out more.

The reports of a magical incident at Mount Saint Helens, which he knew to be the site of Ehran's sanctum, has disturbed the High Prince. He fears that this personal battle of Ehran's may have gone a step too far. The High Prince prefers that the outside world remain ignorant of the internal politics of Elves. Any hint of dissent might provide political leverage to one of the national or corporate powers. The High Prince has already enough problems dealing with the demands of the militant Tir Na Og Sidhe of the British Isles. He doesn't need local trouble.

To investigate this troubling matter, he has dispatched four members of the *Bratach Gheal*, the White Banner, his personal guard. They are Allaech, the leader, Aimsir, Sruth, and Taelech.

Allaech

As the highest-ranking member of the Bratach Gheal present, Allaech is the leader. The responsibility for the success of this journey falls to him, which does not much please him. Observation and a smattering of personal experience have taught him how dangerous it is to risk insulting Ehran and his ilk. He will do his best to fulfill the High Prince's orders, but is likely to accept whatever solution involves the least number of complications.

Though born in Phoenix, Allaech has lived in the Tir all his adult life. He is accustomed to the styles and manners of "modern Elvish society," at least as set forth by the High Prince and his followers. What he sees in Althain is at once intriguing, astounding, and frightening.

B	S	Q	C	I	W	M	E	R	Armor
4 (8)	4	7	5	3	6	(8)	6	5 (8)	3/3

Dice Pools: Defense (Armed) 5, Defense (Unarmed) 7, Dodge 7
Skills: Armed Combat 5, Athletics: 5, Car 3, Elvish 4, Etiquette (Tir Tairngire) 4, Firearms 5, Negotiation 3, Persuasion 4, Stealth 3, Unarmed Combat 7
Special Abilities: Physical Adept, Initiate (Grade 3), Increased Reaction 3, Increased Body Attribute (+4)
Gear: Reinforced Ballistic Leathers (3/3), Sword (4M2, +1 Reach)

Aimsir

Aimsir, a combat-oriented mage, believes that Ehran the Scribe is one of the voices that will lead the Elven people from the underclass. She met him once while working security at a Tir social function, but he will not remember and she will not care that he doesn't. Aimsir is awed by Althain, which contains so many things she has never before seen. She is not perceptive or knowledgeable enough to understand the implications of these new things.

B	S	Q	C	I	W	M	E	R	Armor
3	3	6	4	6	6	(7)	6	6 (9)	3/3

Dice Pools: Defense (Armed) 4, Defense (Unarmed) 5, Dodge 6, Magic 14

Skills: Armed Combat 4, Athletics: 3, Conjuring 4, Elvish 4, Etiquette (Tir Tairngire) 3, Firearms 2, Magical Theory 4, Special Skill: Gaelic (Centering Skill) 4, Sorcery 7, Unarmed Combat 5

Special Abilities: Initiate (Grade 2)

Gear: Ares Light Fire (Explosive ammo), Reinforced Ballistic Leathers (3/3), Sword (4M2, +1 Reach)

Magic: Fire Elemental (Rating 4, 3 services); Quickened Personal Combat Sense 4

Spells: Fire Cloud 4, Heal Moderate Wounds 5, Mana Missile 3, Personal Clairvoyance (Extended) 3, Physical Mask 3, Stun Missile 4, Stunblast 4

Sruth

Sruth is a ringer, a plant from the Tir Tairngire "secret police" whose elite members are known as Paladins. Not a full Paladin, Sruth was planted in the Bratach Gheal to keep an eye on it and its members. Being chosen to accompany Allaech was sheer luck. If he survives the visit to Althain, what he sees and hears could prove damaging, or at the very least embarrassing, to Ehran in the future.

Though remaining aloof from most of the proceedings, Sruth takes a dim view of Ehran and the goings-on at Althain, even though he barely understands them. He is especially angry to see non-Elves present, not to mention shadowrunners.

B	S	Q	C	I	W	M	E	R	Armor
5	5	7	4	4	3	—	3.48	5	3/3

Dice Pools: Defense (Armed) 7, Defense (Unarmed) 3, Dodge 8

Skills: Armed Combat 4, Car 2, Elvish 2, Etiquette (Tir Tairngire) 5, Etiquette (Tribal) 3, Firearms 4, Rotor 3, Unarmed Combat 4

Cyberware: Alpha Clinic installed; Boosted Reflexes 2, Chipjack, Cyberear, Cybereye w/ Video Link, Datajack, Headware Memory (70 Mp), Skillwire 3

Gear: Ares Crusader MP (APDS Ammo), Linguasofts: Japanese (3), Spanish (3), and Salish (3) all loaded into Headware Memory, Reinforced Ballistic Leathers (3/3), Survival Knife (5L3)

Taelech

Taelech is at a critical juncture in his life. He is unhappy but unsure what to do about it. As a young Elven child living in Dallas, he imagined Tir Tairngire as the refuge, the paradise for Elves. Now he has been there enough years to see that it is far from the "Land of Promise."

He is especially troubled by what he perceives as a "hidden agenda" among certain members of the Tir hierarchy, Ehran the Scribe included. He will carry back with him to the Tir the sights and the implications of what he sees in Althain. Of all the Bratach Gheal, Taelech is (with the possible exception of Aimsir, the most willing to explore.

B	S	Q	C	I	W	M	E	R	Armor
6	6 (7)	7 (8)	3	3	4	—	3	5 (7)	3/3

Dice Pools: Defense (Armed) 7, Defense (Unarmed) 3, Dodge 8
Skills: Armed Combat 7, Athletics 2, Cycle 2, Elvish 2, Etiquette (Tir Tairngire) 2, Firearms 6, Gunnery 3, Unarmed Combat 3
Cyberware: Muscle Replacement 1, Wired Reflexes 1
Gear: Combat Axe (7S2, +2 Reach), Reinforced Ballistic Leathers (3/3), Remington Room Sweeper (Explosive Ammo)

RESOLUTION

Allaech does do most of the talking for the group, demanding to know what is going on, where Ehran is, demanding to see him, and so on. He will attempt an air of knowing the score, all the while trying to pry every bit of information out of the runners. He will speak first to the most respectable-looking (by his standards) Elf in the player-character group. If none is present, he will choose another Metahuman. He really does not care who he speaks to as long as he gets answers.

Allaech received no orders concerning the shadowrunners and is as surprised as anyone else to see them. He will immediately assume they are Ehran's goons. Allaech is the bearer of a "Princely Order" requesting that Ehran and this Harlequin (if he can be found) appear before the High Prince with regard to their current activities. He has been instructed to deliver the Order only to Ehran and will be adamant about that aspect of it.

Depending on how the gamemaster and the players handle the situation, some conflict could very well occur. If provoked, the Tir Elves will immediately move to make this a hand-to-hand fight. Aimsir also has orders to use her Stun Blast heavily, regardless of who might be in the blast radius.

Shortly into this, Ehran's real goons should arrive. Comprised of the remnants of his team from the **Future** segment, the group should also contain a number of Elven Street Samurai, Mages as well as Elven-converted Mercenaries, Combat Mages, and such. The gamemaster will balance this group as he sees fit, based on the current situation involving the Tir Tairngire Elves, the player characters, and their respective conditions. The intent is for the Tir Elves and the runners to team up against Ehran's real goons when they appear.

The gamemaster has another option: the Dragon is in the basement. The restraining spell around it has been leaking away ever since the Harlequin/Ehran spell combat, and he could become free right about now if the gamemaster so wishes. The Dragon's first action will be to escape. In his confused and pained state of mind, that means going up. Directly above him is the Main Hall where the runners are confronting the Tir Elves.

A crazed Dragon suddenly breaking through the floor in the midst of the two groups might just be enough to defuse the situation. The Dragon, whose stats are below, is so crazed he ignores the effects of all injuries as far as Target Modifiers are concerned, though Initiative Modifiers should still be applied. For more on dracoforms, specifically the Western Dragon and its powers, see pages 176, 180-81, and 190 of **Shadowrun**, as well as p. 10, **Paranormal Animals Of North America**.

Dragon

B	Q	S	C	I	W	E	R	Attacks
13/5	8x3	32	4	3	7	(10)	6	9D3, +2 Reach

Powers: Enhanced Senses (Thermal Sense), Flame Projection

Once the Dragon has been subdued or defeated, Allaech will be frustrated by the circumstances, dumbfounded by the appearance of the Dragon, and adamant that he be taken to see Ehran. The shadowrunners present will be the ones to decide if they and the Tir Elves get to see the end of Ehran and Harlequin's sword fight.

If they do, Allaech will react frantically to Harlequin's and Ehran's disappearances. Seeing their escape as his failure, he begins to rant and rave in Elvish, gesticulating wildly, in the "Why Me?!?" tradition. Aimsir's reaction will be dumbfounded wonderment because she realizes that no one she's ever met knows the kind of magic that allowed Ehran and Harlequin to disappear. She will immediately assense the area, but find nothing.

If a point needs to be made of it, the language that Ehran and Harlequin speak to each other in the exchanges above, and in the introductory story, is not Elvish. No one, not even Allaech, has ever heard it before.

Once Ehran and Harlequin are gone and Allaech's self-pity has run its course, an odd light will come into his eyes. He will turn to the runners and say "Wait! You saw what happened. I can take *you* back to the High Prince!"

The runners may, of course, have some objection to this. They can reason it out or they can fight it out. Their choice.

If the situation is resolved amicably, the Tir Elves will leave Althain to report back to the High Prince. Sruth will recommend this, and Allaech will somewhat dejectedly agree.

Depending on how things turned out, the gamemaster may have a slight problem getting the runners to leave Althain. The easiest way to spur their departure is for Ariel to appear to one of the runners with a warning that Ehran is returning and has already begun preparations to reactivate the security systems. If they do not leave now, she says, they might never leave.

Why is Ariel being so nice to the runners? She sees them as potential tools against Ehran in the future. See her description in **Counterstroke** for more information. She is able to take these actions because none of Ehran's orders prevent her.

If the runners attempt to remove any of Althain's art pieces, Ariel will warn them strongly against doing so. Remember, these are Ehran's heirlooms. Until now he was willing to overlook the runners' involvement because they were a legitimate part of Harlequin's challenge.

Should the runners complain about not getting paid by Harlequin for their work, Ariel will sneer disdainfully and then remind them of the sword Harlequin tossed just before he vanished.

Let us hope that logical heads ultimately prevail and that the runners realize it's time to leave. After all, do they really want to be here when Ehran gets back?

WRAPPING IT UP

There are a number of ways that **Present** could end, which is why the normal **Picking Up The Pieces** section for that segment has been included with this master section.

One way or another, the runners will exit Althain. It may be calmly, with due haste, or as part of a running battle with the Tir Tairngire Elves. However it happens, they will eventually leave, then discover immediately that they are unable to return.

Any attempts to find Althain again will be fruitless. Ehran has reactivated his masking and illusion security spells to completely hide it. As far as the runners are concerned, it has vanished from the face of the earth. They will be able to find many of the caverns that lead to it, but they will never locate the chasm, stone bridge, or tunnel again.

The runners will also have to find their way back to Seattle. They may or may not have prearranged this. In either case, the traffic around the mountain has increased considerably by now, despite the S-S Council's attempts to discourage tourists and gawkers. The sheer volume of people may assist the runners' escape. Then again, more people mean more security forces to control them. The Tir Elves all have diplomatic passes and the associated immunity, so they are not worried.

PAWNING THE SWORD

One of the runners ought to remember the sword that Harlequin tossed to them immediately before vanishing. It is, in fact, their final payment for services rendered. The rapier is an heirloom, a 16th-century antique. Its exquisite craftsmanship makes it obviously valuable. How valuable exactly is up to the gamemaster.

Styles of play vary between different **Shadowrun** groups. Some games are low-income, scrounge-for-nuyen games, while others have a much higher cash flow. The gamemaster should take into account the needs and style of his game before placing a value on the weapn. The base value should, however, be about ¥100,000 nuyen.

To fence the weapon, however, the runners will certainly have to find an appropriate fixer. Their normal one will probably not do, though he will certainly offer to take it off their hands at roughly 15 percent of real value. (If the runners are foolish enough to do this, they should see a newsvid report about a rare rapier being sold at auction for millions.) An individual who deals in fine weaponry is not usually the kind of person who has street contacts, opening up a whole new storyline for the gamemaster to explore. The runners may learn the name of a reclusive weapons collector who might be interested in the rapier. The only problem is that he's a wiz virtual-reality programmer for UCAS Data Systems and holed up in their compound in Denver. The possibilities are endless.

FUTURE EVENTS

The first piece of news that the runners will hear about Ehran is that the release of *Mankind Revealed* has been delayed for six months. The story is that release has been postponed because Ehran is ill and would be unable to make promotional appearances right now. Within six months, Ehran the Scribe will return to the limelight as fit and hale as ever. He will also be sporting two ears.

Should the runners ever again have contact with Ehran or ranking members of the Young Elven Technologists who may be aware of what has occurred, relations will be neutral, but reserved. Ehran has instructed everyone to take no retaliation against the runners. Vengeance against pawns is forbidden by the rules of *chal'han*. This does not mean that members of Ehran's entourage or YET will bend over backward to thank the runners for screwing up their boss' life.

Allaech's report, or lack of it, will have no affect on any future dealings between the Tir and the shadowrunners. Naturally, their involvement and their images are now recorded in a some file if Sruth lived through Althain. Again, this does not mean the runners will be honored guests of the High Prince, either.

As for Harlequin, the runners will hear nothing at first. If they attempt to use one of the Fixers or Mr. Johnsons met through this adventure, they will have no luck contacting. A month or so later, one of the runners will receive a custom photo holocard mailed from Phoenix, Pueblo Council. The photo shows the city's downtown area at night. Clearly visible is the figure of Harlequin bowing grandly to the camera. If the characters examine the photo closely enough, they will notice another figure in the background, slightly out of focus, that could be Jane Foster. She seems to be talking to an old, short Ork carrying a soccer ball. The back of the card reads: "My God, it's hot. Wish you were here. —H."

KARMA

At the very least, the runners are still owed Karma from **Present.** The way in which this adventure is structured does not present many opportunities for Team Karma. The gamemaster should award a blanket 8 points or so, plus 1 point for each adventure segment in which the full player-character team participated.

Award Individual Karma per the rules on page 160 of **Shadowrun**.

MASTER LEGWORK

This section covers the Legwork that the characters could undertake at any time during **Harlequin**, as opposed to the investigations that are specific to only one story segment.

The various pieces of information, listed under each entry as Excerpts, are easily available from one of the public databases.

SYLVAN INFORMATION SYSTEMS

—*BEGIN EXCERPT:* **Seattle Corporate Record, last amended October 2050**

Home Office Location: Seattle, UCAS
President/CEO: Malachi Morgan
Principal Division:
   Chief Products/Service: Multi-media/hypermedia publications and industrial software.

Business Profile:
   Sylvan is known in the publishing industry as an "Elven house," meaning it publishes Elven authors or designers almost exclusively. Sylvan also has publication rights to all works by Elven social theorist Ehran the Scribe.

Security/Military Forces
   Sylvan maintains an in-house security force. Its computer system is rumored to be fairly well defended.
—*END EXCERPT*—

Appropriate Contacts
   Any Corporate Type, any Media Type.

Available Information (Target 4)

Successes	Result
1	"Yes, I've heard of them, a multimedia production company, if I remember correctly. They specialize in tri-vid and simsense hypermedia presentations, plus a lot of conventional publications. I think they design database programs, too. A real information corporation."
2	"They've got themselves a real cash cow with the exclusive rights to Ehran the Scribe's stuff. I hear they're planning to publish his lecture material the way Campbell's was in the nineties."
3+	"Sylvan's got a whole section of hotshot deckers coding stuff for some of the biggest corps in UCAS. That's where the company really makes its nuyen."

YOUNG ELVEN TECHNOLOGISTS (YET)

—*BEGIN EXCERPT:* **Seattle Political Database, March 2051**

Headquarters: Seattle, UCAS
Leader: John Winter

Policlub Officers
   Indoctrination: Nick Francis
   Recruitment: Patricia Stein
   Security: Alex Manke

Profile

An influential Metahuman policlub, the Young Elven Technologists is located in the Puyallup Barrens. Its major benefactor, Ehran the Scribe, underwrites most of the policlub's expenses through extensive lecture tours across North America. Additional funds come through benefits and personal contributions.

The Young Elven Technologists currently meet in an old (pre-Awakening) fire station they purchased from the city.

Security

Though the YET's meeting hall is in a nasty section of the Barrens, the policlub rarely encounters any trouble there. This may be attributed to either the Young Elven Technologists' disdain for violence or, considering the upbringing of its membership, its superior firepower.

—END EXCERPT—

Appropriate Contacts

Any contact who has lived in the Seattle area for more than six months will have heard of the Young Elven Technologists.

Available Information (Target 4)

Successes	Result
1	"Yeah, they've been around at least three years, maybe more, but I only really started hearing about them in the last year or so. They say some of the core members used to be in a Metahuman gang that started up after the Night of Rage. After Ehran The Scribe—you know, the Elf writer guy—hooked up with them somehow, WHAM! they're a big-shot policlub. Go figure."
2	"The boys from YET have been having it out with another Elf group, the Association Para-Nobles, or something. The APN got their heads greased the last time out, and I hear they're bucking for blood."
3	"YET's been doing some heavy recruiting at the University and the decker BBSs. The club does the head-hunting, then funnels the chummers to some multi-media production and development place out in the Barrens. Nah, I don't remember which one."
4+	"Oh yeah, I remember, Sylvan Information."

ASSOCIATION PARA-NOBILIS

—BEGIN EXCERPT: **Seattle Political Database, August 2050**

Headquarters: Seattle, UCAS
Leader: Aaron Mitchel (aka Xeric)

Policlub Head Officers

Six members of a governing council. The individuals identified on registration papers are Xeric, Allair, Erendahl, Thiran, and Blaine Deathedge.

Profile

Known as a radical policlub, the APN propounds a hard-line "back-to-nature" philosophy for Elvenkind. They have been known to use aggressive, violent tactics.

It is believed the APN has an active membership of 200 in the Seattle area. There are no reports that the APN has spread into other political regions of North America.

The APN currently meets in a building near the Renraku Arcology in the vicinity of Post and University.

Security

The APN relies on its own members for security.

—END EXCERPT—

Appropriate Contacts

Any Gang Type, Metahuman, Metahuman Rights Activist, Ork Rights Committee Member, Snitch, Street or Plain Clothes Cop, any Street Type

Available Information (Target 4)

Successes	Result
1	"Those guys are drek-brains. Real blatherers about living in the woods and getting back to nature and such. So where do they hang? By the Arcology. Only figures, right?"
2	"They've mixed it up a couple of times with the Young Elven Techies. Their respective points of view sort of butt heads. It's gotten really violent a few times. You'd think that Ehran fellow would do something to calm it down, but he hasn't."
3+	"And get this—THEY AIN'T REAL ELVES! Can you believe it? The inner-circle jokers are all posers. Cosmetic reconstruction, fake ears, the whole works."

EHRAN THE SCRIBE

—*BEGIN EXCERPT:* **Who's Who in UCAS, 2050 Edition**

Ehran the Scribe rose to national prominence within the last fifteen years, first as a contributor to the Opinions sections of major metropolitan newsfaxes and then as a published author and commentator. His first non-fiction work dealt with the sudden rise of the Metahuman underclass and the social changes that accompanied it. Though not a best-seller, it garnered him much critical and academic praise.

Now regarded as a social theorist, Ehran is best known for his full-length works *The New Magic, Life After 2001, Mankind Ascendant* (a Pulitzer prize winner), and *Metagenes: Future Spiral.* Among his better-known essays and articles are *Debunking the Neo-anarchist Myth: Why Humanity Needs Leadership, Toward a Stable Society, Latinitis:The Inadequacies of Zoological Terminology in the Awakened World.*

Little is known of his history, though he has made comments concerning his youth in the Chicago "Shattergraves" region. There are no records of formal education, nor has he claimed any. Ehran's only current connection to politics is his backing of the Young Elven Technologists policlub.

He currently maintains residences in Seattle, Portland, and New York.

—*END EXCERPT*—

Appropriate Contacts

Any Corporate Type, Government Type, and Media Type. Also any contact associated with High Society.

Available Information (Target 5)

Successes	Result
1	"Ehran. Interesting fellow, has one of the sharpest minds I've ever encountered. You always have the feeling there're ten layers of thought going on behind his eyes."
2-3	"He's listed as a backer of the Young Elven Technologists, but I think he calls the shots. I also hear he's tied up in the politics of Tir Tairngire, which makes for an interesting cross-connection."
4+	"God, that Elf scares me. Have you ever seen him angry? I mean really angry? I think he really understands *power.* His aura is mundane, but I know people who've seen him do magic."

HARLEQUIN

The only available public information concerns the definition and source of the word harlequin. The gamemaster should encourage his players to research it themselves, or have a dictionary or encyclopedia available for them.

Appropriate Contacts

Any.

Available Information (Target 4)

Successes	Result
1	"Harlequin? Harlequin? A clown kinda guy? Like maybe the Halloweeners? Hah, just kidding. No. Never heard of him."
2+	"Yeah, yeah, psycho-chummer. Wasted himself summoning an Elemental a coupla years back. Wife sold him for parts." (**Gamemaster's Note:** See page 87 of the **Shadowrun** rules for the fate of this particular Harlequin. It is not the same Harlequin of this adventure.)

GETTING THERE BY AIR

Thus far most **Shadowrun** adventures have been set in Seattle. Now, however, the borders are expanding. In **Harlequin**, three of the eight segments (well, four, counting **Present**) take place outside of Seattle. **Past** in Bavaria, **Spiritual** in Amazonia, and **Future** in Columbia, Missouri. To reach any of these places, the runners will have to travel by air. This section tells how that's done.

CHOICE OF TRAVEL

Before the runners go anywhere, they have to decide *how*. Commercial or private?

COMMERCIAL

In 2050, commercial carriers fly just about anywhere, but they won't necessarily fly everyone. Like neighborhoods, commercial airlines have Enforcement Ratings (see **Sprawl Sites**, page 124). Most, if not all, the larger airlines are considered to have a AAA Rating. This means that if an item is listed on the Weapon Fines and Punishment Table on page 123 of **Sprawl**, it's forbidden to carry it on the aircraft.

Most airlines have provisions that weaponry can be carried in checked luggage (no carry-ons, chummers) and stored in the aircraft cargo holds. These holds are inaccessible during flight.

Keep in mind, however, that they will only store these weapons if 1) the weapons are legal in the area from which the flight originates, 2) the local police are notified on landing, regardless of whether the weapons are legal at the destination point, or c) the bearer is licensed to carry said weapons.

If the traveler has an appropriate permit or license, Class E Weapons (Pistols) can be carried aboard the aircraft. Usually, such permits are issued only to legitimate security forces recognized in the originating and destination areas.

It is, however, a little difficult to check cyberware. Class CA cyberware is normally ignored because it is virtually useless without the associated weapon. Note is made, however, in the passenger manifest of the presence of this gear.

The bearers of Class CB cyberware have it a little tougher. In order to fly on most commercial carriers, they must wear cybersystem restraint cuffs (CRCs). These are small, padded units that clamp into place on each wrist. The cuffs do not restrict movement.

What they do, however, is restrict cyberware usage. Each contains a special set of sensors designed to detect and react to the use or activation of certain pieces of cyberware. Note that this cyberware must have previously been detected and the CRC be custom-programmed for the specific devices. (See **Passing Through Security**, p. 145).

Note that airport security systems cannot detect Boosted Reflexes, so they cannot be calibrated against. More sophisticated tests are required.

Whenever a character wearing the CRC uses or activates a cybersystem which has been calibrated against, roll an Activation Test of 6 dice against a Target of 2. Only 1 success is needed for Activation. Note that these successes can be neutralized by expending Karma. Just be prepared to spend a lot to do it.

On the subject of Wired Reflexes and the like, characters who have such systems may opt to enter combat *without* engaging them. To do this, they must make a Willpower Test against the level of the system before rolling Initiative. Only one success is needed to forestall activation. This test must be made *every* combat turn before Initiative is rolled for that turn. If the CRC activates, its effects will be resolved on the character's first action, before he can do anything.

The most common CRC device consists of a TASER restraint system. High-voltage capacitors are built into the CRC and discharge into the flesh of the wearer when activated. Upon activation of the CRC, the wearer is subjected to a 4D4 Stun attack from the shock. Normal armor and Dermal Armor *do not* help in this case.

Note that each system is only good for three shocks before the capacitors are expended.

Nastier versions of this device exist, but are used predominantly in prison or law-enforcement restraint situations. Upon activation, a 6D6 shaped-charged micro-explosion detonates on each wrist (only conduct one attack). This alone will kill most normal people. Again, these restraints are used only in the most dire circumstances. Even law enforcement agencies, no matter how oppressive, wish to avoid the possibility of accidental detonation.

The CRCs can be deactivated if someone makes a successful Electronics (8) Test with a base time of 1 minute. A microtronics tool kit is required. Failure means an immediate Activation check should be made.

COMMERICIAL COSTS

Travel costs money, chummer. Check it out below:

AIRFARE COSTS TABLE

Distance	Cost
Intrastate	100¥ (Coach)
200¥ (1st Class)	
Interstate, same Region	200¥ (Coach)
400¥ (1st Class)	
Interstate, different Regions	300¥ (Coach)
600¥ (1st Class)	
Transcontinental	450¥ (Coach)
900¥ (1st Class)	
Intercontinental (Conventional)	900¥ (Coach)
2,000¥ (1st Class)	
Intercontinental (Sub-orbital)	1,600¥ (Coach)
4,000¥ (1s5 Class)	

PRIVATE

Private carriers also go just about anywhere and will carry just about anyone, for a price. Virtually any arrangements can be made with them, as long as the client has the nuyen to spend. It's a seller's market, chummer.

To find the private carrier, the runner must make a Corporate Etiquette Test against a Target Number equal to the number of Weapon Classifications he wants ignored on the flight.

To negotiate the price of the flight, assume the pilot (or whomever) has a Negotiation Skill equal to the Weapon Classification the passenger wants ignored. The cost can be adjusted by 5 percent per new success.

Suborbital private travel is not available, but the other classifications on the table above are. For a private carrier, however, multiply the cost by the factors below:

PRIVATE CARRIER FACTORS

Factor	Multiplier
Base Cost	x3
Ignore Class A-G Weapons and CA, CB, and CC Cyberware	No Charge
Ignore Class H and I Weapons	+1
Ignore Class J Weapons	+2
Ignore Class K Armor	+1
Ignore Class L Ammunition	No Charge
Arrival Fees	About 100¥ per person, per category*

*View this as bribery costs for the local constabulary. Not all airport securities are corruptible, and so the price may vary, depending on one's destination airport.

PASSING THROUGH SECURITY

The ultimate test comes when a player character has to pass through security. Most airports use either the Detekt-It™ portable wand system or the Gateway™ station system. The Detekt-It™ system is only good against weaponry; it does not detect cyberware. Gateway™ works to detect both.

System	Rating (Weapons*)	Rating (Cyberware)
Detekt-It™, Alpha	1	—
Detekt-It™, Beta	2	—
Detekt-It™, Delta	3	—
Detekt-It™, Gamma	4	—
Gateway I	3	1
Gateway II	4	2
Gateway III	6	3
Gateway IV	8	4

*includes cyberweapons

The Detekt-It™ wands come in four rating levels: Alpha, Beta, Delta, and Gamma. In each case, the wand's rating is pitted against the Concealability of the weapon in question. A Beta wand, Rating 2, for example, would call for a roll of two dice against the weapon's Concealability. Only 1 success is needed to detect the weapon.

The "Concealability" of cyberware is factored somewhat differently. Subtract the Essence Cost from 6, round up, and double. This new result is the effective Concealability of the cyberware, with one exception: cyberweapons do not have their result doubled. Additionally, cyberware that is heavily biotech-based, such as Muscle Replacement, Boosted Reflexes, and Retinal Duplication, has its result tripled, not doubled.

RUNNING HARLEQUIN

THE BIG PICTURE

In most adventure games, the gamemaster is the only one who knows the master plot. Particularly in a campaign setting, he is the one who weaves together different plots according to the demands of another, deeper storyline that may remain hidden from the player characters.

That is not the case in **Harlequin,** where even the gamemaster does not see or know the big picture. Ehran and Harlequin's dance of blood and vengeance is the secret, master story, while the storyline involving the runners is only an offshoot of that deeper plot. The gamemaster knows only enough of the storyline to interweave a number of adventures, gradually letting their surface plot become revealed. About all he and the player characters can do to find out the truth is make educated guesses about the master story, based on the little information they can obtain and the few interactions between Ehran and Harlequin they actually witness.

FASA has already done something similar in **Bottled Demon,** a previous **Shadowrun** adventure. The "bottle" and its effects are described in the adventure, but the true nature of the object is never revealed. The reason for the secrecy is the same in both adventures. Future game products will be based on hidden elements of **Harlequin** and on the true nature of the bottle. As the gaming continues and additional products come out, both players and gamemasters will become involved in storylines that have been building or hinted at for many, many adventures. Gamemasters are not the only ones who might read an adventure book like **Harlequin,** so we don't want to give away any surprises.

This does make it slightly more difficult for the gamemaster, who must create certain situations and instigate various actions without knowing the reasoning behind them. Every effort has been made to structure **Harlequin** in a way that makes this only a minor difficulty rather than a stumbling block.

The player characters are only pawns in the struggle between the feuding Elves. If the runners do (inevitably) try to interfere in that conflict, the gamemaster should present Harlequin and Ehran as individuals of such power and intellect that they are prepared for virtually any situation. Thus, if a runner attempts to shoot at Ehran, the Elf has a Bullet Barrier, and so on. He or Harlequin might also have an Elemental or Spirit along for protection. In the two instances when Harlequin and/or Ehran appear in person, the gamemaster can deal with any potential problems by having the two Elves operate at such a powerful level that the runners can do nothing to harm them or deviate them from their paths of action.

The player characters should walk away from **Harlequin** feeling that they have been involved in the affairs of two people whose personal power far outclasses their own. It is for this very reason that neither Ehran nor Harlequin are given game statistics in the adventure. They don't need them. Within the scope of these mini-adventures, each has the power and ability to perform whatever action he wishes. Should any runner become, shall we say, "unruly," either Elf will use magic to neutralize him temporarily.

Both Elves are full-powered hermetic magicians and Initiates of incredible rank. By extrapolating the effects of existing spells, it should be no problem to give either Elf control of any situation. Give the players the chance to roll as many dice as they wish in an effort to negate or counteract the spells. Let them come oh-so-close to resisting and then fail. The master story demands it. The players should have no idea they're being manipulated.

ROLEPLAYING EHRAN AND HARLEQUIN

Ehran and Harlequin have distinct personalities. Ehran rarely jokes, except in those moments when his adrenalin is pumping. He is normally studied and solemn, though he can become quite passionate and convincing when he speaks. He has the ability to hold an individual's or crowd's undivided attention on virtually any subject. He is charismatic and eloquent, with a voice and manner that speak of sophistication and elegance.

Ehran appears to be in his thirties, looking slightly older than most Elves. He blames this on an "exuberant youth," though he refuses to go into details. Standing at just over two meters, he has a strong, square face and piercing green eyes that reveal his emotions when he speaks. He is always, even at his worst, dressed impeccably in beautifully tailored suits from the finest shops in Spain and Tokyo.

Harlequin, on the other hand, is chaos personified. His attitude, manner, philosophy, dress, and accent are subject to change at a moment's notice. He is quick-witted, but sometimes his wit depends on some obscure reference that possibly only three other people in the world understand. He is quick to anger and equally quick to forgive…usually. If his anger lasts, as it has for Ehran, it will become a consuming passion.

The gamemaster should play Harlequin as a wild, almost elemental force. He is prone to rambling and raving on the most arcane subjects, but what he says is often fascinating and revelatory. Both he and Ehran are powerful mages. Unlike Ehran, however, Harlequin will display that power openly, even to the point of blatantly displaying that he is capable of a level of magic the runners are not. He *is* like Ehran in Masking his aura.

Harlequin is half a head shorter than Ehran and of slightly lighter build. His clothes are more typical of an inhabitant of the Sprawl except that he always seems to be slightly behind the times. He wears a long, many-pocketed coat with numerous

PLAYER HANDOUTS

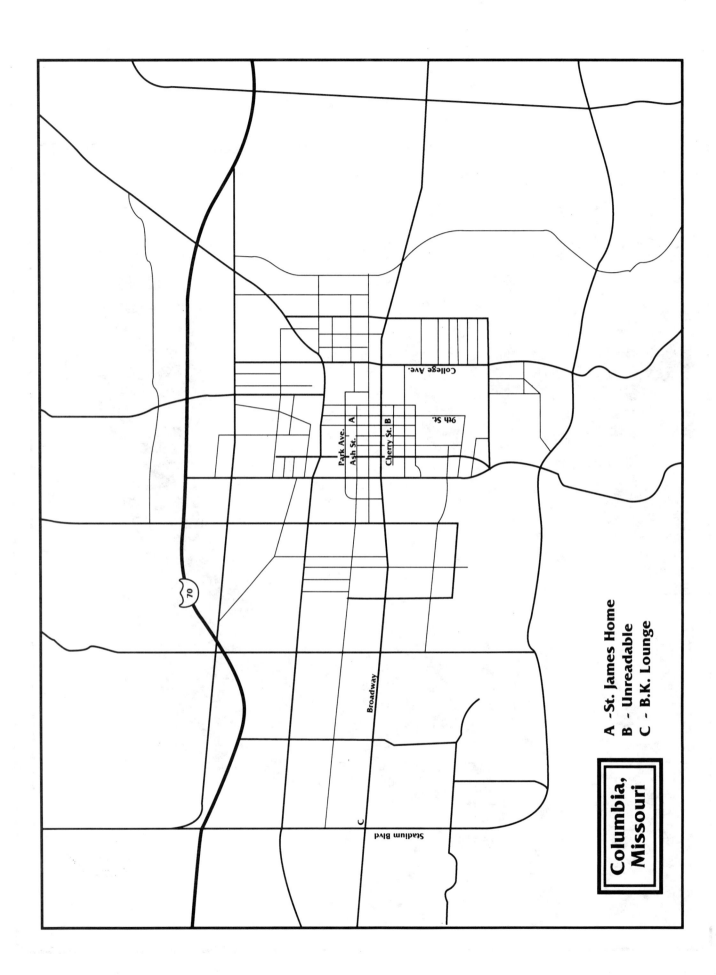

Columbia,
Missouri

A - St. James Home
B - Unreadable
C - B.K. Lounge

College Ave.

Park Ave.
Ash St.
A

Cherry St. B
9th St.

Broadway

Stadium Blvd

C

70

COLUMBIA, MISSOURI (UCAS)

—From a UCAS Board of Tourism publication, *"Traveling: The Real Story,"* August 2050 edition.

Columbia is first and foremost a college town. The University of Missouri, Columbia was the first land-grant university west of the Mississippi and the town grew up around it.

Located in the center of what was once the state of Missouri, Columbia is equidistant from Kansas City, the first city of the West, and St. Louis, the last eastern city. As a result, Columbia is a common meeting place between the two metroplexes.

Columbia is a city of growth. Consistently ranked among the most educated cities in the nation, fully 86 percent of the population above age 18 has some college credit. Skilled labor is both cheap and abundant. Prices tend to be a little higher in Columbia than for a similar town elsewhere, but the cultural attractions and pleasant setting make it worth the price to the 80,000 people who call Columbia home.

GETTING TO COLUMBIA

Columbia is located on Interstate 70, which leads west 200 kilometers to Kansas City and east an equal distance to St. Louis. Highway 63 runs north and south, tying Columbia to Jefferson City 48 kilometers to the south and to several small towns to the north. The roads are all maintained in fair, if not good condition, with I-70 providing the best groundway. Highway travel remains the principal method of delivering goods to the Columbia area.

In all cases, travel within the Columbia area is unrestricted. Travelers from Seattle would find it a welcome change from the hassles that stem from the regulations of being surrounded by the NAN and Salish-Shidhe. The Missouri River flows to within 16 kilometers of the city limits, providing the town with an alternate form of transportation. The towns of Rocheport, Booneville, and Jefferson City all do a brisk river trade, reviving the tradition of their forefathers who plied the river with goods hundreds of years ago. From the Missouri, goods are often transported via flat-bottom barge along the numerous smaller rivers of the general area. Chief among these smaller rivers is the Osage.

The single major airport of the region is the Columbia Regional Airport. Small by big-city standards, the airport handles 50 to 75 flights per day. Because of the limited landing area, these flights are limited to smaller commuter jets and rotor/winged craft. There are also a half-dozen regularly scheduled daily dirigible flights.

Security at the CRA is definitely not up to big-city standards. Columbia, Missouri, is hardly a hot spot, so they make do with a set of metal detectors and a host of passive alarms keyed to sound when certain substances are detected. Most travelers are not even aware they are being scanned.

GOVERNMENT

Columbia government is little changed since the final years of the 20th century. Voters make their choice through telecom elections, just as in the past.

The head of city government is the mayor. The two-year term does not offer any form of salary or incentive. Most Columbia mayors must also hold day-jobs to support themselves.

Each of the nine wards of the city elects a representative to serve at a two-year term on the city council. These offices are also unsalaried. The city is also zoned to elect two state representatives and one state senator to the state congress in Jefferson City. These three offices are considered the pinnacle of success in the local political arena.

The actual power in the city government is wielded by the city planner. Hired by the city council, this individual handles most of the day-to-day business of running the city. He or she is hired for a one-year term, with an option for the council to renew. Most planners are retained until they leave to accept some other job, often despite disastrous mismanagement.

All city services are funded by tax nuyen collected from the citizens of the city and county. The city still provides all services except for sanitation and power. The various wards contract out their sanitation needs, while the Calloway County Nuclear Power Corporation in the nearby city of Fulton provides Columbia's power. The city council will soon be considering a proposal to subcontract out to local law enforcement security companies, especially for the more secure neighborhoods.

POINTS OF INTEREST

The city of Columbia is dominated by the University of Missouri, whose nearly 30,000 students swell its size by a third when all are present. The school offers many fields of study, ranging from electrical engineering and industrial management to matrix geometry and theories of applied sorcery.

The campus has some of the city's most beautiful and well-maintained buildings. The liberal arts college hosts a variety of special events that includes everything from choral and theatrical performances to lectures and political debates. Contact the local Extension Office for more information on special events and performances.

Supplementing the University of Columbia are Columbia College and Stephans College. Though much smaller than the university, these two institutions also sponsor a wide array of exhibits and performances. The CC fall art show is especially anticipated by the city residents and collectors alike, as the college repeatedly attracts some of the most gifted art students in the UCAS.

Along the fringes of the city are parks and recreation areas. Residents of Columbia can use these areas free of charge, or for a modest fee when a park provides such special facilities as tennis courts or a baseball diamond.

SHADOWS OF THE CITY

Columbia has its share of crime and urban unrest, but these are confined to isolated instances and scattered areas. The only organized crime to speak of are several resident street gangs and the occasional go-gang that springs up for a month or two.

Of the local gangs, only four have been around long enough to be considered more than a loose pack of hoodlums. The Pretenders go-gang is the longest-lived, and they like to rove the highways between the surrounding cities. The number of their raids has, however, remained small enough that the county police have not invested much time or effort to hunting them down.

Guys in Sunglasses is the biggest gang in the city. Something of a neighborhood watch, these locals are mostly interested in keeping the "college boys" and "frat rats" away from the local girls. Fights between the Guys and various university organizations are often brutal and lethal.

The Flames is an all-girl gang based in the downtown area. Mostly from well-to-do families, its members limit their activities to rolling drunks and petty larceny.

The final group, the Spirits, is rather new. Springing up in the residential areas of the city, they are reportedly responsible for a recent string of violent incidents and break-ins.

The computer grid in Columbia is especially secure. With all three colleges offering degrees in computer science, the town has to fend off an abundance of would-be deckers who would love to crash through a corp's system in search of goodies. Most of the truly talented wiz kids graduate to bigger and better careers in the corporate jungle.

GETTING AROUND

Columbia is a strange mixture of roads, loops, and one-way streets. Though most locals can get around just fine, a "tourist" (which is anyone who has lived in the city for less than two years) will find it hopeless. Tourists can usually tell you where you are and offer limited information about general directions, but little else.

Motorists use individual electric cars that are recharged at local stations. Plans for an electrical grid has long been in the planning stages, but debate over the eventual contractor and the cost involved have kept it from becoming a reality. For now, commuters make do with the local recharging stations.

Mass transit is reasonably priced, but is rarely convenient or dependable. Lack of public support of the system is what makes its service dicey at best. Anyone who does not mind a wait can get anywhere in the city via the Columbia Area Transit System (CATS) for the price of five nuyen.

ENTERTAINMENT AND MEDIA

Columbia has more night spots and restaurants per capita than almost any other city in the UCAS. Fast food, cafes, diners, and formal restaurants crowd every nook and cranny of the city. Bars, dance halls, clubs, and dives cater to every sector of the population, but most focus on students and younger crowd.

The Mizzou Tigers compete in all college sports. Farrow Field is the home of the university's combat football team, still looking for an elusive bowl bid. Hearnes Center is the home of the university-sponsored Black and Gold Bengals, the local UrbanBrawl team. The Bengals offer the only professional sports program in the city. For other professional sports, one must make the trip to K.C. or St. Louis.

Because of the presence of so many university students, Columbia plays host to a wide variety of rock bands. Often used as a settlement site when promoters decide to play the western UCAS, the town will briefly swell in size by one as much as a third when groupies gather at Hearnes or Farrow to hear their favorite bands.

Visitors to the city may be surprised at how well-informed is the local populace on current world and local events. This is primarily due

to the university's School of Journalism, which offers its students valuable experience covering local and regional events. With so many students fighting for so few stories, the competition is fierce and the results often superior.

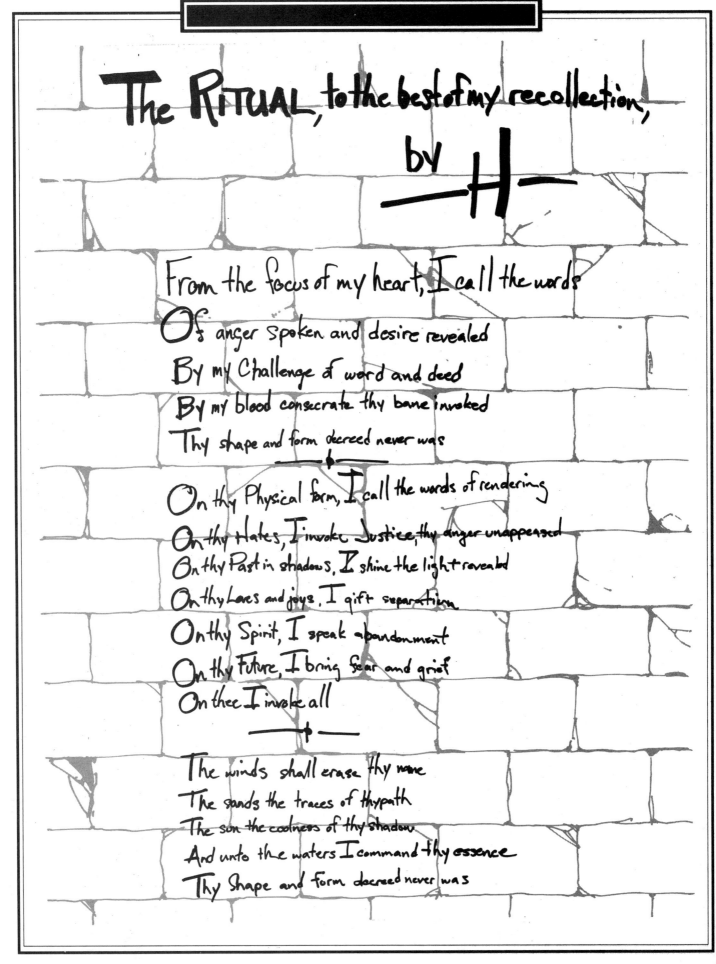

The RITUAL, to the best of my recollection, by H—

From the focus of my heart, I call the words
Of anger spoken and desire revealed
By my Challenge of word and deed
By my blood consecrate thy bane invoked
Thy shape and form decreed never was

On thy Physical form, I call the words of rendering
On thy Hates, I invoke Justice, thy anger unappeased
On thy Past in shadows, I shine the light revealed
On thy Loves and joys, I gift separation
On thy Spirit, I speak abandonment
On thy Future, I bring fear and grief
On thee I invoke all

The winds shall erase thy name
The sands the traces of thy path
The sun the coolness of thy shadow
And unto the waters I command thy essence
Thy shape and form decreed never was

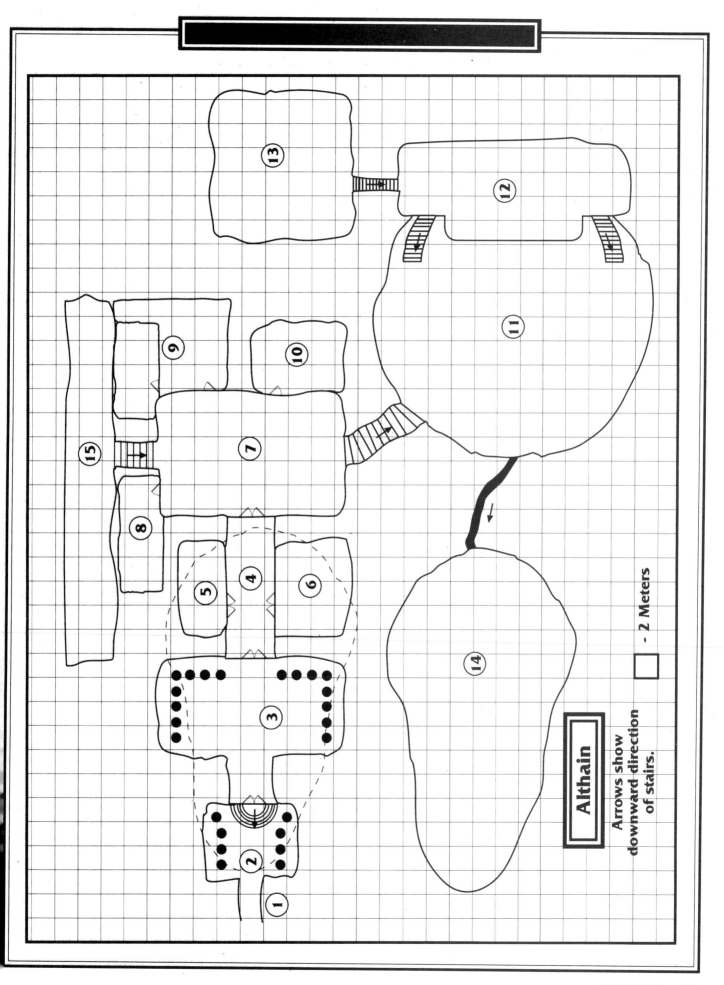

Althain

Arrows show
downward direction
of stairs.

☐ - 2 Meters